Computers in Amateur Radio

by Steve White, G3ZVW

with contributions by other authors

Radio Society of Great Britain

Published by the Radio Society of Great Britain, 3 Abbey Court, Fraser Road, Priory Business Park, Bedford MK44 3WH.

First published 2013

Reprinted 2014 & 2017

Printed Digitally 2020 Onwards

ISBN 9781-9050-8685-6

Publisher's note
The opinions expressed in this book are those of the authors and not necessarily those of the publisher. While the information presented is believed to be correct, the authors, publisher and their agents cannot accept responsibility for consequences arising from any inaccuracies or omissions.

Front cover: Kevin Williams

Compilation, editing and typography: Steve White, G3ZVW

Production: Mark Allgar, M1MPA

Printed in Great Britain by 4Edge Ltd of Hockley, Essex

Contents

Meet the Contributors

Internet Remote Control
Wojtek (Berni) Bernasinski, G0IDA/SP5GU

My interest in radio began at primary school, when a friend made a crystal set from an electronics kit. The fact that it needed no battery simply amazed me and from then on I was hooked! My first job was repairing radiopagers at a company where, as well as taking my Morse test first then my RAE, my friendly manager gave me the opportunity to build radio projects. This is something I still enjoy and do today.

In 1993 I studied Electronics at the Warsaw Technical University in Poland, during which I got a job in the mobile phone industry as a voicemail and text messaging engineer. In 1998 I left for Germany, where I set up voicemail and text messaging servers and services for new mobile phone companies. One leap in technology where I was directly involved in was the implementation of GPRS in the Deutshe Bahn railway mobile network, who were the first to use it in world. In 2000 I changed my career and embarked on getting an Airline Transport Pilots Licence.

I am a keen contester and have won numerous events and been awarded many trophies and certificates. I am now a commercial pilot working for a major UK airline and live in an urban area with lots of noise and little space for a 80m antenna, so have made a complete remote station. Thanks to a friend who lives in a very quiet location my antenna is at his QTH, over 100km from my home. With it I am able to enjoy working five HF bands, hearing stations I would never have done before.

Antenna Modelling
Ian Birkenshaw, G4UWK

I became a short wave listener at the age of ten and was first licensed as G8ZAG in 1980. I have a BSc in Electronic Engineering from the University of Wales and am now retired from a career in Civil, Military and Space Communications and Computer Networking, having worked both in the UK and overseas. My last working role was as a Radio and Communications Technology Consultant for the National Health Service.

I became interested in antenna modelling to help in the development of better low profile directional antennas for DXing from difficult urban environments. This can best be described as 'work in progress'.

Automatic Packet/Position Reporting System
Chris Dunn, G4KVI

I live with my wife who is also licensed, in Midsomer Norton, near Bath. My interest in radio started at school while bored in Chemistry and I went on to pass my RAE in 1980.

I was very active during the 1980s and tried almost all aspects of amateur radio. I worked for many years as a Field Engineer in the Cable TV industry. I'm a member of RAYNET and spent several years as a group controller.

I have been involved with APRS for several years and set up MB7UB, the Bath digipeater. I am also currently the repeater keeper for the GB3UB repeater at Bath University.

HF Terrain Modelling
Alan Hydes, G3XSV

I was first licensed in 1968 and served a couple of years as Secretary of Southgate ARC, before leaving for Southampton University. I gained a BSc in Electronic Engineering in 1974. My career since then has been in the computer industry, starting with IBM as a graduate R&D engineer at Hursley Park near Winchester. In 1982 I moved to Hewlett Packard, firstly in Wokingham and later transferring to Bristol.

I have always been interested in the HF bands, DX, and particularly in contesting. On moving to Bristol I became involved with the Bristol RSGB Group. I have been Chairman of their contesting arm, the Bristol Contest Group, for a number of years and am delighted with the success we have enjoyed, especially in field days and IOTA.

My interest in HF terrain analysis came about when trying to pick good HF contest sites and to understand what types of antenna and heights were needed.

Electromagnetic Compatibility
John Pink, G8MM/F5VKU

After leaving college with a degree in physics, I followed a long career in the field of measuring instrumentation and radio communication. After working for Redifon Communications and the Plessey Company I joined Hewlett Packard and was able to further develop an interest in microwave technology. I became a specialist in precision measurements using automatic network analysers at both low frequency and microwaves. I remained with HP for over 15 years, serving from time to time on various ITU-R working groups. I remained with US-based companies for almost all my working life, working with Scientific Atlanta on satellite earth terminals for a number of years and then as Managing Director of Wiltron Measurements - a company specialising in microwave instrumentation for over 17 years.

From 1990 until retirement I was Director and General Manager of the UK arm of Anritsu, the renowned Japanese measuring instrument company. During this time Anritsu-Wiltron developed a number of leading edge products, including scalar network measuring systems, microwave power meters and a Bluetooth protocol analyser. Although in a senior management position, I was able to remain in touch with technology. I retired in 2002 and have been actively engaged in EMC matters with the RSGB EMC committee. I am also a member of various BSI committees and working parties concerned with EMC.

I was licensed in 1960 as G3OQB and in 2003 was able to get the callsign G8MM re-issued, which had been in the family since 1937. I currently also hold F5VKU.

Raspberry Pi
Peter Goodhall, 2E0SQL

In 2000 I became interested in amateur radio after finding out about digital modes. After a couple of years as a shortwave listener I took the Foundation Licence in 2002, attaining the callsign M3PHP. In 2008, after leaving Buckinghamshire New University with a degree in Multimedia Technology – Web Design, I attained my Intermediate Licence.

Since leaving university I have been working as a freelance web developer for a variety of clients, which lets me play about with all sorts of computer technology, although my work is heavily biased towards technologies that work on Linux based systems.

My interests in amateur radio centre on anything I can use a computer to further the experience, I'm still keen on digital modes but also contesting and recently operating through amateur radio satellites, both portable and from home. I also help run a large number of amateur radio websites, including HamTests.

Software Defined Radio and Data Modes Software
Mike Richards, G4WNC

Inspired by my father, I took to radio and electronics construction at a very early age and we spent much of my early teens putting radios together. We were fortunate to have two excellent component stores locally and most Sunday evenings were spent window shopping. This informal apprenticeship served me well and set me up for a great career with BT that spanned some 40 years. During that time I worked on just about everything from poles and holes through to broadcast services, with a significant time dealing with the then emerging field of data communications.

My writing career started about 25 years ago when I was asked to write the RTTY column in *PW*. Since then I have been writing regular columns and reviews for a variety of magazines. First licensed as G8HHA, my amateur interests really took off in the 1970s when I was able to link my Compukit UK-101 computer with a friend's TRS-80 using full duplex on 2m and 70cm and an old 300-baud modem. Since then my interest has focused on the digital side of amateur radio.

Logging Software
Mike Ruttenberg, G7TWC

I have been licensed since 1994 and operate mainly in contests due to limited facilities and restricted environments in London locations over the years, indeed contesting is my lifeblood. I have been a regular attendee at the contest stations of various groups over the years and have won sections of CQWW and CQWPX events on SSB and CW.

I work in Information Technology as a Quality Assurance website tester and love nothing better than making sure the PC in my shack is optimally set up. I have ten years of experience in database management from previous employment in a database marketing company, so cross-checking logs and 'looking under the hood' of the database file behind N1MM to take maximum advantage doesn't phase me. I feel at home with most modern logging software packages – specifically N1MM, MixW, SD, WinTest and Writelog – but also have experience of older packages.

D-Star
Dave Thomas, MW0RUH

My passion for radio came about from the days of CB. I was introduced to some local amateurs around that time, but didn't take things further. In 2006, whilst volunteering, I was travelling with a paramedic officer when the vehicle radio burst into life. The officer explained that the transmissions were detectable on a scanner - an item I had in my possession at the time. Following the monitoring of these transmissions, I searched the Internet for other possible local trans- missions. It was then I then came across the new amateur radio licensing structure. I was hooked and took my Foundation licence exam in February 2007, followed by my Intermediate licence exam in August 2007. Initially I operated on HF and VHF, SSB and data (including SSTV and PSK31).

In 2008 I discovered D-Star and began to assist in the promotion of the mode by giving talks and demonstrations at local radio clubs. I am the Administrator for GB7CD in Wales, the only D-Star repeater that is owned and operated by South Glamorgan RAYNET, of which I am a member. I also hold a NoV for MB6BA, Wales' first simplex D-Star Gateway. I work full time for a Local Authority and in my spare time respond to 999 calls on behalf of the Welsh Ambulance Service, also assisting a local search and rescue group, the Cardiff and Vale Rescue Association.

Propagation Modelling
Gwyn Williams, G4FKH

My career in radio started in 1965 when I joined the Royal Air Force and trained as a Telegraphist, which means that I was taught to type and to send and receive Morse. I was lucky enough to be stationed at an overseas station where Morse was the only means of contact with the outside world. It was during this time that I became interested in propagation. Upon my demob I went into communications (IT) in the City of London. I passed my RAE in 1975 and became G4FKH.

It was inevitable that I would combine my hobby with computers and automation and now write programs in PERL for propagation prediction pur- poses. I use all the programs that I examine in my chapter, as well as some that do not go into.

My HF propagation predictions appear in *RadCom* and on the RSGB web site. I also prepare propagation predictions for the magazines of two other national radio societies and maintain a few databases in Access, which the 5MHz group use and publish on their web site.

Slow-Scan Television
Paul Young, G0HWC

My interest in radio started when I was around 12 as a Short Wave Listener. Later I was into CB radio and finally I got around to taking the RAE in 1985. A year later I got my A licence. Once licensed I soon got into SSTV and built myself a Robot 1200 clone, designed by G3WCY and G4ENA. My first move over to SSTV on the PC was with Pasokon SSTV, by WB2OSZ.

I was also involved in packet radio when it was all the rage and ran packet BBS GB7AAA. Wile living in Northampton I was an active member of the local radio club and served on the committee for a number of years.

Over the years I have worked in PMR and cellular communications. These days I drive a truck around the UK and sometimes run SSTV from it while parked up at night.

All other chapters
Steve White, G3ZVW/AF6SU

I became interested in electronics and radio at an early age, having been brought up in a home that had a cupboard full of electronic components. I heard my first radio amateur on a home constructed crystal set and passed the radio amateurs' exam at the age of 17, while still at school. After leaving school I followed an engineering career in telecommunications, initially with Post Office International Telegraphs and then various computer and communication companies. In parallel with work I was always involved with my local radio club, serving in various posts on the committee for over 20 years and taking an active interest in home construction, contest operating and helping newly licensed operators get themselves set up.

At various times in the 1980s and 1990s I tutored students who were studying for the radio amateurs' exam, helping a large number of them gain their amateur radio licence. I developed a method of teaching the basics of Morse code in a remarkably quick timeframe and for over ten years organised amateur radio events.

In 1997 my technical experience and broad knowledge of amateur radio in general led to me becoming the Technical Editor of *Radio Communication* and in 1998 the Editor. After leaving RSGB I became a regular contributor to *RadCom* and I have also written for other magazines in technical and non-technical capacities. For the last twelve years I have produced the *RSGB Yearbook,* the *Rig Guide* and was also Pat Hawker's biographer.

My interest in amateur radio is still mainly centred around home construction and contesting, and I am regularly active on the bands.

1.
Introduction

by Steve White, G3ZVW

When electronic computers first became available to the public they were too expensive for all but the most wealthy or enthusiastic to aspire to owning one. Their functionality was also extremely limited. Without such things as BASIC interpreters, machine code programming was the order of the day. This, and the fact that memory was expensive, resulted in programs that were compact, but not intuitive to write or debug. As technology advanced, memory became less expensive, storage and transferring data between machines became more straightforward, and programs easier to write.

Radio amateurs were quick to discover that a computer could be used in conjunction with their hobby to make operating easier or provide something extra at the station. When the Internet started to become popular it was clear that the world was going to change dramatically and some people thought it spelt the end for amateur radio, but it wasn't to be. Computers became appliances that just about everybody wanted, competition between companies resulted in prices tumbling, and the hitherto technical challenges of building one disappeared. Computers simply became tools that did jobs.

These days it is practically impossible to avoid the microprocessor and just about everybody has some computing power at their disposal, even if it is only in a household appliance. Computers are practically an essential part of amateur radio, but few of us use them to do everything they are capable of doing.

For the purposes of this book, the machine discussed will the the IBM compatible type. Such machines usually run a version of Microsoft Windows.

Desktop machines are easily modified, as the devices and connectors are standard and there are numerous companies manufacturing compatible moduled and devices for them. To a lesser extent the same applies to laptop PCs.

Selecting a Computer for The Shack

There are a number of criteria that you should consider when selecting a computer for use in the shack. The computing power of the average modern machine will be perfectly adequate for most purposes, except perhaps when used in conjuntion with a Software Defined Radio. Rather, the aspects of selecting a computer are more to do with integration into the station and ergonomics.

Audible Noise
The last thing you are likely to want in your shack is a computer that has fans so noisy they can be heard when you transmit or prevent you from hearing a weak station when you receive, so select a machine with quiet fans. CPU fans tend to be the noisiest, but the type of fan used depends on the heatsink on the CPU chip. A better heatsink might enable the use of a quieter fan, and they are relatively easy to swop out.

Laptop computers score highly in this respect, because they do not have fans on their power supplies and their CPU fans are very quiet.

Electrical noise
Some desktop computer cases are better quality and offer better screening than others. Equally, more expensive power supplies are likely to incorporate better filtering. Genrally speaking, the more you pay for a case, the better screened it is likely to be; and the more you pay for a power supply, the better filtered it is likely to be.

Laptop computers employ external power supply modules. Some of these are more electrically noisy than others. Users should be particularly wary of cheap, third party replacements.

If you are going to buy a new computer from a shop, it can be useful to take a portable receiver with you and check how much noise emerges from the case, cables, power supply etc, by placing it close to each of them in turn. You might get some puzzled looks from the shop staff, but you won't be laughing if you get your new machine home and discover that it causes interference.

You will find more in the EMC chapter on how to select a good PC case, how to suppress electrical noise and how to wire your station to minimise noise pickup.

Size
If your shack is small you are hardly likely to want a physically large computer in it, but generally speaking the bigger the screen, the better. If space is really at a premium, a laptop computer is likely to be your best option.

Connectability

First and foremost, make sure your computer has all the ports that you are ever likely to need.

Few modern PCs have parallel printer ports (sometimes very useful for keying), and some do not have RS232 serial ports. If required, you can use plug-in cards to provide you with these interfaces.

Some computers have few USB sockets, some have more. If yours does not have enough, a plug-in card or a hub that will give you more is relatively inexpensive.

If you are going to use a laptop computer that you don't leave in the shack permanently, to reduce the number of times you have to plug in and unplug all your peripheral devices, consider buying a USB hub. This will enable you to plug items such as interfaces, a keyer, mouse and keyboard into it and then make one connection to the computer.

Operating System

Without an Operating System (OS) a computer can do nothing, Windows and Linux being the ones most commonly found on modern PCs. A computer then needs programs to perform specific functions.

Software Packages

Software packages (programs) that the general public tend to be familiar with are those used for e-mail, Internet access, word processing, spreadsheets, drawing, the management of digital photographs etc, but there are numerous specific packages that can be of real use to radio amateurs.

In a number of the chapters that follow, some of the contributing authors take detailed looks at some applications and specific software packages. Please be aware that it is not unheard of for patches to be required for some of these software packages to run under certain operating systems. Also be aware that programs don't remain as they are. By this I mean that bugs are fixed, facilities are added, functionality and appearance is changed, etc. The odds are that if you have been running an amateur radio related software package for some considerable time, it has been updated. A check of the Internet should reveal if you are running the latest version, and if you are not you should consider downloading and installing the latest one.

Something you should already be aware of is that a CD with a useful selction of amateur radio software accompanies this book. Details of the software are given in Appendix 2.

There are innumerable online calculators. Some of these are looked at in a separate chapter, but the very nature of the Internet is that it is highly dynamic. New web sites are appearing all the time and old web sites disappear almost as quickly, so it would be impossible to even attempt to provide an exhaustive list of what is available out there. The best that any of us can hope for is to use search engines to find what we want.

In fact the hobby of amateur radio is extremely well served when it comes to software packages, because a lot of radio amateurs are technically-minded and have an interest in programming. Those who are capable of doing so tend to develop new packages to solve a particular problem, and these days the logical method of distribution is via the Internet. Although it is necessary to pay for some of these software packages, many are free. We have our fellow, philanthropic radio amateurs to thank for that!

2.
Datamodes

by Steve White, G3ZVW

Computers have revolutionised datamode operation for radio amateurs. With their advent we were no longer restricted to the use of huge, clunking, mechanical teleprinters, although there is nothing to prevent us from using such equipment if we choose. Neither were we restricted to the modes that these machines were capable of employing – invariably only one per type of machine.

The first advances in electronic datamode operation took place pretty much as soon as personal computers became available, usually by the use of an external modem. By about 1980 there were modems and software packages available for the computers of the day; machines such as the Tandy TRS-80. IBM introduced their Personal Computer in 1981, but it was too expensive for most people to consider having one at home. Besides, in the first half of the 1980s Sinclair Electronics established a strong presence in the UK computer market, first with the ZX80 and later the ZX Spectrum. Huge numbers were sold and a wide variety of communication (and other) programs written for them. There were numerous other brands and types of computer available for the home market, but software wasn't compatible across the platforms.

Code tables for the common datamodes described here can be found in the Code Tables chapter.

Morse

The original 'datamode', Morse code is attributed to Samuel Morse, but the Morse in use today – and which has been is use for over 150 years – is not the same as the code developed my Samuel Morse.

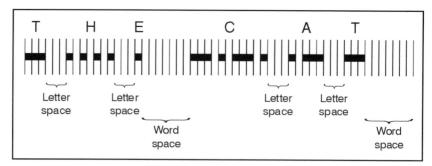

Fig 2.1: An
example of two
words sent in
Morse, with
vertical lines to
show the official
timing and
spacing.

With Morse, the dots, dashes and spaces are all intended to vary in proportion to one another, as transmission speed varies. Depending on the speed of transmission, it may sound like a heterodyne (steady whistle) that is switched on and off. As **Fig 2.1** shows, a dash (usually pronounced 'dah') should be three times the length of a dot (pronounced 'dit'). The space between the letters of a word should be the same length as a 'dah', i.e. three times the length of a 'dit' and the space between words should be seven times the length of a 'dit'.

Depending on its use and the ability of individual operators, Morse may be sent at widely differing speeds. On VLF it may be sent *extremely* slowly. This is known as QRSs operation, where a 'dit' may be many seconds long. Such slow Morse would be sent by computer, because manual operation would be too tedious. At the receive end, it would also be detected and displayed on a computer. This is because at extremely slow speeds a computer running a Fast Fourier Transform program can detect and display a signal that is not audible to the human ear.

The speeds that are commonly sent and copied manually by an operator range from about 5-40 words per minute, although speeds in the 20s are the most common.

Prior to the development of modern datamodes, looped recordings of high-speed Morse (often at 80 words per minute) used to be employed by Meteor Scatter enthusiasts. Whilst incomprehensible to the human ear, repetitive high speed Morse messages sound slightly rhythmic. On receive, fragments of transmission (for that is all that are typically received in a meteor scatter contact) would be recorded on tape and then played back at slow speed, for the receiving operator to copy by ear.

Morse is normally transmitted by on/off keying (Amplitude Shift Keying), although many beacon stations use Frequency Shift Keying. Although not often referred to in such terms, Morse code is the International Telegraphic Alphabet No.1.

Baudot (RTTY)

The so-called International Telegraphic Alphabet No.2 was developed for numerous reasons, not the least of which is that Morse is not easy to receive and decode with a mechanical machine. This is primarily because, irrespective of the sending speed, not all the characters take the same length of time to transmit. Emile Baudot overcame this problem in the 1840s, by developing a code in which all the characters were the same length. This permitted receiving equipment to be synchronised for each character sent.

The construction of RTTY data is shown in **Fig 2.2**. The standard Mark condition tone is 2125Hz (logic '1') and the Space condition tone is 2295Hz (logic '0'). The grey areas are 1's or 0's, depending on the characters being sent. Transmission of each character commences with a 'start' bit. The length of the start bit – indeed all the bits – depends upon the rate of transmission. For a 50 baud transmission (as used by the Telex network), the length is 20 milliseconds. For 45.45 baud transmission (as commonly used by radio amateurs), the length is 22 milliseconds. The start bit is followed by five data bits (10010 for a letter D), then 1.5 stop bits. The extra length of the stop element of the character is to give mechanical teleprinters the opportunity to come to a halt before the next character arrives.

Five data bits give a possible 32 combinations, which is not sufficient for transmission and reception of the 26 letters of the alphabet, the numbers 0-9, and common punctuation marks and control characters such as a bell, new line, carriage return, etc. This problem is overcome by dedicating two of the 32 possible character combinations for Letters Shift and Figures Shift. In Letters Shift, the 26 letters of the alphabet plus some common functions (carriage return, new line, space) are possible. In Figures Shift, numbers, punctuation, a few symbols and the same common functions are available.

RTTY is normally transmitted by a process known as Frequency Shift Keying (FSK) or Audio Frequency Shift Keying (AFSK). In a loudspeaker this results in a wobbling sound, because the transmitted signal is being switched between two frequencies. During periods when no data is being transmitted but the transmitter is still on, there is a steady tone. Practically any two audio tones can be used, the standard

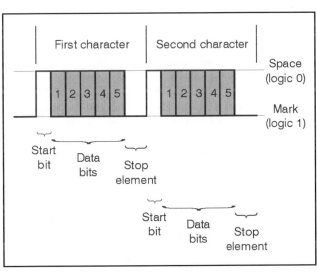

Fig 2.2: How RTTY characters are constructed and transmitted.

Mark-Space shifts being 85Hz, 170Hz, 425Hz or 850Hz. The most popular shift used by radio amateurs on HF is 170Hz. 85Hz tends to be used at VLF, because the bandwidth of antennas is extremely small, while sending RTTY at higher rates requires a bigger frequency shift and consequently greater bandwidth. When FM or SSB is being used, the two tones are usually 2125Hz and 2295Hz. These two frequencies ensure that any audio harmonics are outside the passband of amateur transmitters, because their audio cut-off is about 3kHz. Data throughput is about 60 words per minute at 45.45 bauds.

Although RTTY is limited by the fact that it contains no error detection or correction, it remains an extremely popular datamode amongst radio amateurs.

ASCII

The original ASCII (American Standard Code for Information Exchange) used electromechanical teletypes that worked at 110 bauds. This equated to an element length of 9ms.

ASCII was a significant improvement on Baudot, because it contained seven data bits. The 128 possible combinations meant that upper and lower case letters could be sent, plus a lot more symbols, punctuation and control characters.

As standard, ASCII does not incorporate error detection or correction, but it is possible to add a measure of error detection by adding a parity bit.

Although there is no reason why it should not be used in its basic form by radio amateurs, it tends not to be. Rather, it tends to be used as the core code for some other datamodes.

PSK31

PSK31 was invented by Peter Martinez, G3PLX in 1998. It employs Phase Shift Keying at 31.25 bauds and has the advantage of requiring a very narrow bandwidth (31Hz). It was designed primarily for real-time keyboard-to-keyboard QSOs, is capable to transmitting all the characters on a keyboard and has even been used to transmit small pictures.

Rather like Morse, where not all characters take the same time to transmit (with the most commonly used ones taking the least amount of time), PSK31 uses a 'varicode' system. More commonly used letters such as 'e', 'n' and 's' employ less bits and take significantly less time to be transmitted. If transmitting a passage of text in lower case letters, a throughput of about 53 words per minute can be achieved, but if the same text is transmitted in upper case letters the throughput drops to about 39 words per minute.

Whilst not supporting error detection or correction, PSK31 is self-synchronising. It is very good at working through noise, indeed it is copyable by a computer when it is too weak to detect by ear. It has a high duty cycle though, which can easily lead to overheating if a transceiver is run at full power. Consequently it is advisable to run equipment at a significantly lower power level than its maximum. 30 watts is considered by many to be more than sufficient on the HF bands.

On air, PSK31 sounds like a pulsating high-pitched whistle. Tuning and frequency stability are critical for correct operation.

Olivia

This data mode was designed by Pawel Jalocha, SP9VRC, to work effectively over difficult radio paths, i.e. those suffering from fading, interference, auroral distortion, flutter, etc. It can work when the signal is 10-14dB below the noise level, which means that worldwide communication is possible using low power.

Olivia has 40 possible formats, this being brought about by the fact that eight possible numbers of tones can be transmitted in five possible bandwidths. There can be 2, 4, 8, 16, 32, 64, 128 and 256 tones, and bandwidths of 125, 250, 500, 1000 and 2000kHz. All these combinations result in differing characteristics and capabilities. The 'standard' formats (bandwidth/tones) are 125/4, 250/8, 500/16, 1000/32, and 2000/64, while the formats most commonly used (in order of use) are 500/16, 500/8, 1000/32, 250/8 and 1000/16. Data throughput is just under 60 words per minute at 1000/8.

The basic code used is 7-bit ASCII and Olivia works by sending characters in blocks of five over the course of two seconds. Multi Frequency Shift Keying (MFSK) is employed, with Forward Error Correction (FEC).

Packet Radio

Packet Radio is a datamode used for sending text messages. It is a time division multiplex system, so more than one contact can take place on one frequency at a time. It also includes full error correction. These two facets resulted in the creation of a worldwide network that supports real-time QSOs and non-real-time contacts via mailboxes. The former is akin to Instant Messaging used across the Internet, while the latter is akin to e-mail, but they were both in widespread use by radio amateurs before many members of the general public had Internet access. On HF, Packet is transmitted at 300 Bauds, while on VHF the rates used are 1200 and 9600 Bauds.

Data is transmitted in frames, which contain a start flag, an ad-

Fig 2.3: The AEA PK232 multi-mode data controller.

dress, text and an end flag. Each frame is identified by the receiving station by a unique number. If it coincides, the receiving station sends an ACK frame and the next frame is then sent.

Packet Radio uses ASCII code in a Link-Layer protocol known as AX25. It can operate between 'dumb' terminals (teletype machines, VDUs etc), which was useful before the widespread adoption of computers. It did however mean that special terminal equipment was required, not just a modem. Such equipment is known as a Terminal Node Controlled (TNC). Common models were the Paccomm Tiny 2 and the AEA PK232 (which also catered for many other modes). See **Fig 2.3**. These days it is common for Packet Radio software to be run on a computer, the sound card being used as the modem.

Packet Radio can also be used in a broadcast mode, which is how the DX Packet Cluster network came about.

AmTOR

Amateur Teleprinting Over Radio (AmTOR) was developed in 1979 by Peter Martinez, G3PLX. It is an adaptation of the commercial system Simplex Teleprinting Over Radio (SiTOR), used mainly by maritime stations.

AmTOR uses Frequency Shift Keying and is sent at 100 baud, usually with a frequency shift of 170Hz. It employs a special 7-bit adaptation of the Baudot telegraphic code that contains a fixed ratio of 4 'mark' bits to 3 'space' bits. AmTOR has two primary modes – A and B – which stand for Automatic Repeat reQuest (ARQ) and Forward Error Correction (FEC).

In Mode-A, stations in communication need to be synchronised and characters are transmitted in groups of three. The receiving equipment (slave) checks each character for the correct mark-space ratio and then sends a single character back to the master – an ACKnowledgement (ACK) if all the characters met the requirement and a Negative ACKnowlegelent (NACK) if any character contained one or more error. There are two codes for the ACK signal – known as Idle Signal A and Idle Signal B. They are sent alternately, and the master checks that it receives alternating ACKs. Receipt of an appropriate ACK informs the master that it can then send the next group of three characters, while receipt of a NACK causes it to re-send the whole group of three characters, irrespective of which character (or characters) were identified as containing a corruption. The whole process – known as a frame – takes 450ms; 210ms to send the three characters, followed by a 240ms receive 'window' during which the transmitting station expects to receive the 70ms-long ACK or NACK response. Mode-A is suitable for communication between two stations and is characterised on air by interleaved long and short chirping sounds. The speed of transmit/receive switching is critical to operation, especially on long distance paths on which the propagation delay is appreciable.

If three or more stations wish to communicate by AmTOR, it is not possible for each of the receiving (slave) stations to return ACK or NACK signals to the master, so Mode-B is used. In this mode the master sends each character twice. Each slave compares the two characters, as well as the mark-space ratio. If the mark-space ratio is met and the same character is decoded twice, it is assumed that there was no corruption and the character is displayed, while a failure of the mark-space ratio or a difference between the two characters results in an 'error' character being displayed. In this mode, AmTOR sounds like high speed RTTY.

It is possible to listen-in to AmTOR transmissions, but without the ability to send NACK signals it is likely that some corruption of messages will occur.

Although it revolutionised RTTY links when it was introduced, AmTOR was very much a product of its time. It was defined and introduced before the days of the microprocessor, so the error detection needed to be simple enough to implement in the electronics of the day. This led to AmTOR having a relatively weak error handling capability, because it detects an error only if the required mark/space ratio of a character is incorrect. This is good at detecting single bit errors, but if two or more bits of a character are corrupted it is possible that a character will still be determined as having the correct mark-space ratio. Another problem with AmTOR is the modulation method used, because FSK suffers from multi-path propagation effects.

PacTOR

Using AmTOR as the model, PacTOR was developed in 1991 by Hans-Peter Helfert, DL6MAA and Ulrich Strate, KF4KV. The basic structure is the same as AmTOR, with its fixed interval data blocks and corresponding acknowledgements, but PacTOR also combines important characteristics from Packet Radio. First of all it uses ASCII code, so the character set is much larger. Also, the baud rate has automatic variability (100 or 200 baud), which enables traffic to move faster when propagation paths are good but still maintain contact when paths are poor. It is an FSK mode with a shift of 200Hz.

PacTOR uses a longer acknowledgment signal than AmTOR, plus a Cyclic Redundancy Code (CRC) checksum to detect errors in the transmission. All this leads to a much higher quality of error detection and correction than Packet Radio or AmTOR. For this reason, PacTOR has largely replaced straightforward Packet Radio on HF.

The PacTOR frame is 960ms seconds. Although there is no reason why it cannot be used on VHF/UHF, PacTOR was designed for use on HF.

A particularly interesting and effective aspect of PacTOR is the so-called 'Memory ARQ'. If a corrupted frame is received, a NACK signal is returned to request a re-send of the frame in error. If the re-sent frame is received for a second time with a corruption, it is then compared to the previous frame (which was stored, rather than discarded). By so doing, it often transpires that the data can be reconstructed, eliminating the need for a second NACK.

A more recent variant, PacTOR II, is backwards compatible with PacTOR, but uses a different four-phase PSK modulation system and much higher speeds.

MFSK

Piccolo was the original Multi-tone Frequency Shift Keying (MFSK) mode, devised for the British Foreign and Commonwealth Office in the 1950s. It used 33 tones, one for each of the characters of the International Telegraphic Alphabet No.2, and one for the idle condition. It was capable of sending 10 characters per second in a 400Hz bandwidth, by switching between tones. Later versions transmitted fewer tones, but transmitted more than one at a time.

As far as amateur radio is concerned, there are a number of MFSK modes, all of which have appeared in relatively recent times. Here are some of the more common ones.

MFSK16 was devised by Murray Greenman, ZL1BPU, in 1999, and developed for MS Windows and sound card use by Nino Porcino, IZ8BLY. It uses 16-tone MFSK at 15.625 bauds. Employing varicode, it is (a) capable of up to 40 words per minute, and (b) accommodating very large character sets. It was designed for working over long distances, but because it employs a low bit symbol rate it is able to handle severe multi-path reception. It is also good for use via NVIS propagation. There is also a more sensitive but slightly slower version – MFSK8 – that uses 32 tones and operates at 7.8125 bauds.

Throb was written by Lionel Sear, G3PPT. It employs either five or nine tones, depending on the version in use. The latest is the 9-tone version. The tones are spaced 8Hz or 16Hz apart, leading to bandwidths of 72Hz and 144Hz respectively. There are three speeds of transmission (measured in Throbs per second), leading to data rates of 10, 20 and 40 words per minute respectively. The baud rates are 1, 2 or 4. Throb uses a special code, which results in a restricted character set. A-Z, 0-9,

<space> and a few punctuation characters are possible. ThrobX is a newer development. It uses 11 tones at a baud rate of 1 or 2 only. In this mode 53 character combinations are possible, so a few more punctuation characters are catered for. Throb works well under poor propagation conditions, but is not widely used.

The **WSJT** suite of communication protocols was developed by Joe Taylor, K1JT for meteor scatter operation and other activities where a signal path might be present only briefly and with poor frequency stability (Doppler shift). For this reason a very high data rate is required, which necessitates wide bandwidth. Three sequential tones are used to send each character at 441 baud, making the transmission rate 147 characters per second (441/3). Within the suite, protocols are optimised for various purposes. FSK441 is for meteor scatter operation. JT6M is for ionospheric scatter and meteor scatter on the 6m band. JT65 is for Earth-Moon-Earth at VHF/UHF and for HF skywave propagation. JT2, JT4 and WSPR (Whisper) are experimental modes.

Hellschreiber

The Hellschreiber ('bright writer', in German) was developed in the 1920s as a simple means of distributing text from central press offices to newspapers. Pictured in **Fig 2.4**, it was also used extensively during WWII for military communications, for non-secret traffic. After that it fell into disuse, but was 'rediscovered' by radio amateurs in the 1970s.

It is a facsimile type mode, whereby characters are 'scanned' and transmitted. There is no encoding of data and no timing or synchronisation. Each character to be transmitted is scanned much like a miniature facsimile, usually with fourteen dots per column and seven dots (vertically) per character. Referring to original type equipment, at the receiving end, a strip of paper would be driven slowly through the equipment, in a similar way that a tape recorder moves tape with a slow running motor and a pinch roller. The paper would pass between a hammer and a spinning 2-turn helix that was inked. As an audio tone was received, it would cause a solenoid to pull the hammer in and strike the paper in two places. This resulted in the characters of the message being received appearing twice along the strip, one above the other. The reason for this is that because there is no synchronisation or timing,

Fig 2.4: Early Hellschreiber machine.

characters would drift up or down the paper strip, off one edge and back onto the other. To minimise drift, the speed of the motor in the receiving equipment would be adjusted manually by the person operating it, but invariably some drift remained. By printing each character twice, one at least would be 100% visible.

The original mode is now called Feld-Hell and is still used, usually employing computers. It uses Amplitude Shift Keying (ASK) at 122.5 bauds and transmits at about 25 words per minute. Interference shows up by corruptions within characters, but messages are often discernable through corruptions. Multi-path reception shows up as a ghost on the received text, but even so it remains quite a useful system for visual use.

There are a number of modern, high-performance variants of Hellschreiber, including multi-tone – known as MT Hell. In this mode (which may use 9, 10 or 12 concurrent tones) a messages can be read direct in the waterfall display often provided with modern datamodes software packages. With MT Hell, characters do not need to be transmitted twice, because they appear perfectly in line in the display. In the event that the receiver is switched to the wrong sideband, the characters simply appear upside down! FSK-Hell uses Frequency Shift Keying rather than Amplitude Shift Keying and is quite good at reducing corruptions caused by noise pulses during the 'off' periods inherent with Amplitude Shift Keying. PSK-Hell uses Phase Shift Keying, similar to PSK31.

MT63

Developed by Pawel Jalocha, SP9VRC, in the late 1990s, this is an excellent mode for sending text over propagation paths that suffer from fading and interference from other signals. It works by encoding text with a matrix of 64 tones over time and frequency. Although this is rather complicated, it provides error correction at the receiving end.

In its most popular configuration, MT63 has a bandwidth of 1kHz and a throughput of about 100 words per minute. There are also 500Hz and 2000Hz versions of the mode, which are achieved by scaling the times and frequencies.

On the air, MT63 sounds like a roaring or rushing noise.

Clover

A commercial system developed by HAL Communications Corporation for amateur and commercial service, based on a special waveform designed by Ray Petit, W7GHM, in the early 1990s. There are several variations, the most widely used being Clover II, but all are only available in equipment made by – or under licence from – HAL Communications.

Clover uses a four-carrier Orthogonal Frequency Division Multiplex

(ODFM) technique, where different pulses are sent on each of the four frequencies in turn. The tones are 125Hz apart. There is a pulse on each frequency in every symbol period, thus it is possible to send many bits of data per symbol, as the phase and amplitude of each of the pulses can be varied. The symbol period is 32ms, so each pulse is centred 8ms after the one before. The pulses are carefully shaped to minimise the bandwidth, which is exactly 500Hz. Transmitter linearity is important for this mode, which has a characteristic chirping sound when heard on the air. Sophisticated error correction and QSO management is offered. It uses a Reed-Solomon block FEC system in all modes. Errors are detected on 8-bit groups of data (bytes). Most errors can be corrected, without the need to send a repeat request.

There are numerous modulation techniques used for clover. The protocol allows these to be changed automatically, as radio conditions permit. The data rate can also change to suit conditions and it operates in a bi-directional synchronous connected mode, exchanging ASCII text.

Clover can be very effective under poor conditions and when multi-path is present, but as a mode it is not as popular as it once was.

WOLF

WOLF was written by Stewart Nelson, KK7KA, the letters standing for Weak-signal Operation on Low Frequency. It can be used for beacons and two-way communication.

Unlike most existing datamodes, which are optimised for a particular signal/noise ratio (and corresponding speed), WOLF can operate over a wide range of signal levels. For example, consider a WOLF beacon transmitting a 15-character message repeatedly. If the received signal is adequate for conventional CW, copy will be displayed in 24 seconds. At a level barely enough for 0.4 words per minute QRSS, copy will appear within two minutes. Even if the signal is another 10dB weaker, the message can still be received, although it can take from 20 minutes to several hours, depending on the frequency stability of the equipment.

The WOLF transmitted signal uses Binary Phase Shift Keying (BPSK) with a specially constructed bit stream. After each data bit, a reference bit is transmitted. In simple terms, the signal has a data channel and a reference channel. The reference stream is a long pseudo-random sequence that is known in advance by the receiver, its purpose being to enable recovery of the carrier frequency and phase, bit timing, and message timing. A message to be transmitted is broken into packets of up to fifteen characters each. The packet of data is then 'source coded' into 80 bits. Forward Error Correction with a 1/6 rate is then applied, resulting in a 480-bit data stream. After adding reference bits, the final packet is 960 bits long and takes 96 seconds to send.

To get the best out of WOLF, *extremely* accurate tuning and excellent frequency stability of both the transmitter and receiver are required.

Facsimile

FAX or HF-FAX is not widely used by radio amateurs, but it is still widely used commercially for the transmission of weather maps. The quality of a received image can be very good, but it can take 10-20 minutes to transmit such an image.

ROS

This is a new, digital mode that criss-crosses symbols both within the permitted bandwith and across time. ROS uses a convolutional code with Forward Error Correction. There are two variants, each of which are designed to work through the 2.2kHz passband of a standard SSB transceiver:

ROSHF is designed for use on the HF bands. There are three symbol rates; 1 baud (aimed at weak signals down to -35dB SNR), 8 baud and 16 baud. In 1 baud mode there are reports of it being able to copy signals that do not even show up on a waterfall display. It can automatically detect the symbol rate being transmitted and adjust dynamically, to take changing conditions into account.

ROSEME is designed for moonbounce communication at VHF. Using 16-tone MFSK, it is very different to ROSHF. The tones are separated by 4Hz, resulting in a bandwidth of 64Hz. The advantage of the narrow bandwidth is that it can scan the audio spectrum and recover a signal wherever it finds it, automatically adjusting for doppler shift.

Interfacing Tips

When using a datamode software package running on a personal computer with a sound card, there are some basic do's and don'ts.

1. Remove, mute or bypass the microphone, or unwanted background noise may be transmitted along with the data.

2. If injecting audio into a transmitter, switch off speech compression.

3. On receive, do not rely on a microphone built into a computer to pick up data listened to through a loudspeaker, provide a wired link instead.

3.
Logging Software

by Mike Ruttenberg, G7TWC

In this chapter it is assumed that you are either curious about or already interested in using software with your radio and that you're looking either for 'getting started' guidance or that you are already experienced but want some sneaky tips. The intention here is to show you the ropes and give you the tips, but let's start from the basics for the uninitiated.

Much of this chapter will relate to contesting software, as many operators have cumulatively many centuries of experience and their learnings and requirements are now pretty standard in operating software, whether or not for contesting.

Whether you're looking to log your ragchew contacts, a data mode enthusiast, you love chasing DX or are a contest-winning operator, there is almost certainly something out there to cater for your needs. Finding a software package that is right for you is a whole different story though.

Unfortunately there is no answer to the age-old question "what software should I use?" It depends on what you want to use it for. You may also use a variety of packages for different purposes; e.g. casual operation logging, award-chasing, contesting, data modes, meteor scatter. This is not a finite list of needs or interests.

Incidentally, although this chapter mentions modes and much functionality, it equally applies to SWLs. Consequently, some powerful packages which don't have transmit functionality in them appear in the listing at the end.

I Want it All!

If you want it all and you want it delivered, ready to go, out of the box, you're in for a disappointment, because no single package does everything. Radio amateurs are blessed with a wide variety of niche interests - more than any one software package can keep up with, given the time and effort to produce code for every interest or techno-logical development.

The next factor is personal taste. Even for the same functionality, people are used to different 'look and feel' (colours, screen layout, etc) or just plain familiarity with a previous product.

Some logging packages allow you to rearrange the screen to your personal taste. Each component can be moved around the screen, e.g. the logging window, the packet window, the bandmap, the grayline map can all be moved around in certain packages. This can be especially useful if you want a lot of modules on screen and use two screens or you want to save screen 'real estate' and only have a small screen. e.g. on a 12" laptop. If the package writer's choice of screen pre-defined layout suits you, that's fine too.

Picking Your Software

It all depends on what are you trying to do, so let's look at some basic questions to help you pick a best-fit solution to your needs.

Assuming you want to log QSOs and you're moving away from paper logging, basic questions need to be asked such as (but not limited to):

- Which mode(s) do you want to use?
- Do you want to (or mind) use packet radio or the Internet (or neither)?
- Do you have Internet access?
- Do you have a PC, a Mac or run Linux?
- Do you want to connect your rig to the PC for it to control the rig, e.g. frequency and mode logged automatically?
- Do you operate on data modes?
- Do you want to see if and when you last made a QSO with the station you're working?
- Do you want to see the other station's name on screen, whether you've worked them before or not?
- Are you a disabled operator who prefers a particular mode, e.g. visual display of CW/data modes?
- Do you use or want to use a voice keyer that sends audio from your computer's soundcard, instead of repeating yourself on the mic over a long period of time?
- Do you mind occasionally giving away points in a contest?
- Do you contest frequently?
- Do you want to design antennas and inspect their radiation patterns?
- Do you want complete silence while operating, so you don't wake the XYL?
- Do you want to monitor beacons?

Each of the above questions is catered for, but no package does them all. Consequently it's a best-fit solution you need to look for.

Cyberphobia

For some, the time-honoured paper log is their preferred method. It works, but see the list that follows for the advantages of using a computer instead. Many things can be done on paper, but when a computer is there for you to use at little or no cost it's certainly worth a shot at trying to use it. You don't need specialist knowledge for any of the packages and there is a lot of assistance for 'newbies'.

Advantages of Using a Computer in Amateur Radio

When using software the computer has the following advantages, in no particular order. Please note that not everything applies to every package.

- An ordinary PC can be used instead of specialist IT equipment, e.g. external decoding modules are not usually required any more. You no longer need teleprinters or external modules to do RTTY, packet radio, etc. Soundcards can do this and PCs are fast enough to cope. In the early days of PCs this wasn't the case but nowadays soundcards can pick out signals below the noise level by using DSP. In fact your rig may now *be* your computer with the advent of SDR.
- Faster logging than on paper especially in a pileup (but note that if you're not familiar with your software this may not be true, so you need to be familiar with the software before you go on a DXpedition where you expect a large volume of QSOs),
- Less chance of mislogging calls or exchanges because you don't need to decipher handwriting later on, and there are files that can help you with partial callsigns to suggest full callsigns if you only have a few characters from the call.
- Real time dupe checking and "worked before" details including when you last worked the other station
- You can submit logs (contesting or general) for some awards to sites such as Log of the World, eQSL and others.
- Computers open up a whole world of other modes and interests with the added ability to work at night without waking the other half as working data modes can be totally silent (data modes are workable in complete silence, as they are visual).
- Upload, validation and awards via LOTW or eQSL
- You can export and/or print QSL card details from some packages
- You can get packet without having a packet modem. The internet contains the packet network online

- Decoding of CW for operators requiring help reading CW
- Recording of the band(s) for later playback/verification/self-training
- Recording of your operation period for checking and correcting your log after a contest/pileup/adjudication
- Enables data modes to be used e.g. SSTV, PSK, RTTY and others
- Allows high speed data to be sent e.g. for MeteorScatter
- Customisable single-press macros to send standard info e.g. locator, name, QSO number, distance calculation etc
- Logs can be sorted on callsign/band/time/whatever field you want
- Back-up. A file can be backed up multiple times and the log installed on multiple computers or even on a network, so it can be accessed or retrieved/copied/moved/shared
- Showing grayline areas on a real-time map
- Data mode packages can be used for decoding utility station broadcasts e.g. synoptic maps from the Met Office, e.g. for SWLs
- Contest functionality can include (but is not limited to):
  - o Networking PCs for multi-op and multi-multi stations/sharing of your log with other stations in your team in real time
  - o Real time scoring, so you can see how you are doing at any time and compare it to previous years
  - o Real-time uploading of scores, so you can see how competitor stations are doing during contests relative to you
  - o See and jump to DX cluster spots as soon as they arrive, often with a single click taking you to the frequency and mode
  - o Support for CW, e.g. sending CQ and handling the exchange at the touch of a button
  - o Sending voice CQs or other messages (saves your voice over a long period and in contests)
  - o Auto-repeat of CQ calls after a customisable period of time
  - o Simplified keystrokes to complete a QSO (Enter Sends Message mode)
  - o Callsign validation. Some software may inform you if a contact is suspected to be incorrect, based on the structure of the call (too long / too short, prefix not valid for that band, etc)
  - o Validation of the contact against the rules, e.g. in contests where you can only work another country/prefix/zone etc
  - o Automated calculation of distances in VHF contest using grid squares
  - o Export of logs to standard formats, ready for uploading to online logging systems, contest adjudicators and awards systems, QSL card printing software
  - o Stats, if you are into that sort of thing, e.g. rate per hour, rate per hour by continent, zones, IOTA references etc shown on screen
  - o If contesting, it may tell you which multipliers are worked or still needed
  - o 'Time on' counters (how long the station has been on the air, e.g. if you are only allowed to operate 36 out of 48 hours)

o Band timer counter (how long the station has been on the band before a band change is allowed e.g. the contests run by *CQ* have 10 minute band timers in some categories)

o The ability to set the operator callsign. This enables one PC to be shared by different operators during operating shifts on a multi-op station. This in turn allows the log to be broken down by operator, for later analysis. It may also allow customised sound files for each operator, so that single-press macros send the correct sound file for the operator on the mic.

This is not an exhaustive list. There is much more besides. All this is done seamlessly by the software and in less than the blink of an eye, while you're still trying to decipher the scribbles on a logging sheet.

I Hate Contesting!

If you don't like contests, don't let the word 'contesting' put you off. General 'DX' modules for everyday logging are almost invariably included and many other features come in useful too, such as checking previous QSOs, the ability to print QSL card labels, submit logs for awards, tell you operator names, tell you distances and bearings, decode data modes and much more.

The software packages that support contesting are generally fantastic general logging programs and many cater for additional modes, whether or not you partake in contests, whether you use these other mode offerings and features or not.

The fact that many software packages support contesting doesn't mean you have to take part in them. Similarly, a basic logging program can still cope with contest exchanges – they just go in the comments field instead of a dedicated field.

Computing Power

Do you need a whizz-bang super computer to use software packages? Not always. Some software only requires a modest PC by current standards. Some software runs under DOS, so a PC from the early '90s will do fine in many cases. For most purposes a Pentium 3 or faster will do, though faster and more modern PCs do the same thing faster and allow greater sophistication.

If you are going to use an old PC, it could be prudent to use a dedicated machine with nothing other than the operating system installed on it and possibly DOS-based or DOS-compatible packages such as SD (current) or TRLog (no longer supported). Some software was written for Windows 95 with only a modest amount of RAM (e.g. 16Mb on a 486 processor).

If you have a Windows machine you may find software that runs fine under Windows 95 or Windows 98, but some more recent packages such as N1MM require a modest amount of speed. Where a computer minimum recommendation of, say, a 500MHz processor is a minimum, if you have a better PC available then the software will respond more quickly after performing the functions you asked it to do.

In short, many PCs will do the job and you don't need a state-of-the-art machine, but an old duffer won't do you any favours either.

You won't usually have to buy a state-of-the-art machine but you would generally need a Windows machine (Windows 2000 or later recommended, but not essential), See each package's minimum requirements for details.

Most modern software is *not* compatible with Windows Vista. Windows 8 is too new at the time of writing to comment on compatibility, but if it works under Vista there is a good chance that it will work under Windows 7, but check your package's user groups and/or website for advice.

Windows XP and Windows 2000 seem to be the stable platforms that are supported. Windows 98 at a push too, but here it depends on the processor speed whether the software still performs to your speed and response expectations. The support for Windows 7 is now better than before, and consequently so is Windows Vista, but check your chosen package's user groups and/or website for advice.

Tip: For Windows Vista/Windows 7 users, a common issue is that a program needs to run with Administrator privileges, so check you're running the program as Administrator (usually right click -> Run as Administrator should do the trick).

Windows XP was a stable (or even advanced) platform that was in use when most of the programs were created, so you should have no issues here. Windows 98 at a push too, but here it depends on the processor speed whether the software still performs to your speed and response expectations.

Windows 8 should work as per Windows 7, but it's too new to tell at the time of writing.

64-bit Architecture

Whilst logging programs are quite advanced, it's not a requirement that one uses 64-bit PCs and software, so a 32-bit machine and operating system is supported, and 64-bit is backwardly compatible. There is no (current) advantage to running a 64 bit machine or operating system for logging purposes, other than that they will not tax your machine's processor as much, as these machines tend to be pretty powerful and the logger should run with ample CPU power to spare.

What about Macs?

Not well supported by developers, due to the prevalence of the Windows-based PC. That is not to say there is no software for it, there is, but it's not supported well enough to include here. The advice and tips that follow though apply equally to Mac packages as Windows/DOS ones.

Users have been known to run packages successfully under virtual machine instances of Windows.

Linux

There are logging and contesting tools for Linux too. However, it's a specialist area. Although it is loved by many, it isn't a large enough subject area to warrant a large amount of column inches here. Only a small percentage of radio users run Linux and many radio packages are supported under Wine. The advice and tips below though apply equally to Linux packages as Windows/DOS ones.

If you're getting started in radio and computing, you most likely have a PC and run a Windows product.

Please note that experience tells me N1MM needs to run under Windows and doesn't like Wine much, so needs to run natively under Windows.

Logging Software

Does software ensure accurate logs?
No, you still can mis-type a call or exchange, or even if you get all the details correctly there is no vouching for the other station copying down all your details correctly.

Which is the best software for logging?
How long is a piece of string (or antenna wire?) This is the holy grail question of logging and there is no unique answer. It depends on your needs, with a rough and ready set of questions as follows:

- What mode are you operating with? Some software supports some modes better than others, e.g. CW/SSB and data modes.
- What operating system are you using? PCs are overwhelming better supported.
- What bands are you using? Some software if dedicated to HF and others to VHF and above.
- What contest(s), if any, are you operating in?
- Are you a casual operator looking to add to your DXCC count with no intention of submitting a log so don't need scoring or serial number logging?

- Some software caters for some contests but not others, some cater for many contests but not 'minor' ones (minor being dependent on the region the coder writers live in, or the participation levels of the contests)
- What country do you live in? The software is most often in English, but some software exists in French, for example.
- Do you mind paying for the software?
- Do you want periodic updates to the software?
- Do you want to use Windows or do you not mind using DOS?
- Do you use a Mac or Linux rather than Windows?
- Do you have internet?
- Do you want to include packet spots via a TNC, the internet, or not at all?
- Do you want to read and send the CW manually or via the computer?
- Do you want to operate on data modes?

As you can see, this is a significant list of variables, and it is sure to grow with the advent of future platforms, technologies and contenders. Google may well throw some of this up in the air but only time will tell as at the time of writing it's just an announcement of the new platform being in development.

How does the software stay up to date?
You may have to check for updates periodically. If you subscribe to the reflector/user group for the software you will see notifications that there are newer versions available to download.

If you pay for your software you may get a period-limited right to updates e.g. updates for one year or for life. Check the terms of the software licence.

Note:
You may have to pay for major updates on some paid software packages.

How do I get new prefixes, countries and/or multipliers in to my software?
When countries split apart, new countries are created/declared or countries issue new prefixes, the software doesn't know about this so it refers to a file telling it which prefixes belong to which country.

Over the years the software developers have settled on a handful of formats for country files, which can be quickly and easily plugged in to a software package. This also helps the scoring in contests if the prefixes are important, as they need to be recognised to be scored correctly.

To do this you need to download the relevant country file (also known as CTY.DAT, though the actually filename may differ depending on your package). You can get a copy from www.country-files.com/cty/ Many contesting and software reflectors announce when a new country file is available for downloading.

Sometimes you need to activate this file in the software, in order for the latest version to be incorporated in to the software. For example, in N1MM just having the file on your hard drive isn't enough, you need to import it into the software. Read the instructions on how to do this.

Does software support multipliers if I am in a contest?

Many contests and awards have different multipliers (mults). Sometimes it's the prefix of the callsign, sometimes it's the DXCC country, WAE country, CQ Zone, ITU Zone, IOTA reference, locator square, province, state, region, county, postcode prefix, operator number or whatever. Every contest or award has its own rules.

Mults are often stored in what are known as .DOM or .SEC files. DOM and .SEC files translate callsigns into the relevant category for the software to recognise the relevant call areas/counties etc for correct scoring. You shouldn't need to edit these. Different software packages treat these differently, and sometimes not at all.

Check which software you use and which contests are supported. If a contest is supported, it probably handles the mults for you, and usually the mult files (.DOM or .SEC files) are bundled with the installation package. Many packages support a wide range of contests, e.g. N1MM, WinTest, SD and even DOS-based TRLog.

You may sometimes have to point the software to the relevant .DOM or .SEC file (e.g. in MixW, when setting up the log) but ultimately it should be supported. Read the manual about how to invoke the relevant mults files in to your chosen package.

If you need additional mult files these can often be found on the Internet or by asking other users on your software support mailing list. Someone usually had the same question and can provide you some guidance.

On-screen indication of mults still needed

Some software lets you view which mults you have worked and which ones are still needed, and some software will tell you on screen that the station you are working is needed on other bands as a mult on, e.g. you have worked GJ on 10m SSB but still need GJ as a mult on 10m CW and 15m CW and SSB. Each piece of software displays worked mults and needed mults differently (if at all). This is a trade-off between best use of computer screen space, software power, software development effort, software cost and, as always, operator skill.

This is not included in the software grid at the end of this chapter, as it depends on the contest whether mults are supported, and in some packages the on-screen mults window can be hidden/moved/made more prominent based on the user's taste.

Tip: Knowing which bands you need a station on is useful, as it can be used to request a QSY to the bands where you need them for a mult. They may have a station on that band already, or they may be prepared to change bands for you and meet you on an agreed frequency. The point is that seeing what mults you still need from a visual prompt, you can boost your score (or country tally or whatever), which you wouldn't otherwise have known you needed.

My mult file isn't correct. The mult isn't recognised. What can I do?
The most common issue is to have a callsign that isn't recognised as the correct DXCC entity. This is often the case for TO callsign prefixes, as all French overseas territories' special prefixes have the same prefix of TO instead of FM, FG, FJ etc. Consequently you may need to "'force' the logger to accept the call at the time of working it (see your manual for how to do this). You can always go back and check the mult file and rescore the contest later.

Most likely you didn't have the most recent DXCC file (CTY.DAT or the equivalent, e.g, wl_cty.dat in N1MM). If you go and get it from www.country-files.com/cty/, load it in to your package (if this step is required) run a rescore and then it should be fine.

How to edit a CTY.DAT file is not covered here as this is a last resort and claimed scores don't have to be (and rarely are) 100% accurate. You will get adjudicated anyway.

What is (and do I need) a partial callsign database file?
For the unfamiliar, if you type in part of a callsign into the logging software and you missed the full call you can get help with identifying who the station is, by using a lookup file of known callsigns.

Basically, it's a list of known callsigns worked by major operators (usually in contests) and put in to a list that is recognised by many software packages. You don't have to use it if you don't want to. For reference it's commonly known as 'master.dta' or 'SCP' (Super Check Partial).

Here's how it works. Say you type in 'G7TW'. The software looks for these characters and shows G7TWC and DG7TW on screen. You can either pick one and type it in to the callsign box or ignore both suggestions. It isn't a replacement for using your ears but it does help to guide you to a callsign or jog your memory.

If your software supports partial callsign databases (see your package's documentation), then you can download it from www.supercheckpartial.com/ It's usually updated about four times a year by K5ZD, following major contests such as CQWW and CQWPX. Your package may have a link directly to the site already built in.

Note: Check the version you download is compatible with your package e.g. WinTest uses a slightly different file structure and so has a dedicated version on the supercheckpartial.com site.

Note: You cannot view the SCP with a text editor, as it's encoded.

Tip: You can edit the partial call file or build one yourself from your previous logs. MEdit software is useful to do this. (www.dxatlas.com/MEdit/).

General Software Tips

What are macros and why are they needed?
Macros are basically message shortcuts assigned to a key or combination of keys. They are useful for data modes, CW and SSB, and save time and keystrokes when sending complex messages. Macros are powerful tools that can be used to send a message and a custom item e.g. your name/callsign/serial number/locator or whatever.

On any program that supports macros, the macros can be personalised however you prefer.

There is a convention that most packages share a general set of common keys, e.g. F1 = CQ. This is good news for most of us, but beware that not all macros and keypresses are the same in all packages. A common example of software packages not adopting the same convention is when wanting to turn CW keying speed up/down.

It is *not* suggested you change the basic key assignment, which is commonly (but not always) as follows:

Key	Function
F1	CQ - e.g. 'CQ de {mycall} TEST'
F2	Send exchange - e.g. 'TU UR RST {RST report} BK'
F3	End of QSO - e.g. 'Thank You' or '73 or Thank you' and go to CQ)
F4	Send my call
F5	Send other station's call (taken from the log window)
F6	'QSO before' message
F8	Request resend of number
F11	Wipe the entry window clean, i.e. bail out of a QSO and start over

Every package has a different way of setting up the commands for the software to recognise it, so read the instructions and don't be afraid to ask for help.

It is suggested that you tackle the modes separately, to avoid confusion as the commands may be different for, say, CW and RTTY, especially if you are using data modes through MMVari or MMTTY. Once you get one mode configured as you like it, then tackle the next one and so on.

For SSB you will need the sound files already recorded to be able to chain them up into usable sequences. More on that later.

The next step of this is to bundle macros together in to the powerhouse that they can be, using 'ESM'.

What ESM is and why you might want it

ESM stands for 'Enter Sends Message'. It is mainly used in contesting. Think of it as a shortcut for many key presses.

Being a shortcut, ESM means you don't have to find and press the key assigned to a macro when you're calling CQ. It's much more useful for 'run' (CQing) stations, but still useful for search-and-pounce (S&P) stations.

Here are examples of how ESM works in a CW station. This may not be the best example of CW QSO etiquette, but let's keep it simple for now.

Scenario 1	ESM off (default)	ESM on
You are running on a frequency	Press **F1** (sends 'CQ G7TWC TEST')	Press <**ENTER**> (sends 'CQ G7TWC TEST')
You hear G3ZVW call you.	Type 'G3ZVW' into log window. Press <**space**> to move to exchange received box. Press **F5** (sends his callsign: 'G3ZVW'). Press **F2** (sends exchange: 'TU 5NN 107 BK')	Type 'G3ZVW' into log window. Press <**ENTER**> (sends 'G3ZVW TU 5NN 107 BK') and moves cursor to exchange received box.
G3ZVW sends exchange (e.g. TU 5NN 005 BK).	Type 005 into exchange box. Press **F3** (sends 'TU G7TWC TEST')	Type 005 into exchange box. Press <**ENTER**> (sends 'TU G7TWC TEST')
Number of F-keys & space keys pressed.	5	0
Number of <ENTER> key pressed.	0	3

ESM Visual Prompting

Software packages normally highlight which buttons are those that would be sent next during ESM.

In the example shown in **Fig 3.1**, G3ZVW has replied to my CQ and I have typed his callsign in. As highlighted, ESM will next send the contents of F5 (acknowledge G3ZVW) and then F2 (my exchange) the next time I press <ENTER>.

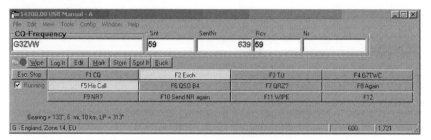

Fig 3.1: N1MM in 'run' mode with ESM switched on.

Scenario 2	ESM off	ESM on
You are running on a frequency	Press **F1** (sends 'CQ G7TWC TEST')	Press **ENTER** (sends 'CQ G7TWC TEST')
You hear G3ZVW call you.	Type 'G3ZVW' into log window. Press **<space>** to move to exchange received box. Press **F5** (sends his call: G3ZVW). Press **F2** (sends exchange 'TU 5NN 107 BK')	Type 'G3ZVW' into log window. Press <**ENTER**> (sends 'G3ZVW TU 5NN 107 BK' and moves cursor to exchange received box.
G3ZVW sends exchange but you don't hear it, so need to ask for a resend.	Find and press **F8** (sends 'NR?')	You haven't logged anything in the received exchange box. Press <**ENTER**> (sends contents of F8 ('NR?')
G3ZVW resends exchange (e.g. '5NN 005 005 BK')	Type '005' into exchange box Press **F3** (sends 'TU G7TWC TEST')	Type in 005 in to exchange box. Press <**ENTER**> (sends contents of F3 ('TU G7TWC TEST')
Number of F-keys + space keys pressed	6	0
Number of <ENTER> key pressed	0	4

With ESM on, you are not expected to press the F-keys, although they are still available for you to use as normal. You could press F5 or interrupt your ESM flow to send a custom message from another F-key, or you could use your Morse key at any point. Using ESM doesn't stop you doing what you want, but it does simplify the basic sequence of tasks and prompt you what is coming next.

ESM also works for SSB (see below about macros and voice files), assuming you have a sound card or DVK.

ESM and Macros for CW

What goes in to your macros is a question of taste, but for the uninitiated you may want a template to work off.

Whilst every package has a different 'dialect' of macro, the idea is generally the same. Consult the software manual for the exact commands for your package. The example below is from N1MM (included on the CD that accompanies this book).

The key thing to do is to try it out. Note that N1MM doesn't support side-tone keying without being plugged in to a rig (a frequently asked question) so I thought I'd mention it.

Key	Function	Macro
F1	CQ	CQ * TEST or CQ {MYCALL} TEST
F2	Send contest exchange	TU 5NN {exch} or TU 5NN #
F3	Thank You (for after the QSO, go to CQ)	TU * TEST or TU {MYCALL} TEST
F4	Send my call	* or {MYCALL}
F5	Send his call (taken from the log window)	!
F6	QSO before	SRI QSO B4
F7	Can be personalised, e.g. '?'	Can be personalised or leave a single blank space
F8	Request number resend	NR?
F9	Resend serial number/exch	5NN {exch} {exch} BK or 5NN # # BK
F10	Can be personalised	Can be personalised or leave a single blank space
F11	Clear the current unlogged callsign in the logging window	{WIPE}
F12	Can be personalised	Can be personalised or leave a single blank space

What DVK is and Why You Might Want It

DVK is short for Digital Voice Keyer. Basically, it's a module or specialised hardware that you record or upload your voice into. At a key press - either on the module or via the computer - it plays back the voice file through the rig. Consult your instructions on how to upload or record the audio and set up the playback.

DVK does not use a computer's soundcard to play back a file. It's basically a soundcard in a stand-alone box and it does what it's meant to very well. Various manufacturers make these for ham purposes.

Macros for SSB

Most operators use a soundcard instead of a Digital Voice Keyer (DVK) for voice keying. In order to send audio files from your keyboard using macros, you need to (1) have or make the sound files you will need, (2) set up the macros in the software, and (3) have a lead from the PC's headphone or Line Out socket into the rig's Patch port (if it has one) or microphone socket. When the radio goes to transmit, any audio from the PC will be sent out on the air, including any PC alerts, software startup sounds etc, so turn those off wherever possible.

This works whether you use ESM or not.

Why use macros for SSB? To reduce the workload on your voice. It is highly recommended, unless you enjoy calling CQ for many hours in a long contest. It's also useful for operators with speech disabilities.

Voice Files Using Your Computer's Sound Card

If you're thinking of using your computer to play your SSB macros, you will need a sound file for each part of the macro you are trying to send. You need to have recorded these before the contest.

You don't need to record all F-keys or every callsign under the sun to do this. 'CQ' and 'MYCALL' will do for a basic setup that saves you loads of effort. For example, you will need a CQ file (saying something like 'CQ Contest G7TWC Contest') and a MYCALL file (saying something like 'Golf 7 Tango Whiskey Charlie'). These normally need to be uncompressed Wave (.WAV) type files.

I suggest using Audacity (free from http://audacity.sourceforge.net/) or other sound recording and editing package is adequate. Remove all leading and trailing gaps from the sound file, so there are no unnecessary silences.

Next, you need to name the file(s) in accordance with the software. For example, N1MM expects all CQ calls to contain the word CQ somewhere in the filename.

Next you need to assign the macro to the sound file. Consult the manual for your package on where to find this and what the software is looking for. In N1MM the path is usually C:\Program Files\N1MM Logger\WAV\

Next, test that the playback works as expected by pressing the macro key, e.g. F1. Do this without the lead plugged into the Headphones / Line Out socket. You should hear your recorded sound file play from the PC speaker.

The most common reason why the file doesn't play is because it isn't in the right location. Also, check the volume setting on your computer is at a comfortable volume and isn't muted.

Plug in your patch cable from the Headphones / Line Out socket to the Patch or microphone socket of your radio. Turn down the power output on your radio to minimum and/or connect a dummy load to your radio. Press F1 to send CQ. If the Monitor function is enabled on your radio you should hear your CQ transmitted.

Common Sound Problems

If you receive reports of distorted audio on playing a sound file from the PC, you almost certainly need to adjust the play volume on the PC. It's very easy to overdrive a transceiver's microphone input from a perfectly clear-sounding audio file. The rig is pretty sensitive and will pick up what it thinks is loud audio (and which we think is perfectly acceptable).

Sometimes a sound file is distorted or too loud when recorded. Listen to it in a sound player (not through the monitor facility of the rig) to determine if it is. Re-record it if necessary. You may be able to adjust the audio level before saving files, within the recording software.

Complicated Voice Files

Some software packages can send audio letters and numbers for you, e.g. the station you are working's callsign and your sent exchange. This is trickier, as you cannot pre-record all permutations of calls etc, so here's the next-best option.

N1MM, for example, looks in separate folders called 'letters' and 'numbers' within in the WAV folder, to get the relevant letters and numbers. It can string them together to make an exchange. It usually sounds like a robot, but it works. I know someone who gets "thanks, nice robot" when using his voice files.

The advantage of using this is that it works well if you have limited voice capacity or have a frog in your throat. The disadvantages are that it is fiddly to set up, sounds unnatural and doesn't cover impromptu replies. Consult your software to find if it supports this functionality.

Auto-sending an Operator's Name

There are some contests in which you need to send the operator's name (or you may just feel like sending it). This can be done with a 'friends' file. Usually it's named 'friend.ini'. Each software package, if supported, will need to be set up separately, so please consult your manual.

A friend.ini file that is generally available and quite comprehensive can be found at http://www.af4z.com/ham/. Personally, I found it quite disturbing that someone I'd never worked knew my name, but I soon got used to it.

In effect, you can create or add your own friends file, by taking the general one and copying the layout and editing the contents using a text editor.

As with any piece of info you log with artificial aids, it isn't a replacement for using your ears. If the friends file says the operator's name is Robert but the station sends 'Bob', then log 'Bob' contrary to what's in the friends file. This is especially so in some contests where operators like to have fun and choose obscure names that aren't based on their real names. It happens!

An example would be a combination of macros that when strung together make up 'G3ZVW de G7TWC GA STEVE UR RST 599 HW?' where 'STEVE' is inserted from a {NAME} macro. The {NAME} macro matched the callsign G3ZVW, which returned the name and this was included. If the {NAME} macro finds no entry for a callsign, no name is returned and the combination macro will be sent without a name.

Tracking Band and Frequency

Depending on your make and model of radio and which software you are running, you can interface it to the software so that it knows what frequency and mode you're on. This information then goes in to the log entries, so that the contacts are logged against the correct band and mode.

This is usually done via Computer Adied Transceiver (CAT) control. Basically, it's a serial port on the back of the rig (although sometimes you require a module to do this, as on older transceivers such as the FT-1000D). You connect the CAT cable to the serial port on the PC. If you only have USB ports, you will need an interface module for this, either a Winkey or other commercially available unit such as one from the Microham range.

Select the rig from the logging software (many packages support a wide range of rigs) and then the relevant information is sent to the rig and back by the software, which has been written to interface with the rig on many pieces of functionality e.g. PTT on/off, frequency, sideband/mode, RIT shift, rotator info and quite a bit more. What is supported depends on the software and the capabilities of the rig. Check the software package, and indeed, check your rig, as not all functionality is the same on all rigs.

CAT control is vital for clickable bandmaps populated by packet spots, since if you click on a spot in the bandmap it can make the rig change mode, frequency and even band to go to the spot.

Sending the Time

Some contests (e.g. the BARTG RTTY) require you to send the time in UTC as part of the exchange. This is usually a macro, and may differ from package to package, so please consult your manual for the macros required.

Rotator Control
Some packages can control antenna rotators. You need to investigate this based on your requirements and the model of rotator you have.

SteppIR Control
Some logging software packages can communicate with a SteppIR controller. You need to investigate this based on your requirements. A good starting point is whether the software supports CAT control. If yes, then can it send this info to the controller unit? It also depends on the model of rig you have. Although it is not the only package to support this function, N1MM is known to support Yaesu FT1000s with SteppIRs attached.

Operator Statistics
For multi-operator stations, some software packages support operator statistics. If you can set the operator's call in the software (separately from the callsign being used on the air) you can create statistics based on an operator's on-time, to see the rate and how some operators performed or how the band shaped-up during their turn at the helm.

Naturally enough, to do this the software needs to know which operator is on the air. Check the instructions of your package on how to change the operator callsign.

Peronal Audio Files
Some software packages can be configured to use specific audio files, depending on which operator is on the microphone. As long as you tell the software which operator is on, the files that correspond to the operator are played.

Data Modes

There are various software packages out there for data mode operation. Many modes exist, new ones are being created from time to time and there are variations on themes (e.g. BPSK63 and 125, MFSK 4 through 64, Olivia 500). As a starting point, let's assume you want to know how to get these on your PC when hooked-up to your rig.

For modes such as RTTY and PSK31, the simplest way is to get your PC to generate the audio tones and connect the audio to the rig either via the 'Patch' port or via the microphone socket. The rig is set to go into transmit a fraction of a second before the audio plays (using the PTT command line keying over a serial or LPT port), and the rig transmits the audio that is fed to it. This is known as Audio Frequency Shift Keying (AFSK).

Alternatively, some modes can be generated by radios natively (e.g. RTTY, packet), in which case you basically tell the radio when to go into transmit and what (but not how) to transmit. This is called

Frequency Shift Keying (FSK).

You will need macros to send the relevant messages and you will need to read the instruction manual on your software package to set up those macros.

See the table at the end of this chapter for a list of packages that support data modes. Note that many packages do not support data modes natively, but are able to interface with external modules that do. e.g. N1MM with MMTTY (for RTTY) and MMVari (for PSK and RTTY). FLDigi and MixW are dedicated pieces of (paid) software that handle a wide range of data modes very well. In addition to the packages listed, others are available.

Packet Radio

Packet Radio is still alive and well on VHF/UHF, but these days the DX Cluster can also be accessed via the Internet. The Internet brings you the cluster faster than ever, and in many cases it can populate a bandmap (a panel on-screen showing you what stations are on what frequency, in frequency order, and can often colour code entries for new countries/zones/prefixes etc).

If you want, posting DX spots can now be done *en masse* from your package, merely by enabling a setting that posts all QSOs from Search & Pounce mode (QSOs made where you weren't the station calling CQ) to the cluster.

Many logging packages now include packet DX Cluster functionality. Look in your manual for Packet access using Telnet, to see if accessing the DX Cluster is supported.

Warning:When it comes to the setting-up of filters, DX Cluster commands can be very complicated.

Note: Not all software packages support networking, so this doesn't always work.

Tip: See below for simplifying Packet use using AR User (aka VE7CC) software.

Tip: If the list of Internet packet clusters on your package is small, you can supplement it with the file of additional clusters from http://www.dxcluster.info/telnet/index.php (if this link doesn't work, look on the Internet for "list of dxclusters").

Tip: Assuming you are contesting or even casually operating, some contests have Assisted entry categories (i.e. the use of Packet/DX Cluster use). By having access to the DX Cluster you can find out about additional contacts and/or multipliers from the DX Cluster during a contest, discover what frequency they are on and jump to them, often by just clicking in the bandmap (if available).

Advantages

● You can find extra multipliers to work, boosting your points
● You can find extra stations to work, e.g. if the band seems dead, you may want to listen on a spotted station's frequency and see if they appear out of the noise for you to work them when you wouldn't otherwise have known they were there
● Some software packages populate a bandmap and may allow you to click on the spot to take you to the frequency and pre-fill the callsign box, ready for you to work them
● Spots can be posted in near-real time for you to see ('near-real time', because the spots may take some time to transfer around the Packet network)
● It is mirrored on the Internet, so even if you don't have access to a VHF Packet cluster you can still access it (see the Tip below). The Internet is usually faster than the Packet network and you can ask for a backlog of spots quickly or set filters on the spots you receive
● Even if you can't hear a spotted station, it can indicate that propagation is around, e.g. if Belgians are hearing Italians on 6m it may be possible that the Sporadic-E cloud will reach the UK's Eastern shores soon
● You can set filters on the spots, so you only receive the mode/band/multipliers you want, e.g. you may only want 80m stations from G who are working CW. This is fiddly to do, but possible. (see the *Tip Make using the cluster over the internet easier* below)

Disadvantages

● Spots can be posted from anywhere, e.g. a US station spot might spot a VK on 80m, but you're in England in the daytime you have no chance of hearing or working the VK, so it is not helpful to see this type of Spot.
● Being on the cluster is no guarantee of you being able to hear the DX.
● In remote locations, you may have no access to the Internet or the DX Cluster.
● The language used by the DX Cluster for you to set filters, send or force an update of Spots can be fiddly (see *Tip: Make using the cluster over the internet easier* below)
● DX Spots can be wrong - callsigns incorrect, 0s and Os transposed, letters typed in the incorrect order, etc. Watch out especially for missing '/P' in Spots, which can affect your score as portable stations are worth extra points in some contests. In short, rely on your ears, not on the screen.

Mobile DXClustering

Now that many mobile phones have GPRS or 3G functionality, the Internet is available wherever you go (subject to coverage), so you can use your phone as a modem for your computer. For more info on this, consult your phone provider or search on the Internet.

Note: There may be costs associated with data usage, so consult your provider and know your tariff. Be especially careful when abroad, as data charges can be astronomic and are usually not covered by your monthly tariff.

Bandmaps

If you are connected to a Packet cluster (whether over the air or via the Internet) you receive the Packet Spots. Some logging packages populate these spots on to a graphical representation of the band, known as a bandmap. Depending on the software you use, this may be clickable, so you can click on the Spot on the bandmap, the rig changes to the required mode and frequency and maybe you get to work them. This is a good way to pick up points if they are a new multiplier.

An example from N1MM is shown in **Fig 3.2**. The colours of the callsigns represent different things: red=multiplier needed, green=double multiplier needed, blue=station needed but not a multiplier, grey=station already worked.

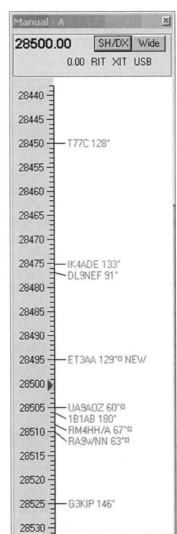

Fig 3.2: N1MM bandmap.

If you have use a Telnet Packet Cluster, to set filters up is hard work and fiddly, and you need to know how to set them in a language that the cluster understands.

Instead of connecting the logging software directly to the Cluster, we put a program in the middle to do all the customisable filtering. A powerful program to do this is AR User software (aka VE7CC), available from www.ve7cc.net. Once installed, you connect AR User to your chosen cluster, but now you can set the bands and modes you want and don't want, or which continents or countries you want/don't want to see spots from. This is done via a graphical interface, so it is much easier to use.

This information can then be sent internally through your PC to the logging software, often using port 127.0.0.1:7300. In your logging software, e.g. N1MM, point the cluster address to IP address 127.0.0.1 port 7300. In simple terms, all network traffic is sent within the computer so that another piece of software (your logging program) can see it.

You need to leave AR User software

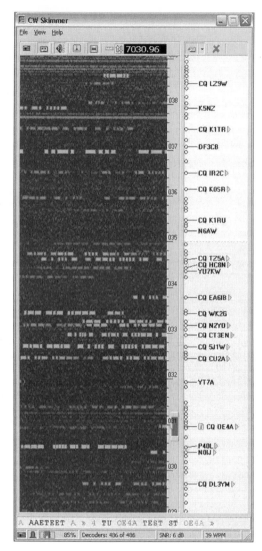

Fig 3.3: CW Skimmer can decode hundreds of signals simultaneously. The usual limiting factor is the bandwidth sent to it.

running and logged on to a DX Cluster in the background while you use your logger. Any action you take on the logger software will run the command for you on the AR User software, e.g. pressing 'SH/DX' on your logging software gets you the most recent spots from the cluster, with AR User doing the filtering for you.

All this depends on which logging software package you are using.

CW Readers

CW Skimmer

Skimmer (included on the CD that accompanies this book) allows you to use the soundcard of a PC to decode the entire audio passband of the rig or SDR unit into intelligible information, i.e. callsigns and/or exchange info.

Basically, you connect the audio from the rig or SDR and it decodes the CW for you. How successfully it does this depends on the quality of the audio, the rig and the passband. If your passband is 500Hz, you may only get two or three stations decoded, but if you pass 150kHz of 20m in from a Software Defined Radio (SDR) you may get - as **Fig 3.3** shows - dozens of stations decoded.

Skimmer is only as good as the signals passed to it, and you being able to 'view' the signal you want to contact (amongst many others also being decoded simultaneously). The power of the software is that it is pretty good (but not perfect) at decoding CW, and with digital technology in an SDR and the algorithms in the software, you can 'hear' stations below the noise level. However, it isn't a replacement for your ears. CW Skimmer can be set to decode only CQing stations or anything it hears.

CW Skimmer is *not* a contest software package, but if set up correctly it can be used to aid an operator in a CW contest as it 'finds' many CW stations and decodes them, thus helping operators find additional contacts. Naturally, the operaator still has to go and work the stations.

The Great CW Skimmer Debate
Whilst there are opponents who believe that this kind of technology is

the death-knell of radio, in past generations there have been those who said that about SSB when AM was commonplace, or when FM was introduced, or even when electricity was invented! You don't *have* to move with the times; you can log with pen and paper if you want. Sure it presents more options, but it doesn't replace using your ears.

Incidentally, the CW Skimmer idea is not new. WriteLog software has had similar functionality for years, allowing users to decode CW on or around their frequency in to plain text, albeit not a whole band simultaneously.

CW Skimmer is available at /www.dxatlas.com/CwSkimmer/ (trial version) and costs US$75 for a full licence.

Note that use of Skimmer in *CQ* Magazine contests (CQWW, CQWPX etc) puts you in to the Assisted category.

Decoding CW

Although not a contesting piece of software, there are pieces of software that help operators with poor CW skills to be able to 'listen' to (or realistically 'watch') and decode CW signals by transcribing what it 'heard' into text on screen. One such package is CWGet, available at www.dxsoft.com/en/products/cwget/ ($35, •30, unlimited free trial).

Basically, you connect the audio from the rig's AF out or similar to your PC's line in or mic socket and let the software decode what it hears.

Advantages

● Allows non-CW operators to operate CW by decoding CW signals
● Allows non-CW operators to work Search & Pounce effectively, by being able to decode the station they are trying to work over a series of QSOs with other stations, and then jump in to make the contact as they know what serial number to expect next. This makes CW less daunting and allows unskilled operators to take their time. This method has been known to work well enough to win certificates in contests such as WPX CW, which has enough categories to accommodate casual, inexperienced operators.
● Clear or strong signals can be decoded easily
● Works best, in the author's experience, when in QRS Corral, i.e. the slow speed section of a contest band (if there is one), as stations coming back send relatively slowly, giving it more time to adjust the listening position of the software (see disadvantages, below).

Disadvantages

● If you have a contesting package open, you need to also have CWGet open to view it. This may use valuable real-estate on your screen.
● When you click on CWGet it is the PC's focus, the logging/contest-

ing package is no longer the PC's focus. If you want to then send something from the contesting package you first need to make it active, which involves an extra mouse or key press, (e.g. ALT-TAB to toggle the focus in Windows) or click the mouse somewhere on the contesting software screen to make it active. This can lose you valuable seconds.

● CWGet is not so good if you are CQing, as stations don't always reply to you on the frequency or at pitch you are listening for. To cater for this there are AutoGTM or GoToMax buttons (used in conjunction with AFC functionality), but it takes a moment for the AFC to act, so you may lose the start of the callsign.

● If you don't use AutoGTM or GoToMax, or even AFC, then you need to click on the signal, which isn't instant because you need to hear or see the station before you can click on it. Once again you may miss some characters of the callsign.

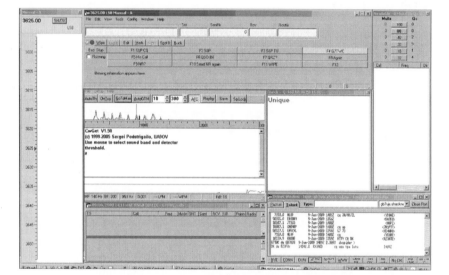

Fig 3.4: CWGet, surrounded by N1MM windows.

Tip: If you position windows of the contesting software around the CWGet screen (as shown in **Fig 3.4**), you may be able reduce the distance you need to move the mouse. This can be a precarious task, which I have used to good effect. It doesn't eliminate the focus issue, but it does reduce it.

Tip: To avoid the focus issue, you may wish to have two PCs active, one for the logging software and one for CWGet, so the PC is always focused on one task, i.e. the logging software on PC1 and CWGet on PC2. PC2 doesn't need to do anything else but 'listen' to the audio from the radio.

Satellite Tracking

For those interested in tracking the positions of satellites, various pieces of software can plot the course of satellites in orbit. Various tools exist such as the free tool Gpredict (http://gpredict.oz9aec.net/) and Orbitron (www.softpedia.com/get/Others/Miscellaneous/Orbitron.shtml).

Amsat have a range of products advertised in their magazine and a section dedicated to software at: www.amsat.org/amsat-new/tools/ software.php Kepler values to track satellite passes can be downloaded from various sources, including (but not limited to) www.amsat.org/amsat-new/tools/keps.php

General Resources

A multitude of maps for CQ and ITU zones, grid squares, prefixes and other useful tools are freely available from: www.dxatlas.com A vast array of tools and article is available from: www.ac6v.com/software.htm and: www.dxzone.com/catalog/Software/

Learning Morse

I have found useful tools such as Koch which incrementally build up your morse alphabet in pairs of letters (free from: www.g4fon.net/ CW%20Trainer.htm).

To practice CW in a contest environment there is the excellent Morse Runner (free from: www.dxatlas.com/MorseRunner/) or you can try G4FON's Contest Trainer (www.g4fon.net/Contest_Trainer.htm). They have adjustable speeds, replicate common macros used in contests and have customisable noise and numbers of stations calling, just like in a real contest. You can start with a nice loud signal with no QRM or QSB and build up your confidence by working 'real' stations without fear of judgment or other stations nearby drowning you out. No radio is required, as it's all done through the sound card.

A variety of Morse training software may be found on the CD that accompanies this book.

Which Logging Package is Best?

This is a question to which there is no definitive answer. There follows a grid for reference, so you can weigh up the pros and cons. It's not a complete list of functionality, but a subset of what core functionality you may wish your logging software to support.

Logging software packages and facilities

Software package	Platform	Cost	Support	Modes	Network support for multi-op/multi-machine use	Packet support	Enter Sends Message (ESM) mode support	Winkey support	HF	VHF	CAT supported	Notes
N1MM www.n1mm.com	Windows	Free	Yahoo group feedback and support forum. Frequent software version updates (approx 3 per month).	CW SSB Data	Y	Y Packet and Telnet	Y	Y	Y	Y	Y	Data modes require external modules, e.g. MMTTY/MMVari/MMPSK RSGB contests supported but UK VHF scoring is unsupported Supports rotator control and StepplR Basic log for non-contest operation provided under module 'DX' or 'VHF DX' For unsupported contests, 'DXSerial' module supports basic serial numbering contests Widespread support for RSGB contests Customisable screen layout. Frequent software updates Responsive and co-operative development team

Software package	Platform	Cost	Support	Modes	Network support for multi-op/multi-machine use	Packet support	Enter Sends Message (ESM) mode support	Winkey support	HF	VHF	CAT supported	Notes
SD (HF logger) SDV (VHF logger) www.ei5di.com	Windows	Shareware (from •10) Free	Periodic updates by its creator.	CW SSB	N	N	Y	Y	Y SD	Y SDV	Y	Software supports UK contests as standard and a large number of additional contests Aimed at single-op unassisted contest entrants. Does not support multi-op networked station operation SDV supports RSGB VHF contest scoring and postcode multipliers
WriteLog v11.x www.writelog.com	Windows	US$30 per 12 months (V10.9 US$18)	Contesting.com Internet feedback and support forum Periodic updates by its creator.	CW SSB RTTY	Y	Y	Y	Y	Y	Y	Y	Includes inbuilt CW and RTTY decoder Minimum Windows 2000 required (for V11) Third party plug-ins available from: http://writelog.com/downloads/third-party
TRLog www.trlog.com	DOS	$60 or $75 initially, $15/year or $100 lifetime	Online e-mail reflector. No new versions since 2006 (though long history of support and stability).	CW SSB	Y	Y	Y	Y	Y	Y	Y Rigs newer than the software may not be supported	Requires dedicated DVK sound card to send audio Does not use the internal sound cards of modern PCs Works on PCs down to 80286 spec (late 1980s)

Logging software packages and facilities

Software package	Platform	Cost	Support	Modes	Network support for multi-op/multi-machine use	Packet support	Enter Sends Message (ESM) mode support	Winkey support	HF	VHF	CAT supported	Notes
MixW www.mixw.net	Windows	V2.x new user US$70 +tax Upgrade from V2.x to V3.x US$50 +tax (free if registered over 10 years - online callsign to check status)	User support via Yahoo groups.	Data: (BPSK [PSK], QPSK, FSK31, RTTY, MFSK, Olivia, Hellschr., SSTV, Fax, Throb, Amtor, Pactor, MT63), SSB, CW.	N	Y see notes	N	Y see notes	Y	Y	N	Widely supports data modes. Olivia mode plugin available via free DLL download from website Version updates released sporadically (often with same version numbering) Poor packet spot interface V2 not integrated with a bandmap QRZ.com lookup supported via external drivers Powerful, but fiddly to get started Has a tendency to merge macros from previous usage, unless told explicitly not to (not always desirable) Export to Cabrillo not intuitive, but is possible Customisable screen layout Winkey not supported, but Microham provide dedicated instructions for their product support at: www.microham.com/ Downloads/MK_MixW_Setup.pdf Telnet packet spot integration (V3) but no link to bandmap. Bandmap not supported

Software package	Platform	Cost	Support	Modes	Network support for multi-op/multi-machine use	Packet support	Enter Sends Message (ESM) mode support	Winkey support	HF	VHF	CAT supported	Notes
Wintest www.win-test.com	Windows	•50 Upgrade from V3 •20		CW SSB RTTY (via MMTTY interface)	Y	Y	V4+ only V3.x not supported	Y	Y	Y	Y	Runs on old-spec Windows machines (166MHz+). Has useful graph for continents worked over time, which can help an operator know how propagation is changing. Customisable screen layout. Robust networking
DX4WIN www.dx4win.com	Windows	V8 $89.95 (less for upgrades from previous versions)	E-mail reflector.	CW SSB PSK31 RTTY	N	Y	Y	Y	Y	Y	Y	Performs basic customisable contesting. Customisable screen layout. Comprehensive awards tracking
Logger32 www.logger32.net	Windows (not Vista)	Free	User support via Yahoo groups.	CW SSB RTTY (via MMTTY) PSK (via MMVari)	Y	Y	N	Y	Y	Y	Y	Although not contesting software, serial number functionality is supported for casual operating in contests
MMTTY http:// mmhamsoft.ca	Windows	Free	User support via Yahoo groups.	RTTY	N	N See notes	N	N	N/A	N/A	Y	Although this can be used as a standalone piece of software, it can also be used as the data engine for other packages, e.g. N1MM, which allow greater networking and packet functionality.

Logging software packages and facilities

Software package	Platform	Cost	Support	Modes	Network support for multi-op/multi-machine use	Packet support	Enter Sends Message (ESM) mode support	Winkey support	HF	VHF	CAT supported	Notes
MMVari http://mmham soft.amateur-radio.ca/MMVari/	Windows	Free	User support via Yahoo groups.	RTTY PSK FSK MFSK	N	N See notes	N	N	N/A	N/A	Y	Although this can be used as a standalone piece of software, it can also be used as the data engine for other packages, e.g. N1MM, which allow greater networking and packet functionality
JVComm32 www.pervisell.com/download/roote.htm	Windows	£49.98 but demo version also	By e-mail to its creator.	HF-FAX weather images, SDUS RTTY SYNOP NAVTEX SSTV	N	N	N	N	N	N	N	Reception-only tool for monitoring HF utilities / amateur radio data. Tx available for ham users with callsigns. Supports Windows 7 including 64-bit, but not Vista. Min spec PC, 166MHz
Ham Radio Deluxe(HRD) and Digital Master DM-780 www.ham-radio-deluxe.com/	Windows XP or better. Mac under VMWare or Parallels	Free without support. Approx US$80 with support subscription, plus free upgrade to V6 when available	Via online forum http://forums.ham-radio.ch/ or individual support with subscription	All the modes available on your rig. DM-780 module supports a large number of data modes	N but multiple sessions can run multiple instances of rigs	Y DXCluster over the internet	N	Y	Y	Y	Y	Software is essentially a graphical front end for your rig. Includes satellite tracking, rotator support, datamodes (DM-780 software), logbook, awards tracking. Advanced contest logging not supported, but ad hoc contest contacts can be logged with contest information

Software package	Platform	Cost	Support	Modes	Network support for multi-op/multi-machine use	Packet support	Enter Sends Message (ESM) mode support	Winkey support	HF	VHF	CAT supported	Notes
FLdigi http://www.w1hkj.com/Fldigi.html	Windows MacOS X Linux FreeBSD	Free	By e-mail to the development team	CW, SSB PSK RTTY THROB Hell Olivia MFSK Thor MT63 Domino Throb Domino WEFAX SITORB	N	N	N	N	Y	N	Y	Powerful program that works across platforms. Wide variety of modes supported. Supports contesting. Modular installation of rig control and other added functionality, based on user's needs. Plugins available for DXCC, LoTW tracking, and eQSL tracking and integration
Minos http://minos.berlios.de	Windows 95/98/ME/XP/Vista Lunix (under Wine)	Free (open source)	Online forum	Logs, SSB, CW & FM QSOs	N	N	N	N	N	Y	N	Simple yet powerful offline VHF/UHF/SHF logger from G0GJV (previous DOS VHF logger author). RSGB VHF contests supported, including postcode multipliers. Excellent callsign and locator part-matching from previous QSOs in previous logs, to suggest callsign and/or locator. Logs can be output as .kml files, showing QSOs overlaid on Google Earth. Supports CTY.DAT. Multiple contests can be run simultaneously, allowing different exchanges to be logged for each

4.
Antenna Modelling

by Ian Birkenshaw, G4UWK

Introduction

The average computer-literate radio amateur might initially ask why he should bother with antenna modelling, not being an antenna designer or guru. However, every amateur is faced with limitations imposed by real estate, available supports, planning permission from the XYL, neighbours or local council and will want to maximise the radiated signal from his QTH within these restrictions.

Antenna modelling using a home computer can answer many questions, particularly in comparing one possible antenna against another. It can also answer questions about the real performance available from commercial antennas, often described in glowing terms by manufacturers or suppliers.

All antenna modelling software likely to be of interest to the typical amateur is based around a modelling system called 'Numerical Electromagnetic Code version 2' or NEC2. This was created in 1981 by the Livingstone Livermore Laboratories in California, the original client being the US Navy. Initially the system was classified, but over the years became available for general use. Originally written in FORTRAN, the code has been translated over the years for use by the Microsoft Windows operating system.

An intermediate version written in BASIC for early PC's called MININEC also exists, but has a number of problems due to it being a cut-down version of NEC2.

NEC2 works by breaking the radiating elements of the antenna to be modelled into small portions called 'segments' and summing the overall electromagnetic radiation from the current and phase on these segments to produce the actual radiation pattern in a mathematical process called 'Method of Moments'.

Readers with a strong physics or maths background may like to peruse the original design methodology. It is available on the Internet at: www.nec2.org

A number of antenna modelling software packages are available based on NEC2. Some of these are freeware and some have to be purchased. It should be stated that the original NEC2 software is far from user friendly. It was written for professional antenna designers using mainframe computers and requires considerable additional add-ons to make it more intuitive and easier to use.

All versions define models on a 3-axis grid, X and Y orthogonally in the horizontal plane and along the Z axis vertically. Some knowledge of basic geometry (sine, cosine and tangent) is essential to model with NEC2.

All antenna elements are defined as wires made up as a number of segments.

A more powerful version NEC4 is available, with additional features beyond NEC2. This still has a restricted security status and requires the user to obtain a licence before purchasing the actual software as part of an antenna modelling package. Unfortunately this costs several hundred pounds and would only be of interest to the serious antenna designer.

A list of available NEC2 based antenna modelling software is detailed in **Table 4.1.**

Product Name	Supplier	Web Site	Free Demo Version?
4nec2	Arie Voos	http://home.ict.nl/~arivoors/	Freeware
Nec2Go	Nova Plus Software	http://www.nec2go.com/	Yes
EZNEC V5.0	Roy Lewallen W7EL	http://www.eznec.com/	Yes
NEC – Win Plus	Nittany Scientific	http://www.nittany-scientific.com	No

Table 4.1: NEC2-based antenna modelling software.

It is left to the reader to select the appropriate package for themselves. They all do basically the same job and any of them will require an investment in time to get familiar with the features. Obviously the software available as freeware or as free demo will be more attractive.

Practical Example

We will now model a real life antenna, the popular G5RV multi-band dipole, complete with transmission line feeder to show how it is done. We will use the NEC2-based EZNEC program for this.

EZNEC is de-facto the amateur standard antenna modelling package, and is relatively easy to use. EZNEC stands for Easy NEC! It is available as a download or CD and runs on Windows version 98. ME, 2000, XP, Vista and Windows 7.

The standard EZNEC V5.0 has a 500 segment capacity; the larger EZNEC+ V5.0 has 1500 segment capacity, allowing more complex or accurate models. These versions have to be purchased.

A free download demonstration version with a maximum of 20 segments is available from the EZNEC website. This is also supplied with the *ARRL Antenna Handbook* on its accompanying CD. The free demo version can be used for the example about to be described, but the number of segments will be restricted to 19 rather than the 51 used. This results in inaccurate feed impedance and SWR values above 10 MHz. However, if this limitation is accepted, the radiation plots are similar.

The capability to model with more segments allows more complex models to be analysed but be aware that processing time increases with the number of segments used.

It is impossible in this short chapter to show all the bells and whistles available or all the caveats inherent in NEC2, but the hope is it will wet the appetite of the reader. A full 185-page manual is available from the EZNEC website.

Fig 4.1: EZNEC Desktop Logo.

Fig 4.1 shows the Desktop Icon for EZNEC. (Version EZNEC+ V5.0) Double clicking on this produces the main EZNEC Control Centre screen – **Fig 4.2**.

This has a top menu, a left hand toolbar with buttons and to the right of this another toolbar with buttons.

EZNEC does not allow you to start with a blank canvas, rather one of the pre-loaded example models needs to be opened and modified to suit the antenna to be modelled. After that, EZNEC always starts up with last antenna modelled. This is automatically saved under filename 'LAST.EZ' when the program is closed. The pre-loaded models enable the first time user to find what each menu item does. Simple models of the basic antenna types, dipoles, yagis, and full wave loops are included in the preloaded library.

Click 'File' and then 'Open' and look for 'BYDipole' in the list of supplied

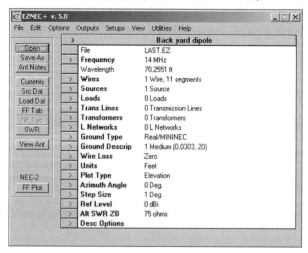

Fig 4.2: The EZNEC Control Centre Window with the sample model BYDipole opened.

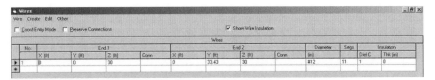

Fig 4.3: The Wires Window for BYDipole.

example models. Left click on this, then click 'Open'. The Control Centre window reveals we have opened the model file BYDipole.EZ which is a 'Back yard Dipole' for 20 metres at a height of 30ft.

Click 'Wires', which opens the Wires definition window – **Fig 4.3**. The single wire dipole is defined as a wire with End 1 and End 2 xyz co-ordinates. The wire is 12 gauge bare copper and is 33.43 feet long at a height of 30ft with 11 segments. The Wires window is where the antenna to be modelled is defined as a series of wires. We will be using only one wire, but more complex models will need many wires and it can be a tedious process to correctly define all of them. Certain tools are provided under the Create function to more easily define structures like radials, loops and helixes.

Note the last two columns, dealing with insulation. This allows antennas with plastic coated wires to be modelled. The effect of the coating is to slightly shorten the required wire lengths compared to bare copper.

We will now turn this 20m dipole into a 102ft G5RV dipole, made of copper wire, 0.1-inch diameter, complete with a 20m $\lambda/2$ feed stub made of 450-ohm open wire feeder. We will then examine the radiation plots and feed-point impedances at the bottom of the feeder.

Fig 4.4 shows the Wires window, modified to create the model of the G5RV.

Fig 4.4: The Wires Window edited for the G5RV. If the Free Demo version is used, the number of segments should be 19.

We have changed the length to 102 ft, the number of segments to 51 (19 if using the free demo version)and the wire diameter to 0.1-inch. To change these parameters, simply highlight each value to be changed and type in the new value. Close the window when finished. The new values are automatically saved.

Note we have used an odd number of segments. This is necessary with NEC2, to allow connection of feed points, or in this case transmission lines to the exact centre of the dipole.

We will now add a 20m $\lambda/2$ 450-ohm ladder-line in the Transmission Lines Window. We need a half wave long line at 14.175MHz made from 450-ohm ladder line with a Velocity Factor of 0.9. This is 32.23 feet long. Real life transmission line losses are 0.082dB per 100ft at 10MHz.

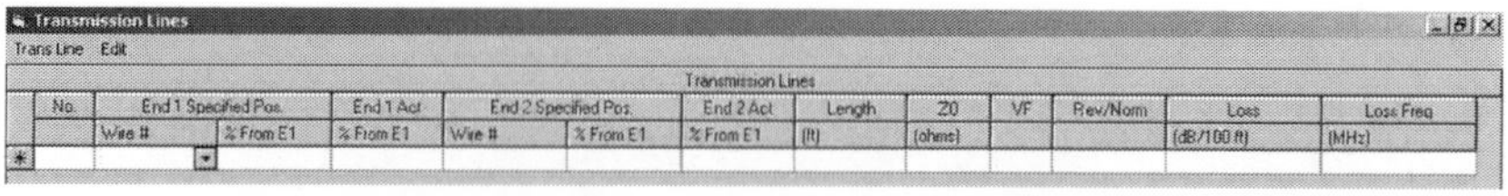

Fig 4.5: Blank Transmission Line window.

No.	End 1 Specified Pos.		End 1 Act.	End 2 Specified Pos.		End 2 Act.	Length	Z0	VF	Rev/Norm	Loss	Loss Freq
	Wire #	% From E1	% From E1	Wire #	% From E1	% From E1	(ft)	(ohms)			(dB/100 ft)	(MHz)

Click on the **Trans Lines** button in the Control Centre window to open the blank Transmission Line window – **Fig 4.5**.

We now enter the required transmission line parameters. End 1 of the line is in the centre of Wire 1 at 50%. End 2 would normally be another wire defined in the Wires window. However, to make life simpler, we use an EZNEC specific shortcut and use a 'Virtual wire' (v1), which does not require a physical location to be defined.

Fig 4.6 shows the completed Transmission Line Window. Close the window.

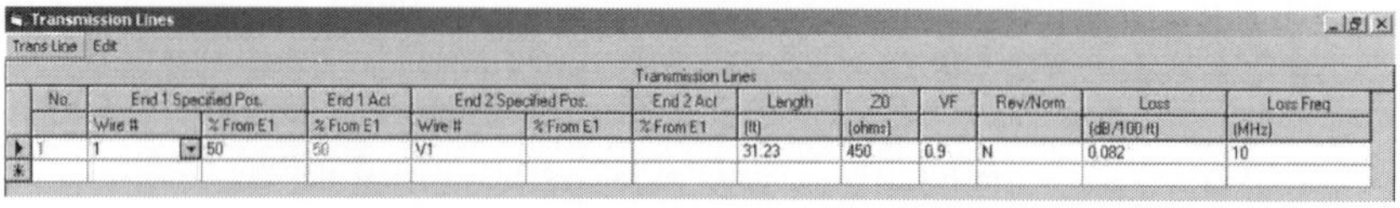

Fig 4.6: The Transmission Line Window completed for the G5RV.

No.	End 1 Specified Pos.		End 1 Act.	End 2 Specified Pos.		End 2 Act.	Length	Z0	VF	Rev/Norm	Loss	Loss Freq
	Wire #	% From E1	% From E1	Wire #	% From E1	% From E1	(ft)	(ohms)			(dB/100 ft)	(MHz)
1	1	50	50	V1			31.23	450	0.9	N	0.082	10

Note that EZNEC V5.0 has a transmission line calculating engine built in, which will calculate the transmission losses for any given frequency and subtract these when calculating the antenna model gain. Impedance transformations down the line are also calculated.

We now move the source from the centre of the wire to the virtual wire at the far end of the transmission line.

Open the **Sources** window. Change the Specified pos from wire 1 to v1 – **Fig 4.7**.

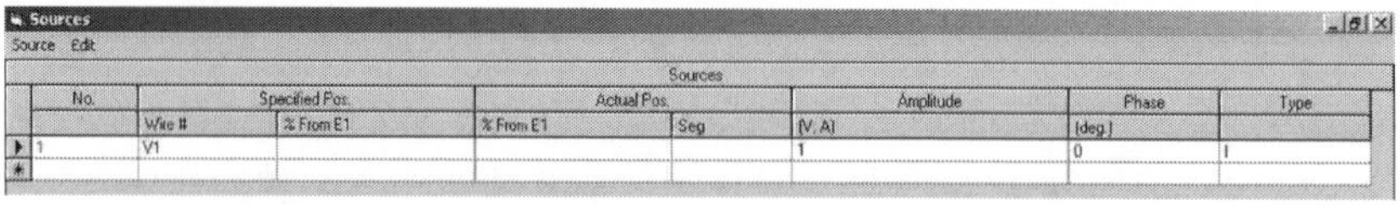

Fig 4.7: The Sources Window completed for the G5RV.

No.	Specified Pos.		Actual Pos.		Amplitude	Phase	Type
	Wire #	% From E1	% From E1	Seg	(V, A)	(deg.)	
1	V1				1	0	I

Note we are using a 'Current' type source with amplitude of 1-amp. Click on OK to close the window.

We will now change a number of other model parameters to better reflect real life conditions.

Click on the **Ground Type** button. In Real Ground Types, click on the High Accuracy button to change from MININEC ground - **Fig 4.8**. The High Accuracy gound model is more accurate than the MININEC ground. Click OK to close the window.

The High Accuracy gound model takes into account losses

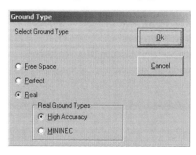

Fig 4.8: The Ground Type Window for the G5RV.

through the ground close to the antenna, the MIMINEC ground does not. The downside is wires can not be directly connected to ground with the High Accuracy ground making accurate modelling of vertical antennas more difficult.

Click on the **Ground Descrip** (Ground Description) button.

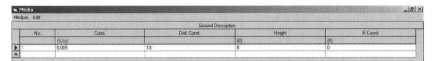

The **Cond** (Ground Conductivity) and **Diel Constant** in the sample model are set to those for very good ground. To make the model more realistic we will change these parameters to those for average ground.

Change the **Cond** (Conductivity) value from 0.0303 to 0.005 Siemens per metre. Change the **Diel Const** (Dielectric Constant) value from 20 to 13 – **Fig 4.9**. Close the window.

This changes these values from those for good ground to average ground. These may not be those pertaining at any particular amateur QTH, the only certain way being to measure them. However, an idea of the likely ground conductivity anywhere in the UK can be obtained from **Fig 4.10.** Also, http://andycowley.net/ant/vmox/gm.html has a useful colour map, showing ground conductivity in the UK and a list of permittivity values for various soil types.

Commonly accepted values for conductivity and permittivity values

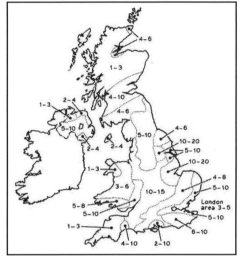

Fig 4.10: Ground
Conductivity Map
for the UK. The
values are in
milli-Siemens
per metre.

Ground Type	Conductivity (Siemens/m)	Conductivity (Milli-Siemens/m)	Permittivity
Poor	0.001	1	5
Average	0.005	5	13
Good	0.0303	30.3	20

Table 4.2:
Typical ground
parameters.

for good, average and poor ground are shown in **Table 4.2**.

Click on the Wire Loss button, click on the copper button to change from zero loss – **Fig 4.11**. Click OK to close the window. We are using copper wire and the resistive loss needs to be taken into account in calculating the actual antenna gain. Click OK to close the window.

Click on the Plot Type button and change from elevation to 3D by clicking on the 3D button – **Fig 4.12** (overleaf). Click OK to close the window.

Fig 4.11: Wire
Loss window for
the G5RV.

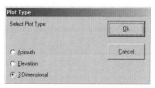

Fig 4.12: The
Plot Type window
for the G5RV.

Fig 4.13: The
Title window,
changed for the
G5RV.

The 3D Plot type allows 3D as
well as azimuth and elevation patterns
to be displayed.

Finally, we rename the model
G5RV and save to filename G5RV.

In the Control Centre window,
click on the description title tile at the
top, (with 'Back yard dipole' in). In
the change window, type 'G5RV
Straight' - **Fig 4.13**, then click OK to
close the window.

On left hand toolbar, click 'Save As', change the filename from
'BYDipole' to 'G5RV', then click 'Save'.

We are now in a position to model the SWR and feed impedances
for each amateur band and plot the expected radiation patterns.

Click on 'View Ant' – **Fig 4.14**. This shows a simple representation

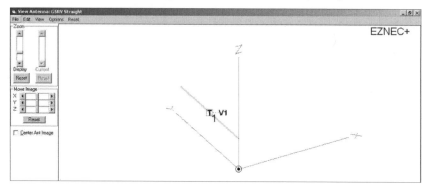

Fig 4.14: The
View Ant window,
showing the
G5RV model.

of the physical antenna. Note the T, representing the transmission line
and v1, representing the source or feed-point at the end of the line. Note
the controls on the left hand side, which allow the image to be zoomed

Fig 4.15: The Set
Frequency
window, set to
14.175MHz.

and spatially manipulated. This
can be useful in a multi-wire
model, to see if all the wires
connect correctly. Close the
window.

Click on the Frequency
button. Change the frequency
to 14.175MHz, the exact centre frequency for the 20m band – **Fig 4.15** –
then click OK to close the window.

At this point those using the free demo version with a wire with only
19 segments instead of 51 will have
got a Segmentation Check window,
containing a Segmentation Check
warning – **Fig 4.16**. This indicates that
the segment is too long for NEC2/
EZNEC to calculate the correct imped-

Fig 4.16: The
Segmentation
Check warning
at 14MHz on the
Demo version.

ance value. The warning indicates that the segment length of 5.3684 feet should be 3.34694 feet as a minimum. Close the window. EZNEC will simply do a best effort when calculating impedance and SWR, but the

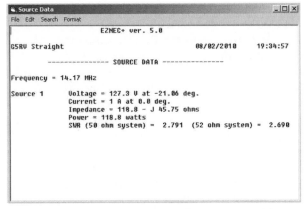

Fig 4.17: The Source Data Window, showing the feed Impedance for the G5RV model at 14.175MHz.

values will differ from a correctly segmented model. The cure would normally be to increase the number of segments but there only 20 segments available in the free demo version. Later in the chapter I will produce a table showing the different values for impedance and SWR for the 19 and 51 segment models as calculated by EZNEC.

Click on the 'Src Dat' (Source Data) button. This window shows the feed-point impedance, SWR and other information for the G5RV at 14.175MHz. **Fig 4.17**.

Click on the 'SWR' button. Change the start frequency to 3.5MHz, the stop frequency to 30MHz and the Frequency Step to 0.5MHz. Click 'Run'. EZNEC now calculates the SWR at the feed point (end of the transmission line) from 3.5MHz to 30MHz in 0.5MHz steps and displays the results in a useful graph – **Fig 4.18**.

Note the dot pointer at 8MHz, which can be moved to each

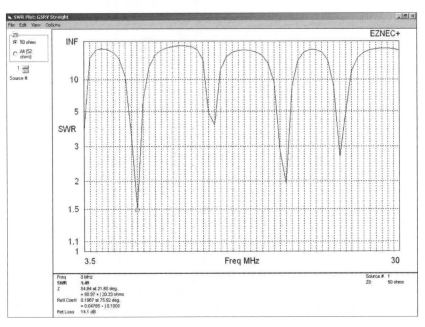

Fig 4.18: The SWR curve for the G5RV Model, from 3.5MHz to 30MHz.

frequency step. The impedance and SWR for the selected frequency are detailed in the bottom left hand side.

As can be seen, the SWR around many of the amateur bands is in fact quite high, not the 2.0 or less often expected. For the G5RV it is normal practice to connect 50-ohm coax at the end of the open wire feeder section to connect to the transceiver (ideally via a choke balun).

Transmission losses on the coax line, particularly at the higher bands and with a longer length of coax, will be quite high. This can be reduced by using open wire feeder or ladder line all the way to the shack and a balanced antenna tuning unit, or placing a remote automatic antenna tuner (AATU) at the base of the ladder line. Either solution will result in lower transmission losses and is a better way of using the G5RV than the 'standard' method.

The SWR plot for any particular amateur band can be looked at by changing the start and end frequencies, and by adjusting the frequency step to an appropriate value. Choosing a small step will take EZNEC longer to produce results.

We will now plot the 3D radiation patterns for each of the main amateur (non WARC) bands. Click the Frequency button and change to 3.65MHz, the centre frequency of the 80m band. Click 'OK' to close the windows.

Click the 'FF Plot' button. EZNEC now calculates the 3D radiation plot for 3.65MHz and displays it – **Fig 4.19**. Note that by clicking on the 'azimuth' or 'elevation' buttons then clicking the 'Show 2D' plot button we can change the view of the plot. Be careful with these 2D plots.

For the azimuth plot, the view depends on the elevation angle

Fig 4.19: The 3D Far Field Plot at 3.65MHz.

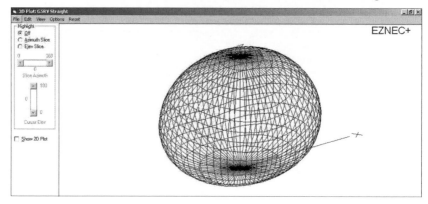

defined by the 'Cursor Elev' slider.

For the elevation plot, the view depends on the azimuth direction defined by the 'Slice Azimuth' slider.

The 3.65MHz 3D plot shows most of the transmitted signal will radiate at high elevation angles, due to the relatively low antenna height. This is fine for local QSOs, but not for DX. Close the window.

Repeat the procedure for other bands by changing the frequency. Note that on 20M, 15M and 10M the radiation pattern is multi-lobe and of lower elevation angle. In the model the antenna is lined up along the y axis, assigning a real life compass direction to the y axis and using a Great Circle map will show the parts of the world where the lobes will maximise DX performance.

The 3D plots for 7.1Mhz, 14.175 Mhz, 21.225 Mhz and 28.5 Mhz are shows in **Fig 4.20** to **Fig 4.23**. Note that at 28.5MHz a segmenta-

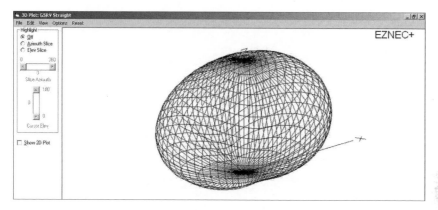

Fig 4.20: The 3D Far Field Plot for 7.1MHz.

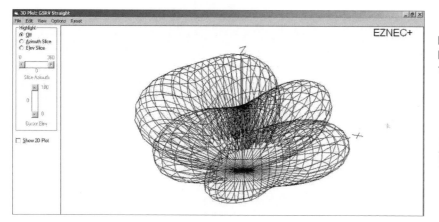

Fig 4.21: The 3D Far Field Plot for 14.175MHz.

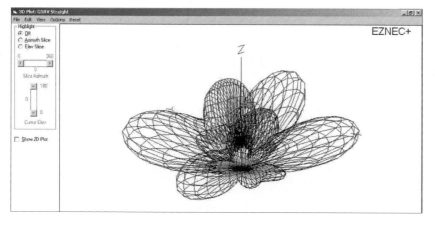

Fig 4.22: The 3D Far Field Plot for 21.225MHz.

Fig 4.23: The 3D Far Field Plot for 28.5MHz.

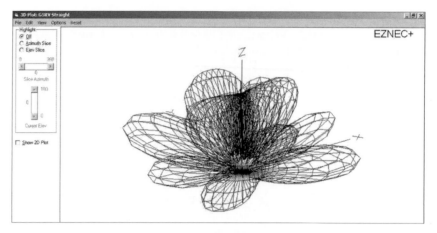

tion check on the 51 segment model will come up.

Table 4.3 shows the different impedance and SWR values derived fro the 19 segment and 51 segment models.

Table 4.3: Differences between 19-segment and 51-segment modelling.

Freq (MHz)	19 Segments Complex Feed Impedance	19 Segment SWR	51 Segments Complex Feed Impedance	51 Segment SWR
3.65	18/54	6.2	18/56	6.5
7.1	63/-158	9.9	63/-147	8.9
14.175	120/-44	2.8	119/-44	2.8
21.225	54/142	9.3	55/177	13.3
28.5	2501/1051	58.8	2733/-556	56.9

Finally in this example, we change the model from a straight dipole to an Inverted-V and show that the performance of this type of G5RV is vastly inferior to the straight version.

Fig 4.24: The Wires window for the Inverted V G5RV Model.

We start with the saved G5RV file.

The Wire Windows for the inverted-V format is shown in **Fig 4.24**. Note that we have used three wires rather than two. There is a short wire in the centre (1.2 inches). This gets around a well-known problem in NEC-2, where wires meet at an angle. The ends of the Inverted-V are 3 feet above ground. In the Wires window, make the original wire 1 the short wire, but change the number of segments from 51 to 1. Add the two other wires, then close the window.

Change the description from 'G5RV Straight' to 'G5RV Inverted V' and Save as 'G5RV Inv V'. That's it!

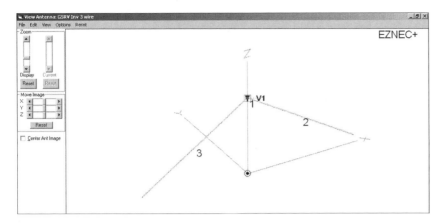

Fig 4.25: The View Ant Window for the Inverted V Model of the G5RV.

The 'Show Ant' window for the Inverted-V is shown in **Fig 4.25**.

Look at the 3D plot at 14.175MHz – **Fig 4.26**. We now have a prominent lobe straight up, just right for picking up ionospheric noise and possibly unwanted short skip signals. Note also that the six lobes in the straight version have gone down to four. Use the Azimuth plot to show that the gain in these lobes is well down on the gain in the lobes in the straight model. Repeat for the 15m and 10m bands – it's the same.

The moral here is to not install a G5RV as an inverted-V! Unfortunately, many amateurs will only have the one support, making the inverted-V format the only one possible. Further modelling will show better antenna solutions than the G5RV for these situations.

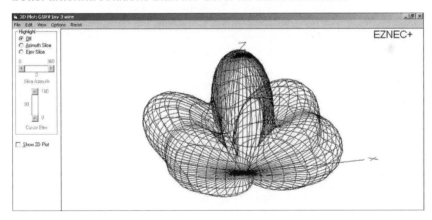

Fig 4.26: The 3D Far Field Plot at 14.125 Mhz for the Inverted V G5RV. The plot has been slightly rotated to better show the pattern. Note the prominent upwards bulge.

Conclusions

It has been shown how easy it is to model basic antennas using EZNEC. In the process, some urban myths about the G5RV have been exposed.

From this it is hoped that readers will be encouraged into further modelling. It can be quite addictive, if you get into it! There is also the possibility of added interest, turning a model into reality and finding agreement between the model and physical reality.

5.
Propagation Modelling

by Gwyn Williams, G4FKH

This chapter will discuss how computers can be used in the shack to better the understanding of propagation. The topics will include information gathering, prediction production and beacon and ionospheric monitoring.

It would be frivolous to attempt a comprehensive list of places online where the various programs and information can be gathered. Instead, the keywords should be inserted into a favourite Internet search engine and this should be used as a basis for finding the required programs and interesting sites. One example of this would be to insert 'Bartels Musical Scales' into a search engine. One of the results will be ftp://ftp.gfz-potsdam.de/pub/home/obs/kp-ap/music/ This shows a list of files in which the K_p index is shown in a musical format. The files are in PostScript, but free programs are available on the WWW to read and display them. This is a little known gem in which the historic K_p index can be viewed in order to visualise or predict occurrences of ionospheric disturbances.

It is of course possible to replicate most of what will be shown in this chapter without the use of a computer, assuming one has a scientific calculator and all the necessary algorithms to do the work and of course an awful lot of paper and even more time. I've been utilizing computers of one sort or another for over two decades to produce propagation predictions and now find the use of them indispensible. Let's continue with a discussion on the type of information required so that we are prepared for the various data inputs our computer programs require.

Internet Information Gathering

It is possible and suggested that those interested register with such agencies as SEC NOAA SWPC and the Aus. IPS site. They will send bulletins each day which include the basic propagation indices. For prediction programs that utilise the VOACAP engine and its derivatives, put 'predict.txt' into your search engine for the sunspot numbers. A_p and K_p indices can be obtained in the recommended fashion. The Solar Terrestrial Dispatch site has a wealth of information and products aimed at the understanding of the current activity on the Sun and its subsequent interaction with Earth's ionosphere. SIDC in Brussels also has an interesting array of information and programs for users interested in propagation studies. There are two other very important sites that are commonly used in propagation research: the Rutherford Appleton Laboratory (RAL), and the Solar and Heliospheric Observatory (SOHO).

RAL is designated as a World Data Centre, so all sorts of archives and data can be found on the site. The section of most interest to those of us interested in radio conditions now or in the near future is the ionogram section. In this area ionogram pictures and ionogram data can be found. Ionogram explanations can also be found on the site. There was also a detailed explanation in the May 2009 edition of *RadCom*. From the ionogram data it is a relatively easy task to single-out a particular data type and graph in order to better understand it. A simple line graph of the F2 layer Critical Frequency (foF2) is shown in **Fig 5.1**.

This graph shows the diurnal effect of the foF2 at the bottom of the sunspot cycle and this time of year. The only real difference that will be seen at the height of the sunspot cycle will be the frequency magnitude. There are day-to-day and seasonal variations, for example during the winter months the foF2 tends to peak around the midday period. The Maximum Usable Frequency (MUF) at 3,000km can also be found within the same data set and will follow the foF2 graph because the two are interlinked. The SOHO site on the other hand contains a large amount of data shown mainly as images taken from the various satellites that have

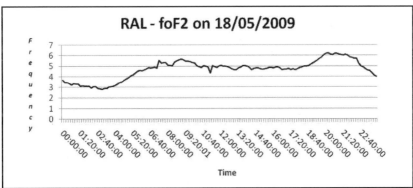

Fig. 5.1: A graph of RAL foF2 at the bottom of the sunspot cycle.

been put into orbit over the last several years. The site also contains a realistic visualisation of the solar wind speed in the guise of a speedometer. Utilizing this information as well as that from the ACE RTSW site, it is possible to pinpoint the timings of such events as flaring and coronal hole occurrences. Both of these later phenomenon adversely effect Earth's ionosphere and its ability to provide skywave communications.

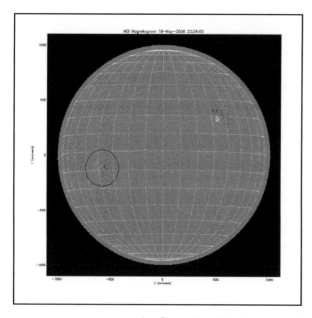

Fig. 5.2: Soho
MDI image taken
on 18 May 2009.

Fig 5.2 shows one sunspot group 11017 in the North Western quadrant and a plage region in the South Eastern quadrant. Plage regions are areas of the sun that have developed magnetically, but not substantially enough to be considered sunspot groups. Sunspot group 11017 belongs to the new solar cycle 24, whilst the plage region belongs to the old cycle 23. This is determined by the polarity of the solar flux of the leading and trailing areas. For this solar cycle sunspot areas in the northern hemisphere have negative polarity leading with positive polarity areas trailing, and the reverse for the southern hemisphere. The polarity flips for each successive sunspot cycle. Occasionally during a solar cycle, a sunspot appears with a reverse polarity. This usually causes large-scale eruptions on the sun that can cause short-wave fadeouts, as well as widely dispersed aurora and Ground Levels Events (GLE's).

Propagation Predictions Programs

There are many different propagation prediction programs. It would be imprudent to include them all, so we will concentrate on just two; REC533 and the W6EL Prop. packages. Both of these are gratis.

REC533
The October 1996 version follows the recommendation ITU-R. P.533 with recommendation ITU-R P.842 incorporated. This version was compiled by M I Dick and S M Harrison of RAL and H Sizun of France Telecom, written for the old DOS operating system. Soon after this date NTIA/ITS of the US Government took over the administration duties and converted the user interface (Graphical User Interface (GUI)) over to Windows. The output was also consolidated into a VOACAP type format, which makes the program especially easy to manipulate programmatically. This latter point, along with its inherent accuracy, has made it the choice of propagation engine for the production of propagation predictions for *RadCom* and other national society magazines.

When searching for this program, put 'HFWIN32' into your search criteria and seek out the Greg Hand site. He is the person who converted the original program and has since rectified any bugs. Greg is now retired but still has an interest in REC533. From time to time he

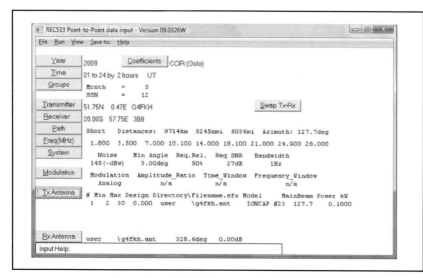

Fig 5.3: The REC533 input screen.

posts a new version onto his web site. The new GUI can be seen in **Fig 5.3** and is the setup page.

The parameters are input by clicking on the labels on the left side and answering the questions. The only information needed from the Internet is the Smoothed Sunspot Number (SSN). All other questions can be answered with regard to your situation. The aerial specified is one that has been constructed from the HFant program that comes with the suite. For the aerial, initially choose IONCAP #23 from the defaults directory. After choosing the aerial, it should be remembered to point your aerial at the receiver, 'at Rx' should be clicked on the received aerial dialogue and 'at Tx' should be clicked on the transmit aerial dialogue. To perform predictions, click the 'Run' button at the top then click 'Circuit'. Close that screen and click 'Run', followed by 'Graph'. Close that screen and the necessary output is now available by clicking on 'View' and either 'Circuit' or 'Graph', as desired. **Fig 5.4** contains is a segment of the Circuit output.

Fig 5.4: Part of the REC533 output file, used for analysis.

There are instructions and manuals on the NTIA/ITS web site for

```
MAY    2009           SSN =  12.                     Path
G4FKH               3B8                   AZIMUTHS <Short> N. MI.      KM
51.75 N   0.47 E   20.00 S   57.75 E   127.68 328.57    5246.2    9715.2
MIN ANG  3.0 DEG
XMTR   2-30 IONCAP #23[user\g4fkh.ant   ] Az=127.7 OFFaz=360.0   0.100kW
RCVR   2-30 IONCAP #23[user\g4fkh.ant   ] Az=328.6 OFFaz=360.0
NOISE -145 dBW          S/N 50% of Days @  27 dB  in   1 Hz RX Bandwidth
Analog


17 19.6  1.8  3.5  7.0 10.1 14.0 18.1 21.0 24.9 28.0  0.0 FREQ 10.9 18.3  21.6
      -    -    -    -    -    -    -    -    -    -    -  MODE
      -    -    -    -    -    -    -    -    -    -    -  ANGL
    -44 -167  -59   -8  -13    5  -35  -34  -20  -39 -999 DBU
    -87 -160  -61  -11  -31    2  -72  -64  -25  -53 -999 dBpW
    -41 -150  -42   18    4   43  -27  -16   25   -2 -999 S/N
   0.01 0.01 0.01 0.12 0.01 0.94 0.01 0.01 0.40 0.01 0.00 FS/N
    -41 -150  -42   18    4   43  -27  -16   25   -2 -999 SNxx
```

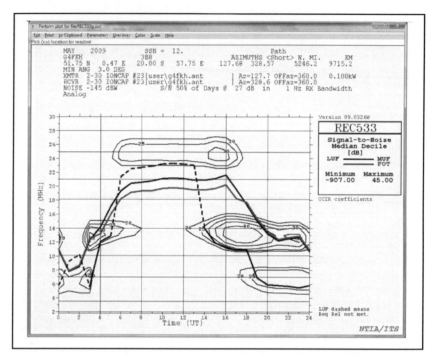

Fig 5.5: SNR output from the REC533 program using the same inputs as previous.

these programs, the manuals for VOACAP and IONCAP are valid for the understanding of REC533. There is also a very good VOACAP Quick Guide available from OH6BG, which explains the output of VOACAP very well and can be adopted for use with REC533. The output segment shown above is for 1700hrs in May 2009, for a circuit between Chelmsford, Essex and Mauritius; it is valid for 50% of the days in the month. At this time on 14MHz the Signal to Noise Ratio (SNR or S/N) tells us that the received signal will be well above the noise and the Medium Field Strength at the Receiver (dBu) tells that we should be able to hear the signal quite well. A figure of -14 and below for the dBu would signify that the receive signal is predicted to be inaudible. The SNR at the receiver is dependent upon a number of factors, such as the aerial and the quality of the receiver, but as a general guideline CW signals should be audible at or above 27dB for experienced operators and probably nearer 35 to 40dB for inexperienced operators. A figure of over 45 or 50dB is usually necessary for SSB reception. Working through the output file in this way will give a very good idea when the circuit will be available and at what signal level. The other output method 'Graph' will provide most of the above information but graphically, as shown in **Fig 5.5**.

This output shows that between about 1600hrs and 1900hrs, 14MHz should be open with an SNR of around 40dB or so. However you will need to verify the dBu by either choosing that parameter from the 'Parameters' choice at the top of the screen or by going to the 'Circuit' output. The thick black line at the bottom which rises at about

0600hrs into a broken black line is the Lowest Usable Frequency (LUF) and drops below 14MHz again at 1400hrs. When the MUF (the top most thick line) is below the LUF no signals are expected to be heard on the circuit, therefore, the island around 0500 to 1700hrs on 24.9MHz is really not a reliable circuit before 1400 when the LUF is computed to be above the MUF, 24.9MHz is also way above the predicted MUF. However, it is always best to check these possibilities as these programs produce predictions and in reality the predicted MUF can be - and occasionally is - exceeded.

W6EL Prop

W6ELProp is quite a different kettle of fish, being not as complicated or sophisticated as REC533. Once the basic parameters have been input, it is a simple matter to make predictions. The package, written by Sheldon C Shallon, W6EL, is well thought of by many radio amateurs. Whilst it does seem to have a tendency to overstate some of the predictions, its ease of use seems to mitigate these shortcomings. The main input screen is shown in **Fig 5.6**.

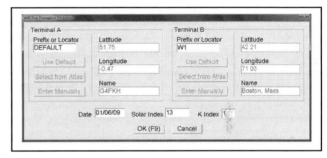

Fig 5.6: The W6EL Prop prediction preparation input page.

The default information comes up automatically (once the defaults have been input) and all that is necessary to input is the 'Prefix or Locator', the 'Solar Index' and the 'K Index'. Clicking 'OK' brings up a basic information screen containing distance and bearing etc. plus a box to click to display the predictions. Part of the output is shown in **Fig 5.7**. It should be noted that the SNR display has been chosen, but it

Fig 5.7: Part of the W6ELProp SNR output.

```
TERMINAL A: 51.75 N  0.47 E  G4FKH      Sunrise/Set: 0356/1957 UTC  Bearing to B: 288.4 deg
TERMINAL B: 42.35 N 71.05 W  Boston, Mass.   Sunrise/Set: 0918/0007 UTC  Bearing to A: 52.6 deg
SSN:  13.0  Flux:  71.3  K: 1                               Path Length:  5295 km
                          SIGNAL-TO-NOISE RATIOS (dB)
UTC   MUF   3.5 MHz   7.0 MHz  10.1 MHz  14.0 MHz  18.9 MHz  21.0 MHz  28.0 MHz
0000 17.1    24 A     47 A     50 A      52 A      53 D      53 D
0030 17.0    37 A     49 A     51 A      52 A      53 D      53 D
0100 16.6    42 A     50 A     51 A      52 A      53 D
0130 16.0    41 A     50 A     51 A      52 A      53 D
0200 15.3    47 A     50 A     51 A      52 B      53 D
0230 14.7    47 A     50 A     51 A      52 B
0300 14.2    40 A     50 A     51 A      52 B
0330 13.8    39 A     49 A     51 A      52 C
0400 13.7    34 A     48 A     50 A      52 C
0430 13.8    31 A     41 A     50 A      51 C
~~~~~~~~~
2230 16.3    -8 A     33 A     46 A      49 A      51 D
2300 16.2     9 A     36 A     47 A      50 A      52 D
2330 16.1    19 A     39 A     49 A      51 A      52 D

Availabilities A: 75 - 100%  B: 50 - 75%  C: 25 - 50%  D: 1 - 25%
S/N suppressed if signal level below -10 dB relative to 0.5 µV or if predicted availability is zero
```

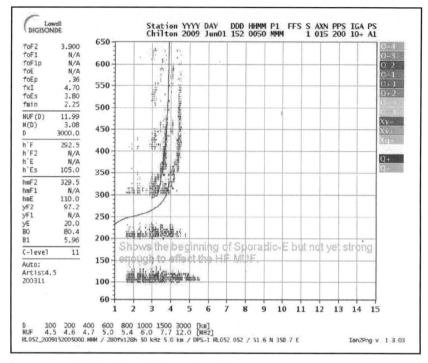

Fig 5.8: RAL Ionosonde display for 1 June 2009 at 00:50hrs.

is also possible to show 'Signal Levels'.

As can be clearly seen, 21MHz is predicted to be open between 0000 and 0030 for between 1 and 25% of the days in June. Unfortunately it can be clearly demonstrated that this is not the case, as **Fig 5.8** is an Ionogram from RAL showing the MUF in the Chilton area.

The reported MUF at 0050 was 11.99MHz. Another program that is available and will be discussed later, Proplab Pro III, corroborates this analysis. That said, this program is more than adequate for showing

Fig 5.9: W6EL Advanced Output Page.

when and at what frequencies to look for openings to particular areas of the world. Other output from this program includes graphical content which unfortunately will not show very well in black and white and a comprehensive advanced feature showing the expected hop configurations at the various frequencies, shown in **Fig 5.9**.

This screen depicts among other important parameters the number of hops necessary to reach the destination and whether they are via the E or F layers. Multiple E-Layer hops are common when Sporadic-E is prevalent. It should be remembered that with multi-hop paths and when Sporadic-E is prevalent, it is possible to bounce a signal off the ionospheric side of the E-Layer (on the second or successive hop), thus avoiding contact with the Earth and negating the losses involved therewith. All-in-all this is a program that it is well worth getting to know, it will also assist in the basic understanding of propagation predictions.

Beacon Monitoring Programs

This next set of programs use disparate methods to assist in the understanding of propagation.

So far LF and VHF/UHF have not been mentioned *per se*. This is because there is a distinct lack of propagation prediction programs designed for these parts of the spectrum. In this section we will talk about beacons and tools for monitoring them. These tools, with the exception perhaps of Spectrum Lab, also show a definite slant towards HF. Beacons can assist us to ascertain what part of the world is open for communication and of course more importantly, when. The NCDXF/IARU Beacon Network is still perhaps the most important group of beacons for the HF bands. Established by the North Carolina DX Foundation (NCDXF), in cooperation with the IARU, it operates a worldwide network of high-frequency radio beacons on 14.100, 18.110, 21.150, 24.930, and 28.200MHz. Beacons are necessarily stable in two ways. Firstly they should be stable in frequency and secondly they should transmit on a timely basis. Monitoring programs have differing ways of keeping an accurate track of time and this will be explained as the various programs are examined. It would therefore be logical to start this section with a look at what programs cater specifically for the NCDXF beacon network.

FAROS
This program was written by Alex Shovkoplyas, VE3NEA in 2006, but unfortunately it is not gratis. However, it is the best program that the author has come across for monitoring the NCDXF beacon chain, whether free or not.

The NCDXF beacon network has eighteen beacons that utilize the five frequencies once every three minutes. For that reason timing is paramount. Faros handles this by monitoring a number of time servers on the Internet. Consequently a broadband connection is necessary if

Fig 5.10: A sample of Faros' output text file.

```
;DATE=2009-06-02
;UTC-      -MHz-     -Call-    -SNR,dB-QSB,%-Evidence-Delay,ms
13:15:00    14      4U1UN     -6.2     100      0.20        50
13:15:10    14      VE8AT      7.3       2      4.25        34
13:15:20    14      W6WX      -7.5     100      0.18        61
13:15:30    14      KH6WO     -7.4     100      0.10         1
13:15:40    14      ZL6B      -5.6     100      0.38       227
13:15:50    14      VK6RBP    -6.0     100      0.24       335
13:16:00    14      JA2IGY    -6.4     100      0.50       242
13:16:10    14      RR9O      -7.1     100      0.10       -18
13:16:20    14      VR2B     -14.2     100      0.12       165
13:16:30    14      4S7B      -6.0     100      0.09       258
13:16:40    14      ZS6DN     -4.9     100      0.26       182
13:16:50    14      5Z4B      -4.5     100      0.48        43
13:17:00    14      4X6TU    -17.5     100      0.15       189
13:17:10    14      OH2B      11.5       0      6.77        25
13:17:20    14      CS3B      -5.5     100      0.28        41
13:17:30    14      LU4AA    -20.0     100      0.05       -43
13:17:40    14      OA4B      -7.4     100      0.22       -53
13:17:50    14      YV5B      -4.9     100      0.16       -51
```

Fig 5.11: The Faros Monitor screen showing which beacons were heard on which bands in the last 15 minutes. The scrolling larger display on the right highlights the last 15 beacons heard.

accurate results are required. The program will communicate with a modern transceiver, changing frequency as required. There is very little in the way of setup, just the normal questions to answer, such as home Latitude/Longitude, COM port and type of audio card. The program then talks to the transceiver and logs the beacons when they are heard. It has a very clever algorithm built in which very satisfactorily identifies the beacons from the background noise and interference and logs the information in text file. A file sample is shown here in **Fig 5.10**.

All the beacons are recorded, whether or not they are audible. For

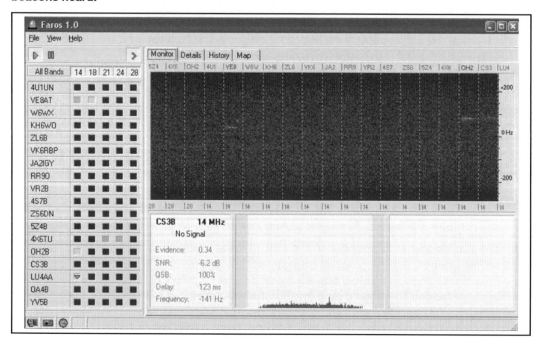

post reception decomposition a method of analysis is required. Whether it is with an Excel spreadsheet or external program becomes the user's choice. To assist in the visualisation of real-time reception a display is shown in **Fig 5.11**.

Going back to the log file information it is only when the SNR,dB is above 0 that signals are actually heard, also the QSB should be much less than 100% and the evidence should probably be around 3 or more. During the period shown and on the frequency shown only two beacons were heard; VE8AT and OH2B. The delay in milliseconds is also of use. With this parameter it is possible to work out when the path is via long-path (LP) as regards the more normal short-path (SP). I've used this parameter for an extensive study of the ZL6B beacon which comes in via LP during the early mornings from about November to about March, the study can be found on the NCDXF web site. There are other displays available as F.g 5.11 suggests but they do not render down too well in black and white. It is possible to download the program for a trial if required. An important application that the author has written uses the output log from this program to prepare an Excel spreadsheet of the output as shown in **Table 5.1**.

The procedure to arrive at the spreadsheet output is quite involved, but we are discussing the use of computers in the shack. The Faros output is firstly run through a PERL program that decides what beacon reports are strong enough to be audible. The output from the PERL program is in Excel format, so it is a simple procedure to then add the file to an Access Database (the author has a 22569 record database going back to April 2006). It is then necessary to run an

Table 5.1: Faros computed output in a spreadsheet format. The figures represent average S-point numbers at the various times.

Faros - NCDXF Beacon Chain Monitoring - May 2009 by G4FKH

QRG	Beacon	00	01	02	03	04	05	06	07	08	09	10	11	12	13	14	15	16	17	18	19	20	21	22	23
14	4X6TU							0						0	0	1	2	0	0	1					
14	5Z4B									0					0	1		0							
14	CS3B							1																	
14	KH6WO							0																	
14	OH2B							3	2	3	1	1	1	1	1	1	1	2	2	2					
14	RR9O													1	1	1	1	0	0	2					
14	VE8AT							1	2	1	1	1	1	1	0	0	0	0	0	0					
14	YV5B															0									
14	ZS6DN																	0							

QRG	Beacon	00	01	02	03	04	05	06	07	08	09	10	11	12	13	14	15	16	17	18	19	20	21	22	23
18	4X6TU									0				1	0	0	0		0	2					
18	5Z4B														0										
18	OH2B							1	2	2	1	1			0										
18	ZS6DN									0															

QRG	Beacon	00	01	02	03	04	05	06	07	08	09	10	11	12	13	14	15	16	17	18	19	20	21	22	23
21	4X6TU									0	0			0	0										
21	CS3B											0													
21	OH2B									0	0		0		0										

QRG	Beacon	00	01	02	03	04	05	06	07	08	09	10	11	12	13	14	15	16	17	18	19	20	21	22	23
24	4X6TU									0	2	1	2	1											
24	OH2B									2	4	2			2										

QRG	Beacon	00	01	02	03	04	05	06	07	08	09	10	11	12	13	14	15	16	17	18	19	20	21	22	23
28	4X6TU									0	1	1													
28	CS3B												0												
28	OH2B									2	2														

Access 'Crosstab' query that puts the output in roughly the format shown above. All that is then necessary is to smarten it up a little so that it looks like the spreadsheet above. Now, what practical use has this spreadsheet? Looking at it closely, it sort of resembles a *RadCom* HF Propagation Predictions page, this output is used to ensure that the HF Propagation Predictions for *RadCom* are in the correct ball park. A lot of the beacons are in the same general vicinity as the destinations listed in *RadCom* so they lend themselves very well to this purpose.

Spectrum Lab

Spectrum Lab is a much more complicated and far more sophisticated creature than Faros, but it can be utilized to monitor most anything including beacons. The main consideration is therefore whether the PC internal clock is correct, if using an older PC, that is older than one using Windows Vista, then it is suggested that this program as well as a lot of others requiring accurate timing be used in conjunction with a GPS time receiver. These receivers can be found occasionally, quite cheaply on ebay. Spectrum Lab is the brainchild of Wolfgang Buescher, DL4YHF, and is basically a Spectrum Laboratory that can be used for applications that are in the audio part of the spectrum up to those in the GHz bands and all frequencies in between. It also has an RDF capability. Built in application files include radio equipment tests, slow Morse reception, and digimodes. However, the first time user will be required to carefully read the instruction manual and make the necessary changes to the setup. This program has a great deal of promise but there is a very steep learning curve involved. The rewards, however, will be great for those able to comprehend the intricacies.

BeSpeak

BeSpeak5 is one of those programs that show when a particular NCDXF beacon is transmitting. Others are available from the NCDXF web site. There is a decent manual and automatic logging feature with this program that quite accurately differentiates between QRM and the required beacon signal. It does this by dis-

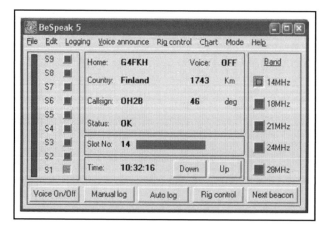

Fig. 5.12: BeSpeak 5 main screen, showing all controls and buttons.

criminating between background noise and Morse. Written by Alan Messenger, G0TLK, it has been developed over the years and has 2D and 3D graphical output. Alan responded quickly when an update was requested to the program, and it enabled a more in-depth discussion here. The entire application is controlled from the primary screen. This and the two other screens used for beacon monitoring are shown in **Fig 5.12**, **Fig 5.13** and **Fig 5.14**.

The three screen shots are used for monitoring purposes. Once the setup is completed it is only necessary to select the monitoring band from the initial screen. With the program controlling the receiver, all the necessary commands are sent to it, making changing bands a one-button clicking action. There is a comprehensive help facility with this program and it is necessary to ensure that it has been read, understood and all the appropriate actions carried out prior to proceeding with monitoring operations. The graphical output is quite good, but does not render down with sufficient accuracy to be displayed here. There is no facility with this program to allow post logging analysis, so it is suggested that those interested download it and try the built-in analysis, after all the program is gratis.

Fig 5.13: Morse discriminator screen and its controls.

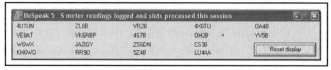

Fig. 5.14: Logging screen. NB: OH2B was logged with an S-meter reading of 1.

GB3RAL

This is the name that the program originator, Peter Martinez, G3PLX, has selected for this application. It provides a graphical and textual output when logging the three 5MHz beacons; GB3RAL, GB3WES and GB3ORK on 5290MHz. These beacons were put in place by the RSGB's 5MHz working group to assist with the understanding of propagation on that frequency and especially to ascertain the extent of NVIS propagation for inter-G working. There is a help system and again it is necessary to read all of the available information and to set the program up as described. Once this has been completed, logging can proceed with

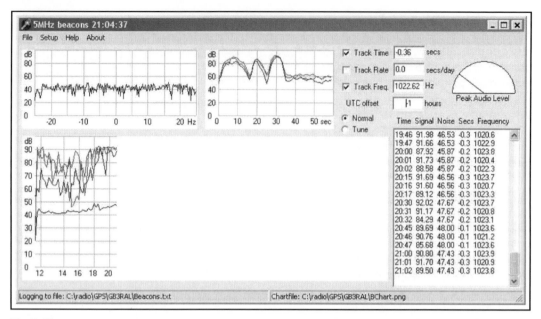

Fig 5.15:
GB3RAL's main
and monitoring
screen.

the minimum of user input. The main screen is depicted in **Fig 5.15**.

The screen shot looks a little busy at first glance, but when you become accustomed to it all the information becomes meaningful. Starting at the top left is the FFT display. When transmitting, beacons should show a peak around the '0' point. The next on the right is the dB output against time of the last three beacons. To the right of these are setup and information displays. The help section should be consulted if clarification is required. The bottom right is a running record of textual output for the recorded beacons. The bottom left is a graphical representation of the three beacons received over time. Fig 12 shows 10 hours of recording. The very top line at the left hand side in the graph is the GB3RAL beacon. The next is the GB3WES beacon and the third is the GB3ORK beacon. The lowest line represents the noise level in the receiver. All this information and more are recorded on disk in a text file. The 5MHz working group would like to receive these files via the WWW. All information can be found on their web site. It is a simple matter to read this text file into a small computer program and do some analysis for oneself, but even without further manipulation Fig 12 shows some interesting trends. For example, the GB3RAL signal started to fall off about 1200. This is because the foF2 dropped. When it recovered around 1800 the signal for that beacon was strong again. This can be directly attributed to nearly NVIS working, while the other two beacons at the receive location are received via the E-layer. In the very early days of the GB3RAL beacon, when analysis was first being performed, it was discovered that GB3RAL was being heard late at night when the foF2 was far below the transmission frequency. To assist with analysis, ionogram pictures were downloaded from the RAL web site and it was discovered that the extra-ordinary wave was responsible for the reception. This was the first time that the author realised that the extra-ordinary wave was as useful for NVIS, as it is at HF frequencies (as will be shown later). Another peculiarity noticed was that the GB3RAL program was showing the reception of signals when they were inaudible, thus they were very weak. It may be possible to exploit this peculiarity by utilizing the more exotic modes using computers.

Ionospheric Monitoring Programs

This category of programs include those that can be used for monitoring the ionosphere and those that can be used to understand the nature of the ionosphere. Also included are applications and datasets that provide basic concepts and measured figures.

ChirpView & Stepper

These are two separate applications from different sources, but used together they provide an excellent way in which the ionosphere can be monitored. ChirpView was written by Andrew Senior, G0TJZ, whilst Stepper was produced by Arend Harteveld, PA1ARE. These are sophisticated packages that come with a pre-requisite of a GPS receiver for accurate timing. A good knowledge of using computers with amateur radio is really another pre-requisite for this pair, as the setup is not at all simple.

ChirpView is a program for receiving signals from ionospheric chirp sounders – transmitters that radiate an unmodulated carrier which is swept at a constant rate across the HF spectrum in order to study ionospheric propagation conditions. These sounders are perhaps unfamiliar to many radio amateurs, but can be thought of as all-band beacons. To receive these signals properly requires a special receiver that tracks the transmitter along its sweep. Such hardware is impractical for most amateurs who are more likely to have an HF receiver with SSB capability. Using such a receiver, a passing chirp sounder signal produces a short chirp in the receiver of around 30 milliseconds duration. ChirpView can detect these chirps and measure their timing precisely to enable propagation to be monitored on the frequency to which the receiver is tuned.

With the above system, Stepper can be used to make the receiver follow the sounder in 100Hz steps to reconstruct ionograms from the detect log. PA1ARE has documentation available to assist those who would like to pursue this idea.

Field Strength

This is an ITU database of medium skywave field strength in dB above 1uV/m, normalized for 1kW EIRP for a total of 181 longpath and shortpath circuits. This database can be used to ascertain when a circuit should be available without the need to consult a propagation prediction program. The database covers two full sunspot cycles. It is necessary to apply to the ITU for free downloads, which are limited to three per annum, otherwise a payment of around 20 Swiss Francs is necessary.

Noise

There is a set of programs available under the above scheme for download from the ITU site. It provides characteristics and applications of atmospheric radio noise data and man-made radio noise. There are three programs in the suite: NOIS1 and NOIS2 and NOISBW. The first two give values of atmospheric noise, man-made noise and galactic noise from Recommendation ITU-R PI.372. The only difference between these two programs is the style of the output. The latter program provides all the parameters relating to atmospheric noise.

GeoMag

Fig.5.16: The world's horizontal magnetic field.

Inserting 'NGDC GeoMag' into a WWW search engine gives the URL's for various programs associated with the earth's Geomagetic state. An interesting world map of the horizontal component is shown in **Fig 5.16**.

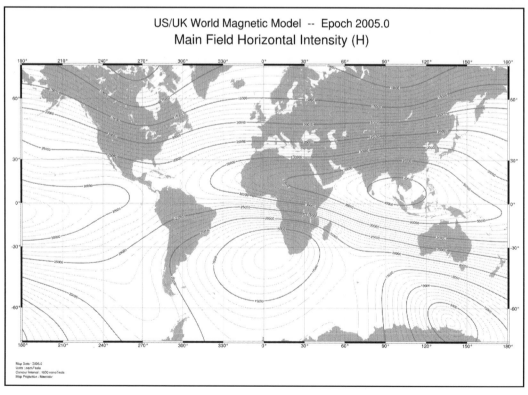

This clearly shows, among other things, that the magnetic equator does not coincide with the geographic equator; it is to the North by roughly 10 to 15 degrees. **Fig 5.17** is of the East component and assists in the visualisation of why North/South paths are generally much superior to East/West paths. Radio signals contain a magnetic property which, to put it very simply, resists crossing these contours.

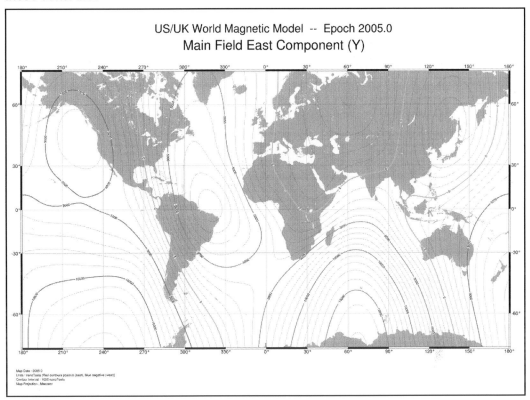

Fig. 5.17: Earth's main field East component.

Proplab Pro

The last piece of software in this section and indeed for the chapter is a propagation laboratory. Produced by the Solar Terrestrial Dispatch; they claim that it is the most advanced radio propagation ray tracing system in the world. It is certainly the most advanced that the author has seen for radio amateurs. It is a state-of-the-art software package not for the feint hearted. It is also a little expensive.

The current version is a lot simpler than previous offerings. The reasons for this are primarily because the majority of the background input is now gathered by the program off the Internet at the click of the mouse, plus it's a lot more complex 'under the hood'. Ray tracing can be performed in either 2-D or 3-D, the two illustrations – **Fig 5.18** and **Fig 5.19** (overleaf)– detail a ray trace from the author's location to 3B8 (Mauritius).

Fig 5.18: 2-D ray tracing output of Proplab-Pro. The start point is on the extreme left and the destination is the little triangle at the right.

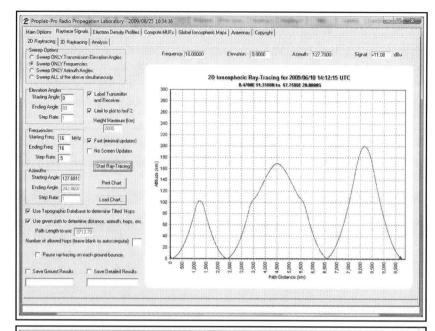

Fig 5.19: 3-D ray tracing output for the same circuit.

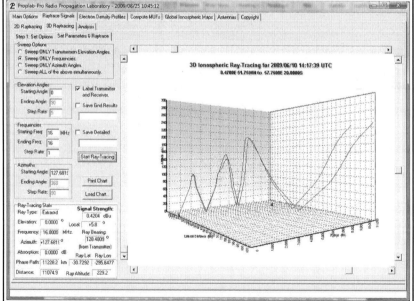

Another output from this package that I particularly like is the world MUF display, shown in **Fig 5.20**.

The contours show the varying MUFs over the globe, but there are a multitude of other parameters available to display. The circuit described is plotted by a great circle line between the two locations along with the day/night terminator line. Hop lengths are known, so it is quite easy to see the frequency in the middle of

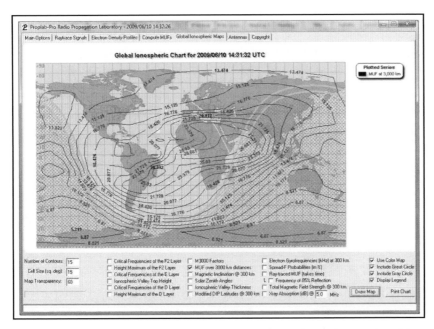

Fig. 5.20: World
MUFs at
3000km.

each separate one. The lowest frequency from these hops should
be about the best for the circuit.

This quick analysis is not always accurate and it is for this reason
and others that ray tracing has been included in the package.

Learning more about Ionospheric Propagation

To fully understand propagation it is necessary to have a firm background in mathematics and basic ionospheric propagation theory. The
programs mentioned previously will then become clearer and more
useful as a consequence.

How does one educate one's self in propagation? Well there are
several ways. One is to trawl the Internet, looking for sites that explain all
about propagation. For example, my own site (http://g4fkh.co.uk/) has a
section on articles that I've previously written for *RadCom*, some of them
for the beginner. Another good example is the wealth of information found
on the NOAA sites, all about different aspects of propagation. Putting a
few queries into Internet search engines produces good results.

The Australian Government's Bureau of Meteorology web site
(www.ips.gov.au/) is another excellent place to start. It contains a wealth
of information. At one time they offered a course on the subject of HF
Ionospheric Propagation, but I could not find it whilst writing this.

Another site that offers a lot of useful information is Solar Terrestrial
Despatch, (http://solar.spacew.com/). They also have a comprehensive
course (very expensive) that will teach those with some previous knowledge a lot more about the subject.

The last but not least way I would suggest those wishing to gain more knowledge is to visit the local library, especially if it is within a large town or city. My own has a number of good reference type books.

Summary

This chapter has attempted to show the usefulness of computers in the shack as far as propagation is concerned. The authors of the various computer programmes are to be congratulated for their hard work and for bringing such tools to a wider audience. Most of the programs mentioned can be enhanced upon, even if it is just organising the output into something more individually meaningful such as averaging or producing medians. There is plenty of scope for the individual amateur to put their mark upon the whole.

Programs available to assist in the understanding of geomagnetism

Name	Function/use
GMCORD	Utility Programs for Geomagnetic Field Studies 1940-2005
GEOMAG	provides field values computed from the International Geomagnetic Reference Field (IGRF) model
SQ1MODEL	Quiet-Day Field Variation, Sq
DSTDEMO	Geomagnetic Disturbance Index, Dst
SUN-MOON	Location of the Sun and Moon
Day Number	Determines the number of the day in the year
POLYFIT	Creates a polynomial equation portrayal of data points
FOURSQ1	Computes the Fourier harmonic spectral components of quiet field records
SORTVAL	Median of Sorted Values
ANALYZ	Mean, Standard Deviation, and Correlation
SPH	Graphical demonstration of Spherical Harmonics

6.
Terrain Modelling for HF

by Alan Hydes, G3XSV

When talking about how good a site is for DX on the HF bands we sometimes hear statements like 'I have a good take-off to the west', or 'I get good reports from the West Coast of the US'. But is there a way of comparing sites or finding out how much gain or loss you are getting from the ground surrounding your antenna? The simple answer is yes... and the results can be quite astounding. This section will describe a practical method and data sources that can be used to analyse a site or compare sites and their DX potential. We will try to answer these questions:

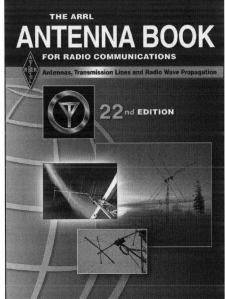

Fig 6.1: *The ARRL Antenna Book.* The accompanying CD contains HF terrain modelling software.

1. What angle of elevation is needed for a specific area of the world?
2. How is the local terrain affecting the signal?
3. What is the best height for the antenna, and can it ever be too high?
4. How will moving the antenna change things?

The methods described here are based on software written by N6BV that has been published by the ARRL in their *Antenna Book* (21st edition). If you want the software, called HFTA (HF Terrain Assessment), it is contained on a CD that accompanies the book (**Fig 6.1**). In that publication there are also details of how it works. Here I will just give an overview of how to use it, how to get terrain data for a particular QTH, and show some example results.

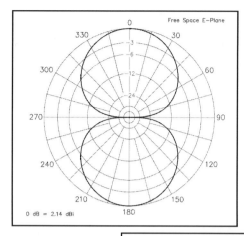

The Basics

Most of us are familiar with antenna gain being shown as E-plane (or horizontal) radiation patterns and H-plane (or vertical) radiation patterns. The horizontal plane is often shown as if the antenna is in free space. For example, the radiation pattern of a dipole is shown in **Fig 6.2**.

In the H-plane (vertical), several radiation patterns are usually shown, because antenna height has great effect on radiation pattern. This is shown in **Fig 6.3**.

Fig 6.2: E-plane free-space radiation pattern of a dipole.

Fig 6.3: H-plane radiation pattern of a dipole at various heights above ground.

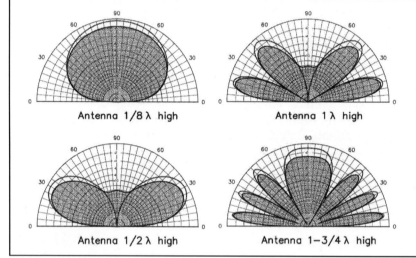

Modelling Terrain Effects

The HFTA software was developed to model how reflections and refractions from the local terrain (see **Fig 6.4**) add up to affect the resultant signal at a remote location.

Fig 6.4: Diffracted and reflected rays.

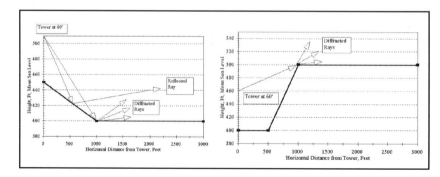

Unfortunately the way that vertical antennas interact with the surrounding terrain is much more complicated and the HFTA software does not attempt to deal with them.

Consequently the main function of HFTA is to calculate and plot the gain of yagi and dipole antennas for different take-off angles over a real ground profile. To do this you just need to provide it with the antenna height and the ground height for a particular direction over a distance of a few kilometres from the antenna.

Getting Terrain Data

The terrain data needed is simply the ground height above sea level along a line starting at the centre of the antenna and extending out several kilometres. HFTA needs a text file that contains two values on each line: distance and height. These can be in metres or feet.

There are several sources of such data.

Printed Maps
Probably the most readily accessible are Ordnance Survey maps. However, it is quite a tedious job to measure along a line and to interpolate the height from the contours. For each data point you need to enter the distance and the height into a line of a text file and give the file an extension of '.pro'. If you use metres as your unit of measure, you will need to put 'meters' (American spelling) as the first line of the file.

Online Maps
An alternative is the use of an Internet accessible map which has built-in terrain data. An example is Google Earth. Unfortunately there does not seem to be a way of accessing the data programmatically, so the process for extracting the height is still quite lengthy.

In Google Earth you can define the line along which you want to collect distance and height data by clicking the 'Add Path' function button. Then click the start point at your antenna location and an end point a few kilometres away in the direction you want to model.

A white line appears on the map and you can now select 'Show Elevation Profile' from the Edit menu. This will show a profile similar to **Fig 6.5**. You can now move the cursor along the elevation profile and record the distance and elevation data point in a profile text file as for printed maps above. About 20 data points was found to be adequate, though 100 is better. Points can be closer spaced near to the antenna, to get better detail close in.

Digital Elevation Models (DEMs)
A far better approach is to use digital elevation data that is available online. The challenge here is to find data that is free or at least very low cost. DEMs covering the UK are mostly provided by commercial

Fig 6.5: How Google Earth can be used to measure height at various distances from a given location.

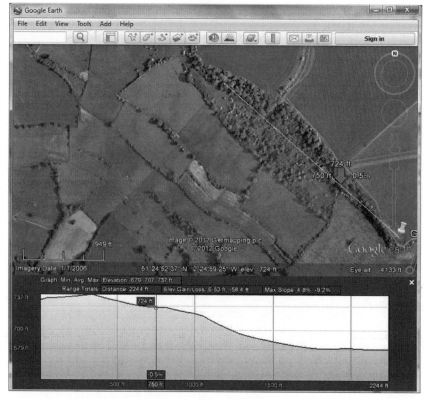

enterprises and the data can be quite costly.

Luckily there is one DEM source that is public domain, as it was created by NASA. In February 2000 NASA ran the Shuttle Radar Topography Mission (SRTM) aboard STS-99. Although raw data is available at http://dds.cr.usgs.gov/srtm/ it is in binary form and therefore needs some processing to produce the .pro files we need for HFTA. Hopefully someone will write a program to do the necessary transformation directly. Meanwhile, there is a temporary method of using this data described later in this section.

What Take-off Angle?

Government communication agencies and major shortwave broadcast stations have been studying take-off angle for many years, in an effort to enhance the strength of their signal into specific parts of the world. Software called IONCAP was developed to simulate the action of the ionosphere at HF frequencies. But as IONCAP is too complex to use directly, calculations were done for all times and stages of the sunspot cycle. The results were aggregated into a small set of data files that are representative of paths between various countries and continents and it is these files that are used by the HFTA software as a reference.

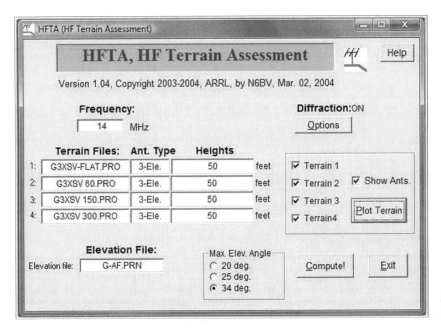

Fig 6.6: Main
HFTA window.

Using the HFTA software

Fig 6.7: Antenna
height and type
dialog box.

Fig 6.6 shows a screen shot of the main HFTA window, which allows you
to enter the names of up to four files
containing terrain data, plus the type
and height of the antenna.

In this example a terrain data file
that represents flat ground has been
used, in order to do comparisons with
typical gain data seen in antenna
textbooks. The other three terrain files
contain data for difference paths,
representing directions 60°, 150° and
300°.

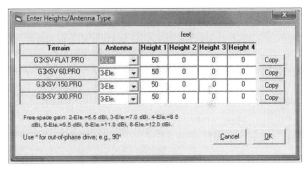

'Ant. Type' or 'Heights' can be changed by clicking on the field.
This brings up a dialogue box shown in **Fig 6.7** to make your selection.

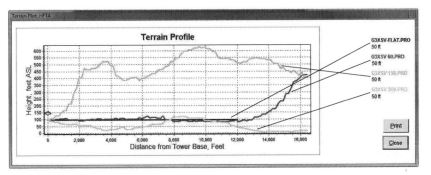

Fig 6.8: Plotted
terrains at bear-
ings of 60°, 150°
and 300°, plus
flat ground.

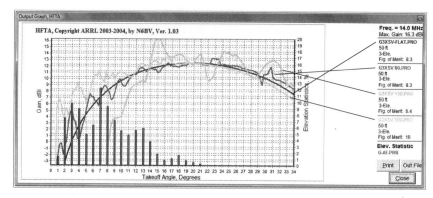

Fig 6.9: Plotted terrains at bearings of 60°, 150° and 300°, plus flat ground.

Note that more than one antenna height can be entered in a row. This models stacked beams. We've entered a single three element yagi with the antenna at 50ft.

Terrain plots

If you select the tick boxes and click the 'Plot Terrain' button you will get a window showing a representation of the terrains shown in **Fig 6.8**.

In this example you can see that the antenna is above land that is approx 100ft and the elevation rises steeply along a path of 150° to a hill that peaks at over 600ft. This is in contrast with the path towards the USA at 300°, where the land steadily drops over the first mile.

Elevation Responses

On the main window you can select a particular part of the world, to see what take-off angles are likely to be useful for that path. In the example we have chosen a path from the UK to Africa which would be appropriate for the 150° path. Click on 'Compute'! The analysis results are shown in **Fig 6.9**.

Fig 6.10: Terrain profile towards the USA from the Bristol CG's site (descending line) and flat ground (straight line).

In this example the most useful elevation angles for Africa are shown as a bar graph. You can probably spot how poor the QTH chosen is for propagation to Africa! Compared to flat ground, the gain is negative all the way up to 14° of elevation, which accounts for most of the propagation to that part of the world.

This is in contrast to the gain for the path of 300°, towards the USA, which shows enhanced gain compared to flat ground. This is between 6dB and 10dB at lower angles.

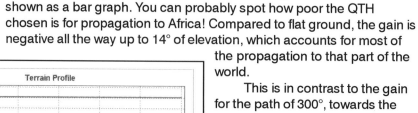

Example and Interpreting Results

Here is an example to show what kind of gain is achievable from the best locations. This site in question is used for Field Day contests by the

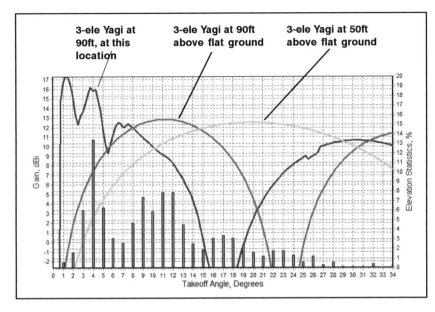

3-ele Yagi at 90ft, at this location

3-ele Yagi at 90ft above flat ground

3-ele Yagi at 50ft above flat ground

Fig 6.11: Gain of a 3-element Yagi at the Bristol CG's group's site, compared to an identical antenna at 50ft and 90ft above flat ground.

Bristol Contest Group. It is located on the edge of an escarpment that slopes away to the west. **Fig 6.10** shows the terrain profile towards midwest USA, showing the antenna at 90ft.

In **Fig 6.11** is the HFTA elevation response for this path, using a 3-element yagi at 90ft. Moving from left to right, the next line is for the same antenna at 90ft above flat ground and the third line is the same antenna at 50ft, to represent a typical home installation.

The bar graph shows the elevation statistics for take-off angles that are useful for the USA. It can be seen that for very low take-off angles of 1° or 2°, the gain relative to the same antenna at home is 20dB or more. At angles under 6°, which are typical for west coast USA, the antenna over the slope significantly outperforms an identical one over flat ground. However, over 8° the performance drops off. This shows that the antenna may be too high for general coverage of the USA and a lower one would be an improvement for some of the higher angle propagation. If it is practical, a better solution is to stack antennas and switch (or split) the power between them.

Conclusions

The combination of the analysis capability and the elevation statistics derived from IONCAP make the HFTA software and excellent tool. It can provide valuable evidence when comparing sites and when trying to determine what height and location would be ideal for antennas. As already mentioned, it can't deal with verticals, but it is nevertheless a valuable tool for any amateur who is serious about picking a site or optimising their antenna system.

Generating .pro files from SRTM data

HFTA has an extensive Help file, which explains how to generate the terrain data from different sources. However, many of these sources are only available for the USA. As mentioned earlier, there is a way to use data from the SRTM. It involves use of web-based software at: http://www.gpsvisualizer.com/elevation

The site consumes input files containing longitude and latitude points and generates height/elevation data for those points. The method we use in our application is to generate a .csv file using an Excel spreadsheet. The same spreadsheet is then used to transform the output data into the format needed for HFTA. **Fig 6.12** shows a screen shot of the start of this spreadsheet with data entry cells shaded.

The Excel spreadsheet is available at: http://g6yb.org/hfta/lat-long-calculator-v2.xls Incidentally, thanks to Matt Jeffery, M0MAT, for help in developing this spreadsheet.

The longitude and latitude of the start point can be found from Google Earth, or from some GPS receivers, to the required accuracy of seconds to two decimal places. Angle is the direction of propagation you want to simulate and can be found from any great circle map of the world. Range and Number of Coordinates can be left as is. Bear in mind that the SRTM data has a resolution of 30 metres, so there is not much to be gained by having points closer than that.

After entering the start point and angle in Excel, save sheet 2 as a .csv file. Go to http://www.gpsvisualizer.com/elevation , click [Choose File] and browse to your .csv file. Select Output type of 'Plain text' and Units 'U.S.' then click [Convert & add elevation]. Cut the height values out of the text box produced from this site and paste into cell A1 in sheet3 of the spreedsheet. Then save sheet 4 as a .PRN file. Change the file extension to .PRO and you are ready to use it in HFTA.

Fig 6.12: Lat Long Calculator Excel spreadsheet.

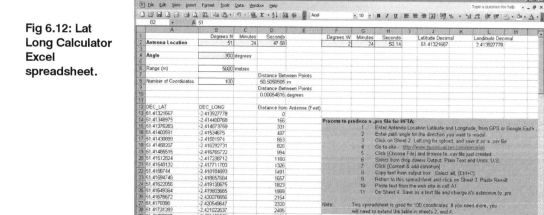

7.
Software Defined Radio

by Mike Richards, G4WNC

Microprocessors have had a massive impact on just about all modern electronics and radio is no exception. Whilst this began with the digital control of local oscillators and noise reduction units, the technology has now spread into the main core of the transceiver and is progressively creeping ever closer to the antenna. In this chapter we will take a look at SDR to see how it works and how we can make best use of it.

What is SDR?

SDR is very broad term that describes any system where software performs one or more of the core functions of a receiver. The first examples to make a widespread impact on amateur radio were the excellent SoftRock receivers and transceivers that were designed and produced by Tony Parks KB9YIG. These comprised a relatively simple hardware direct conversion receiver/exciter with an analogue IQ output (more on this later). The IQ signals were fed to a standard PC soundcard, where tuning and demodulation took place. Dealing with filtering, demodulation and final tuning in software brought about great flexibility as the performance and features could be completely trans-formed with new software. It is this ability to introduce changes and upgrades with ease that makes SDR technology so attractive. In addition to the great flexibility offered by SDR, the use of Digital Signal Processing (DSP) techniques facilitates the inclusion of filters and advanced demodulation systems that would be virtually impossible with conventional hardware circuitry.

There are three key technologies that are at the heart of SDR and we ought to take a look at these before moving-on to real-world systems. They are:

Analogue to Digital Conversion (ADC),
In-phase/Quadrature Data (IQ data), and
Fast Fourier Transforms (FFT).

Analogue to Digital Conversion

As you are no doubt aware, all computer systems talk in numbers, so before a microprocessor can do anything useful in radio the analogue signals need to be digitised. The method of achieving this has remained stable for some time and involves measuring and storing the instantaneous level of the analogue signal at a very high speed. You can visualise this as taking regular measurements with a digital voltmeter (see **Fig 7.1**). So how frequently do you think we need to take measurements

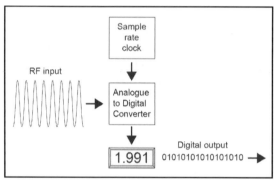

(samples) in order to create a realistic digital equivalent of the original signal? The fundamental work to determine this was first published in 1928 as the Nyquist-Shannon sampling theorem. The theorem states that you must sample at a rate that is at least twice as fast as the highest frequency component you want to digitise. Therefore, to digitise an audio signal that contains frequencies from 20Hz to 20kHz you need to take measurements at 40,000 times per second, i.e. twice 20kHz.

Fig 7,1: Illustration of the analogue to digital conversion process.

The other vital point to consider is the accuracy or resolution of each sample. You can think of this in terms of how many digits you have available on your digital voltmeter. If you were to use an 8-bit measurement you would have just 256 possible values for each measurement which may be a bit too coarse for many purposes. As a result, it is common practice to use 16-bits or greater for radio applications – a 16-bit sample contains 65,536 possibilities for each measurement. When the ADC process is complete, the result is a data stream of 16-bit numbers that are generated at the sampling frequency. Returning to our simple audio signal, that would produce a data stream running at 16 (bits) x 40,000 (sample rate) which is 640,000 bits per second. As you can see, one of the problems with the ADC process is the relatively high-speed data streams that have to be processed.

So where in the receiver chain do you put the ADC? In many systems the ADC in the computer's soundcard is employed and whilst this works very well there is so much more you can do if you can move the digitisation closer to the antenna. At the time of writing there have been a number of systems introduced that digitise the entire spectrum from VLF through to 30MHz or more! Most of these employ some digitally switched band-pass filtering close to the antenna followed by some modest amplification before sending the entire spectrum to the ADC.

From my earlier explanation you will know that the sample rate would need to be twice the highest frequency, i.e. at least 60MHz with 66.666MHz being a popular choice. When combined with 16-bit samples, that gives a data rate from the ADC of 16 (bits) x 66,666,000 (sample rate) = 1.067Gb/s. Now that's a lot of data to process and is way too fast for most home computers to handle. To tame this data rate a process known as decimation is employed. This is the digital equivalent of a mixer and local oscillator in a conventional receiver. The decimator reduces the bit rate and extracts a segment of the sampled 30MHz spectrum that can then be passed to the PC for processing (**Fig.7.2**). In most practical designs the size of the extracted segment can be controlled by the software running on the PC and ranges from a few tens of kHz to 10MHz or more. Rather than passing a single data stream to the PC for processing,

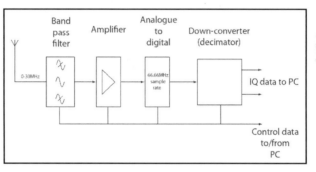

Fig 7.2: Block diagram of a digital HF receiver.

two data streams are presented, one that's in-phase and the other that's delayed by 90 degrees and is known as quadrature. These two streams are the In-phase (I) and Quadrature (Q) data I mentioned earlier. The hardware used for this decimation or down conversion has to be extremely fast and many of the current designs use a Field Programmable Gate Array (FPGA). This is a large array of high-speed gates and logic devices on a single chip that can be programmed and interconnected by software to create highly customised functions.

IQ Data

So, if sampling a signal at the Nyquist sample rate produces a good representation of the signal, why do we need to bother with In-phase(I) and Quadrature (Q) signals? Put very crudely, you can imagine IQ-data as stereo for digital signals! In the same way as stereo audio allows your ear/brain combination to determine the location of instruments and provides a sense of space and increased detail, so IQ data facilitates the extraction of more information from our digitised radio signal. Let's just look at IQ data in a little more detail to see how that works.

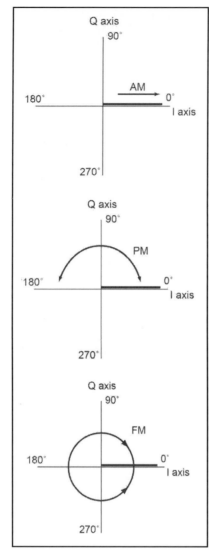

Fig 7.3:
(a) IQ data for an amplitude modulated signal,
(b) IQ data for a phase modulated signal,
(c) IQ data for a frequency modulated signal.

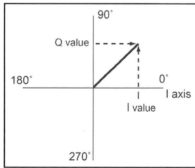

Fig 7.4: Using IQ values to control vector position.

I've shown an IQ polar diagram in Fig 7.3a-c. Here the I axis represents a change in amplitude of the carrier wave, whilst the Q axis shows any change in the carrier's phase. If we start with amplitude modulation, the only part of the vector that changes is the magnitude along the I axis and this changes in response to the modulating signal. Let's now move on to look at what happens with simple phase modulation, where a 180 degree shift is used to convey a digital signal. In this case the vector amplitude remains constant but the vector will flip between 0 to 180 degrees in response to the modulating signal. Frequency modulation can also be demonstrated and the vector will remain the same length but will rotate clockwise to show an LF shift and anti-clockwise for an HF shift.

If we take control of the I and Q values we can adjust the values to generate amplitude, frequency or phase modulation with comparative ease (see **Fig 7.4**). In addition to these relatively simple modulation systems, by manipulating the IQ data we can generate a range of complex modulation systems that employ both amplitude and phase modulation that would be very difficult to implement with traditional hardware. Using IQ data the generation of simple or complex modulation schemes can be completed entirely in software which brings tremendous flexibility. The resultant baseband IQ signal can then applied to an IQ up-converter to produce the final operating frequency. The up-converter is a relatively simple device that mixes the IQ data with a pair of local oscillator carriers at 0 and -90 degrees and then combines the result – see **Fig 7.5**. This makes for a very elegant modulation system that can handle a huge range of operating modes at any carrier frequency.

When it comes to reception with SDR systems, IQ data is the vital ingredient, as monitoring the change in IQ values over time will reveal the modulating message regardless of whether it's a form of AM, FM, PM or a combination of all three, thus providing a simple multi-mode demodulator.

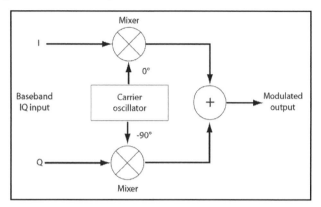

Fast Fourier Transforms

Fig 7.5: Transmit up-converter for baseband IQ data.

Another important process in the development of SDR and digital signal processing in general has been the use of Fast Fourier Transforms (FFT) to analyse sampled data streams from the ADC. One of the great operational benefits of practical SDRs is the presentation of band segments in spectrum analyser style. This enables the operator to quickly locate active stations within a band and to use the click of the mouse to tune to that station. Converting the sampled data stream into a spectrum analyser format is handled by the FFT, so let's take a quick, non-mathematical, look at how this works.

The FFT is an ingenious mathematical algorithm that can examine a stream of sampled data from an ADC and separate the stream into its component frequencies. It does this by dividing a section of the sampled data into a number of bins (containers), each of which contains a narrow band of frequencies – see **Fig 7.6**. It then measures the energy in each bin and it is this data that's used to feed the spectrum display or drive other facilities. The size of each bin is dependent on the sample rate of the digital signal and the number of bins used by the FFT. When using FFT to analyse an audio signal we might typically have a sample rate of say 44kHz so that it can accurately capture frequencies as high

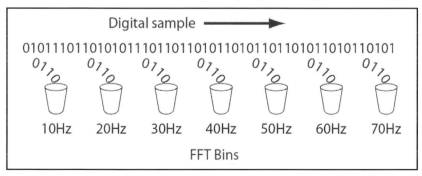

Fig 7.6: Illustration of using FFTs to convert data samples to FFT frequency bins.

as 22kHz. If we then analyse this signal with an FFT using 8,192 bins, each bin would be 22,000Hz (highest audio frequency) / 8,192 (number of bins) = 2.69Hz wide which would produce a very fine resolution spectrum display. One other point to note - the Nyquist-Shannon theorem applies to FFTs and to provide the 8192 FFT bins the FFT needs twice as many samples or points, i.e. 16,384.

One of the problems associated with the FFT algorithm is the assumption that each analysed sample is continuously repeating. Not too much of a problem you might think but if the beginning or end of the sample chops through a signal that's rapidly changing, the abrupt cut will theoretically have lots of harmonics and the FFT will attempt to show that by spreading the energy over many bins. This would spoil our otherwise clean spectrum display. The solution is to apply some more digital wizardry to gently reduce all samples to zero at the beginning and end of the measurement period. The filter that achieves this is called an FFT Window and you may find that you have a choice of windows available – especially in FFT measurement systems. If in doubt, the most useful general purpose window is the Hamming – see **Fig 7.7**.

In addition to using FFTs to display the frequency spectrum, they can also be used to create superb filters. As the FFT can be used to separate the incoming sampled data into narrow FFT bins, filtering the signal can be just a case of deciding which of the bins should be kept and which should be discarded. Using the audio example from earlier that would mean we could create band-pass, low-pass or high-pass filters with adjustments in 2.69Hz steps! This is a very simplistic view of FFT based filters but should give you an idea of how they can work.

Fig 7.7: FFT Hamming window.

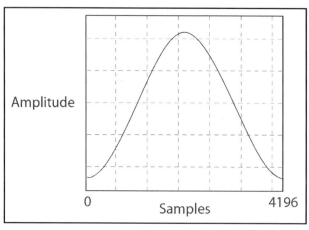

Amplitude

0   Samples   4196

FFT Parameters

When you start using SDR systems and other FFT based systems you will find that the software often provides user adjustments, so you can fine tune the performance. In this section I'll give you some guidance on what the various settings mean and how you can make best use of them. Probably the first to look at is the FFT points or sample size. This is simply the number of samples that the FFT will use to calculate the spectrum display and determines the resolution of the display. Setting this is always a compromise, as higher FFT point (sample) sizes provide increased detail in the display but also increase the processing and display time. The trick is to find a setting that works best with your combination of computing power and the type of signals you are monitoring.

The next adjustment to consider is the smoothing or averaging. Without any smoothing the spectrum display will often look very jerky, erratic and difficult to interpret. However, a small amount of smoothing will quickly even-out the display and make it much easier to read. The amount of smoothing or averaging to apply is really down to personal choice but this rarely needs to go above 4 unless you are looking for a very specific signal type. If you set the smoothing too high you will miss some short duration transmissions altogether.

Practical Systems

By way of an introduction to practical SDR systems, let's start with a look at one of Tony Parks' SoftRock receiver kits. These are wonderfully simple receivers and transceivers with remarkably good performance. **Fig7.8** shows a block diagram of the popular SoftRock40 receiver, which is is a single-band receiver for the 40m amateur band that employs SDR techniques for the final tuning and demodulation. The RF section includes a band-pass filter to help reduce the level of out-of-band signals. The output of this is applied to a very effective Quadrature Sampling Detector. You will note that the output from this stage comprises the vital I & Q signals that carry the 48kHz wide baseband signal. Although the baseband signals are true IQ components they are still analogue at this point in the process. These baseband signals are then amplified and sent to the left and right inputs of a computer soundcard. For the SDR to work correctly the soundcard does need to be able to sample at 96kHz or greater and be able to digitise the full 48kHz of the baseband signal.

Fig 7.8:
SoftRock block diagram.

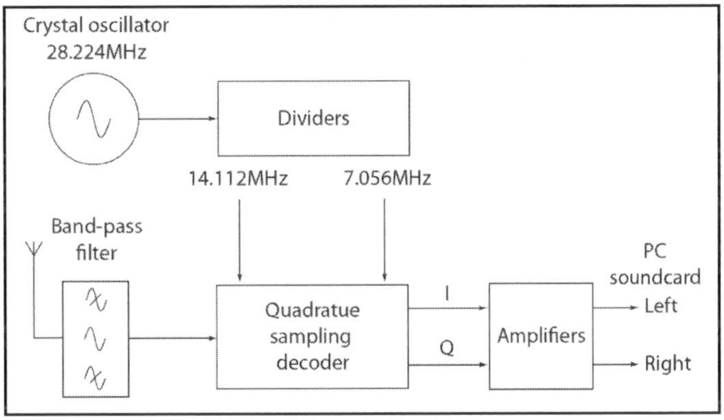

Once in the PC, the digitised IQ signals are processed to create a spectrum display of the band, provide variable filters and demodulate the chosen signals.

In the transceiver version of the SoftRock 40, the Quadrature Sampling Detector (QSD) is supplemented with a Quadrature Sampling Exciter (QSE). In many respects this is

93

similar to the IQ up-converter (see Fig 7.5) as it takes baseband IQ information from the computer's soundcard and combines this with phase shifted local carriers to produce the modulated RF signal. However, the QSE has many performance advantages over a simple up-converter.

The software that handles the SDR element of the transceiver is freely available for download from the Internet as PowerSDR Console. As you can see from **Fig 7.9**, PowerSDR includes a huge range of advanced features that would normally only be available on the most expensive conventional transceivers. The basic operating principles of the SoftRock series have been commercialised and form the foundation of the excellent FlexRadio series of SDR receivers and transceivers.

Fig 7.9:
PowerSDR main
screen.

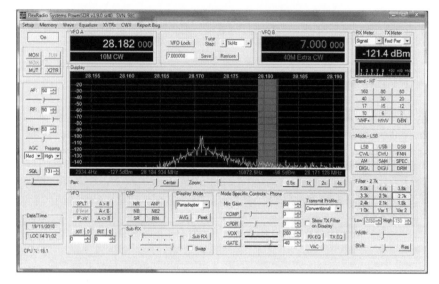

Full Spectrum Digitisation

An example of an alternative SDR approach can be seen in the RFSPACE SDR-IQ module which is available as a ready assembled unit with just two connections – USB lead and antenna! Inside, the SDR-IQ uses hardware from Analogue Devices to digitise the full 500Hz to 30MHz spectrum and down-sample this back to 190kHz segments that can be displayed and decoded using SDR software on the PC (Fig 7.2). This is very much a black-box approach and the hardware can be tucked away, as you don't need to touch it during operation. In addition to providing a full coverage SDR HF receiver complete with filters, etc. the SDR-IQ can also be configured to operate as a Panadaptor with many popular rigs so that you can view entire bands and click-tune to select the desired frequency. To achieve this functionality the RFSPACE-IQ includes a serial port connection on the rear panel that links to the CAT port on the transceiver. Similar full-spectrum SDR approaches can be seen in a number of other high-end receivers such as the Winradio Excalibur and the SSB LAN-SDR.

Open Source Project

Amateur radio has always prided itself as being at the forefront of innovation and for creating an environment where enthusiasts and experts can experiment with new technology. Those principles are alive and flourishing in the world of SDR thanks to the High Performance SDR community. This group can be found on-line at http:// openhpsdr.org/ and comprise a group of experts that are developing open-source hardware and software that will combine to create a state-of-the-art software defined transceiver system. The project has been divided into modules to maintain flexibility and to enable sections to be easily upgraded. One part of the project that falls outside this principle is the Hermes module which is a complete, single-board 160m to 6m SDR transceiver. Hermes has been developed by combining modules from the main SDR project and is set to be very popular now it has been released.

FUNcube Dongle

The FUNcube Dongle project, like so many good initiatives, came from a desire to bring radio and electronics to young people in an exciting way, using low cost hardware and software. As is often the case with this type of project, the resulting receiver has attracted great interest from enthusiasts and hobbyist all over the world. There are two flavours of FUNcube Dongle, the original v1.0 provided coverage from 64MHz through to about 1700MHz with a gap between 1100MHz and 1270MHz. This is an excellent receiver that originally sold for about £100. Unfortunately the manufacturer of the tuner chip went into liquidation, so this model is no longer manufactured. As a result the team had to re-design the dongle hardware to provide the promised hardware support for the FUNcube educational satellite project. The design team excelled themselves and produced a design with more than double the number of components in the same case, but with improved all-round performance (see **Fig 7.10**). Improvements were wide ranging and included extended frequency coverage from 150kHz to 1.9GHz (but with a gap between 280MHz and 420MHz). The v2.0 also added a temperature controlled crystal oscilla-

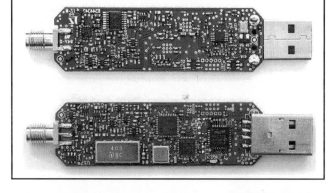

Fig 7.10: A look inside the FUNcube dongle.

tor (TCXO) for improved tuning accuracy and stability. Performance on the critical 2m and 70cm bands was further improved through the use of SAW (Surface Acoustic Wave) filters for these bands.

Both version of the FUNcube Dongle use the direct conversion technique, with the analogue IQ signals from the tuner chip being digitised by an internal codec (CODer/DECoder). The original v1.0 employed a 96kHz sample rate, providing a maximum bandwidth of just under 96kHz for the SDR software. The v2.0 version doubles the sample rate to 192kHz, giving a shade under 192kHz of bandwidth to the SDR software.

Using SDR Software

Software is the essential ingredient to any SDR system and there are an ever growing number of software packages around, all of which are undergoing frequent upgrades as this new technology blossoms. The main players at the time of writing are PowerSDR that works with the FlexRadio SDR hardware, HDSDR which is an updated version on WinRad, SDRsharp and Simon Brown's (HB9DRV) excellent SDR-Console. This latter program has recently been completely re-designed and Version 2.0 includes support for a wide range of hardware systems and can run with up to six receiver panels simultaneously! There will doubtless be more developments as time progresses.

Fig 7.11: SDR-Radio main screen.

Let's just spend some time running through how to use a typical

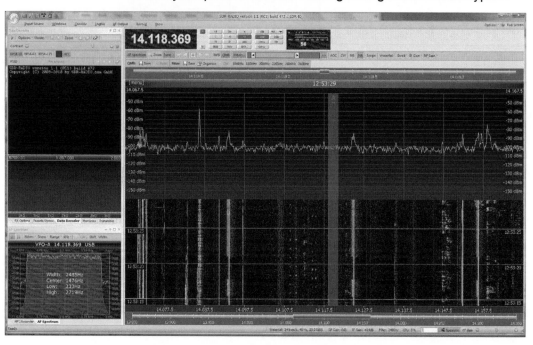

SDR software rig and for this example I'll use Simon Brown's SDR-Radio. One of the first things to remember with just about all SDR systems is that you have to start the radio and choose your input source. As SDR software operates on an IQ data stream this can come from a number of sources including data files that have been stored to disk. The facility to store radio spectrums as IQ data is used extensively by security services for surveillance work. Getting started in SDR-Radio is done by pressing the Start (or Play) button from the Input Source menu. Once started, the display should burst into life with a spectrum display of the currently selected band. You will usually find an assortment of display options in most programs but the most useful for amateur radio is the combined spectrum and waterfall display as shown in **Fig 7.11**. This display shows a spectrum analyser display in the top section with frequency plotted horizontally and signal strength vertically. Below this is a scrolling waterfall display that plots frequency horizontally but the signal level is shown by the intensity and colour of the plot. As the waterfall scrolls relatively slowly, the display builds a pattern of the signal over time which is extremely useful for signal recognition. When you first encounter this type of display it may seem a bit daunting but you will soon find that this combined display reveals a huge amount of information about the signals on the band. In **Fig 7.12** I've shown a segment of the 20m amateur band and highlighted a number of signal types that are instantly recognisable from the waterfall pattern they create.

Tuning SDR rigs also involves new skills, as there's no tuning knob to spin! With SDR, tuning is normally carried-out with the mouse and simply clicking the desired frequency on the display immediately sets

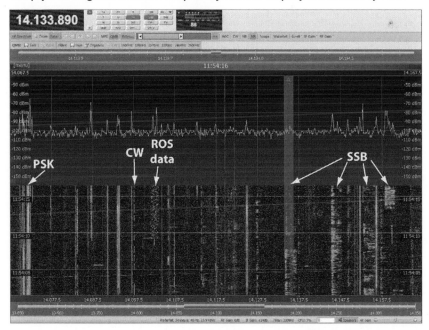

Fig 7.12: Signal recognition using a waterfall display.

the demodulator to that frequency with fine tuning completed using the mouse wheel. This makes tuning around the bands extremely quick and easy. For more precise frequency setting there is normally the option to type-in the frequency or to use up and down arrows to get to the desired setting. You can also change the scale of the frequency axis and zoom-in on a particular band segment. This can be very useful when the bands are busy to help spot a clear frequency.

One of the areas where SDR really excels is filtering and the software always includes some mouth-watering options. In the SDR-Radio software there is a separate audio spectrum display available that shows a spectrum analyser display of the audio frequencies which is overlaid with the shape of the current filter (**Fig 7.13**). To change the shape or width of the filter you simply grab one edge with the mouse and drag it to the desired setting! This is very powerful, especially as you can see the signals as you change the filter so if you have an interfering signal you can drag the filter edge to cut it out whilst having minimal effect on the wanted signal. The filter sides are extremely steep, so you can create some incredible filtering with the click of a mouse! As with all the SDR parameters any changes you make within the software can be saved as pre-sets so that you can recall them for use later.

Another often overlooked feature that is unique to SDR is the facility to record IQ data direct to your computer's hard disk. By recording the IQ signals of a particular band segment you capture all the activity in that segment and can therefore replay and decode it at a later date. IQ recordings are so much more powerful than conventional audio recordings be-cause, you are effectively replaying the RF signals so you have the full range of filtering and demodulation options at your disposal. With many systems you can also set the playback to loop; very helpful if you're trying to resolve a difficult signal. Recordings can also be linked to a timer so that you can capture transmis-

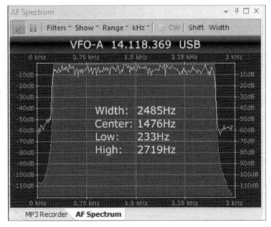

Fig 7.13: SDR audio frequency spectrum and filters.

sions when you're not at home. Receiving weather pictures from the NOAA low orbit satellites is a good example where scheduled recordings can be very helpful.

The SDR receiver also has full access to all the other parameters that you would expect from a high quality rig such as AGC, CW filter, noise Blanker, noise reduction, speech processing, etc. You can also expect to see encoders and decoders for many of the more popular data modes being incorporated into the main SDR software.

SDR - The Future

Now the revolution has started and advanced hardware is becoming available at very competitive prices, we will doubtless see evermore advanced black-box transceivers with all the functions controlled by computer. This opens-up the option to mount the hardware much closer to or even on the antenna system, thus eliminating all the problems associated with getting RF to and from the shack. In the commercial world, SDR is very attractive, as it facilitates the production of universal radio hardware modules that can be software configured for a wide variety of different roles. This flexibility has particular appeal in the military arena, where the interworking of air, land and sea forces from different nations is becoming increasingly important.

8.
Data Modes Software

by Mike Richards, G4WNC

In this chapter I shall be running through a selection of the most popular data modes software programs. I've included a comparison chart that show you the range of features available from each multi-mode package, to help you choose the best one for your operating interests. I will show you how to install and configure each of them, plus some operational tips to help you get on the air as quickly as possible. For the purpose of these examples, all programs were downloaded from the Internet using the listed sources and installed on a clean build of Windows 7 running on a basic (1.7GHz) dual core Pentium processor. I also took the opportunity to test them on a Windows 8 Pro system with a similar specification processor. One easily solved problem with Windows 8 is caused by the Smart Screen filter that's built into Windows 8. This checks the software publisher and a few other things against a centrally stored list in an attempt to protect you from malicious software. However, most amateur software developers will never get on Microsoft's list, so the software gets blocked. If you want to run the software, you should click on the "More info" text link and then choose "Run anyway". I've noted any other specific program compatibility problems in the software descriptions.

Data modes software types

When it comes to data modes software, there are two groups of software. The first group are general purpose, multi-mode systems that attempt to cover as many modes as possible within a single application. These are a popular place to start, as you only have to familiarise yourself with one set of controls and you can operate many different modes. The second group are specialist programs that only cover a single mode or a very small group of similar modes. These are often the only way to go for some modes (such as ROS), but do generally offer better results for their specific modes. You will often find that these packages have been written by the inventor/developer of the data mode in question, and for that fact alone they are likely to be particularly effective.

Is downloading safe?

Whilst there is always an element of risk when downloading software, there are a few simple steps you can take to minimise them. The first is to make sure you are using a good quality Internet Security Suite. Whilst some of the free ones are very good, you always get more comprehensive cover with the paid versions. Personally I use Sophos Antivirus, as I have found it to be very effective over many years of use and it has protected both mine and my family's PCs admirably. NB: I don't get any kick-backs from Sophos for saying that. I pay like everyone else!

Besides having a solid antivirus system, it's worth making sure you download from a safe site. In most cases that means downloading from the software author's site rather than a mirror or other site that is promoting the software. The links I have provided in this chapter are either the author's original or an approved distributor. I have personally checked all the links at the time of writing and I've scanned the download files to make sure that they are virus free. That's about as far as I can go to ensure that the links published here are safe for you to use.

Virtual computing

If you install and uninstall lots of software on a Windows PC, the registry and other settings will gradually get clogged and your system will eventually slow and become less reliable. However, if you want to try lots of software without compromising your main PC, virtual computing is the way to go. A virtual PC is a specialist software package that emulates a computer within your PC. When you run this application you are able to load Windows, Linux or any other operating system without affecting your main PC. Once the new operating system in installed you can connect to the Internet and download/install all the software you like without affecting your main PC. The software is actually installed onto a file that's owned by the virtual PC. Connections to the outside world for Internet, sound, printing, USB ports, etc. are all handled automatically by the virtual PC software, as it creates a bridge between the virtual PC and your hardware. The two most popular Virtual PC packages are the Oracle VirtualBox and VMware's VMware Player. Both are free downloads and work extremely well. I've shown web links to them in **Table 8.1**. You will need a reasonably powerful PC with at least a dual-core Pentium or equivalent to run this software successfully. A lesser machine will be too slow and probably grind to a halt.

Table 8.1.
Virtualisation
software links.

Software	Link
VMware Player	http://www.vmware.com/products/player/
VirtualBox	https://www.virtualbox.org/

Macros

The use of macros are commonplace across most data modes but newcomers are often unsure where to start, plus the use of macros can be intimidating for a new user as the distant station bombards you with stacks of stored text! Let's start with a brief introduction to macros. They are not at all complicated and are little more than a collection of stored text messages that can be recalled with a single key press. They are used to store all the routine information that is exchanged in most QSOs. A good example is the basic handover between overs. The sending station would typically end an over with something like 'G4ABC de G4DEF PSE K'. If you had the text 'de G4DEF PSE K' stored in a macro you would only need to type his call and then press a single button to add the stored text and make the complete handover message. The same can be done with details such as name, QTH and your equipment. By making use of these simple stored texts you can carry out a basic QSO with minimal typing.

Modern data modes software take macros a step further and provide special character combinations that can be used to control the flow of information. A good example is transmit/receive switching in FLDIGI, where adding the characters '<TX>' automatically switches the program to transmit and '<RX>' switches it back to receive. Many also have methods of capturing the other station's call, so it can be automatically inserted into a macro. The actual macros you need will depend on the mode in use, as operating practice varies between modes. You will also find that most software is supplied with some generic macros already setup, so you will just have to modify them to suit your operating style.

Transmitter drive level

All the software discussed here uses the audio output from the PC's soundcard to drive the transmitter. Because of that it's important to be able to adjust the output level, so as not to overdrive the transmitter. Whilst some data modes do not require the transmitter to operate in linear mode, others do, so for beginners I always suggest running the transmitter in linear mode. A simple way to ensure this is to switch your data modes program to transmit and adjust the audio output level so that the ALC just starts to kick in on the transmitter, then just back off the drive slightly. You will find that the required drive level varies between mode and band, so it is helpful to have an easily accessible gain control potentiometer in the transmit audio path. This can be a home-made arrangement (well screened), or built into your interface unit. Whilst most data modes software includes a facility to adjust the transmit audio level a manual control is faster and much more convenient.

Waterfall displays

These have become the standard tuning indicator for the vast majority of data modes software. The waterfall is simply a spectrum display that shows the signal level as different brightness or colour dots. Each sample produces a single line of dots and subsequent lines follow behind, to create a scrolling display. The reason this display makes such a good tuning indicator and signal detector is that it shows an historical record of what's been received over recent minutes. Even if a station has stopped transmitting, you can click on the historical trace to set the correct tuning point. For modes like the ever-popular PSK31, a spectrum display will show the entire band's activity in one sweep, so it becomes very easy to spot new signals and to move around the band segment.

Soundcard troubleshooting

Most of the problems encountered by newcomers to data modes are associated with getting the audio from the rig to the software. The solution is usually very simple, but you need to adopt a logical fault finding process or you will soon get in a muddle. The first step is to make sure your rig is switched-on and tuned to a band with some activity. A good place to start is the PSK section of the 20m band on 14.070MHz. Make sure the mode is set to USB. Next you need to check that an audio signal is emerging from your rig. One way to do this is to plug a very sensitive pair of headphones (high impedance) into the audio output connection on the rig – you should be able to hear something. If all is well at that point, plug the lead back into the computer (the line-in jack is best). In most Windows systems you should see a speaker icon in the bar at the bottom right of the screen. Right-click and choose Recording Devices. That will open-up the Sound panel with the Recording tab activated. If all is well, you should see some activity in the bar graph display to the right of the device name. If the bar graph is dead, double-click on the device to open-up its Properties panel and choose Levels. In this section make sure the slider is well advanced and check that the speaker icon is not on mute. Close that panel and return to the Sound –Recording tab and you should see activity in the bar graph. If the tests so far have worked and you have signs of life in the Sound – Recording tab but not on the waterfall, then you need to look at the software setup. The precise steps will depend on the software you're using, but you need to access the configuration and make sure you have selected the correct sound card and input. If this fails I suggest you visit the support forum for your software to see if the users have any suggestions. In my experience, audio path problems are usually very simple to solve, providing you adopt a logical approach.

Multi-Mode Software

FLDIGI

Web link: http://www.w1hkj.com/Fldigi.html
Yahoo Group: http://groups.yahoo.com/group/win-fldigi/join

Created by W1HKJ, FLDIGI (**Fig 8.1**)is one of the most comprehensive and versatile systems currently available. Operating system support is excellent with versions for Windows, Linux and OS X. You can even get this to run on the Raspberry Pi!

Installation
For Windows, download the Windows Setup package from the Downloads page of the site and save it to a convenient location – Windows Downloads is fine. The download should be quick, as the file is only 4MB. When the download is complete, double click the .exe file to start the installation. If you accept the default options during installation, the software will install in the Program Files directory with desktop and toolbar links to launch the software. That completes the installation.

Configuration
Running FLDIGI for the first time will take you to the configuration wizard that will guide you through the important settings that will allow you to get on the air quickly. The first step is to enter your call sign, name and station details. It's worth thinking about this, because the data stored here will be used in the transmit macros that you'll be using to save typing whilst on the air. The next step is to select the audio input and output settings and for a Windows system you should tick PortAudio and choose the recording and playback sound cards that you intend to use. The Settings and Right Channel tabs can be left at their default settings. The final step of the configuration wizard is to set up the Rig Control settings. If you don't use a rig control system you can ignore this panel. Users of rig control systems will need to refer to their rig control instructions to establish the correct

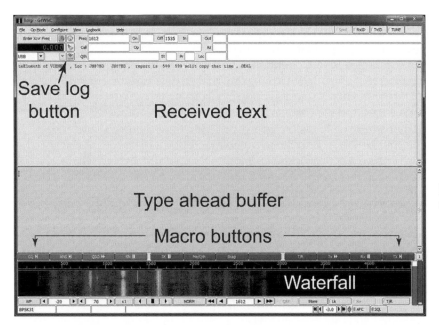

Fig 8.1: FLDIGI
screen layout.

settings for this panel. That completes the basic configuration, but if you want to make any changes at a later time all of FLDIGI's configuration settings are accessible via Configure on the main menu bar.

Operation
As you can see from the software table, FLDIGI supports a very wide range of data modes and this versatility is one of the reasons it is so popular. Considering the versatility of FLDIGI, the interface has been kept remarkably simple, but I'll run through the important sections here. At the very top, mode selection is done via the OpMode menu item. The section immediately below the menu bar is a logbook entry panel, where you can keep a record of your QSOs. You will see that there are entry fields available for all the vital information, such as call sign, operator name, QTH, signal reports in and out, etc. When you've finished your QSO you need to press the save button to store the information in the electronic logbook. This store button is the lower of the stack of three buttons to the left of the log.

Immediately below the log is the received text panel. This is where all the decoded text messages are displayed. You will also find your transmitted text shown in this section after it has been sent, but it will be coloured red so it's easy to identify. This panel effectively keeps a full running log of all your QSOs in the current operating session.

The pale blue panel below is what's known as the type-ahead buffer. It is where text messages can be created and stored prior to transmission. The contents of this section will be transmitted as soon as you switch to transmit.

Immediately below the type-ahead buffer is a line of macro buttons.

These are pre-configured with sample macros that you can edit to suit your operating style. Editing macros is very simple in FLDIGI – just right-click on a button and the macro editor will open up. FLDIGI has a very powerful set of macro commands and it's worth taking some time to read the excellent user guide to make the most of this feature. However, to get on the air quickly it is very simple to customise the default macros. When you've updated the macros, go to File – Macros – Save to store the updated macros to disk. When you re-start the program at a later date you will need to re-load those saved macros.

The next section is the all-important spectrum display, where you can view all the available signals and use a simple left-click of the mouse to tune-in to a specific signal and start decoding. Finally there is a set of controls for the waterfall display, transmit/receive switching, etc.

Tips:
Here a few operational tips for FLDIGI that might make life a bit easier.

Escape key – This is an emergency stop button, which instantly stops transmission and puts you back into receive mode. It's great when you do something daft like transmit in the wrong mode and just want to abort.

Type-ahead – If you click to place the cursor in the type-ahead buffer the output will stop at that point. This is very handy, as you can prepare a message and only let it go out when you're ready.

Right-click browse tune – if you're in a QSO and an interesting station pops-up in the waterfall you can right-click/hold on and FLDIGI decode it and flip back to your QSO when you release.

Signal Browser – Providing you have a reasonably powerful PC, you can use the Signal Browser to simultaneously decode all the signals in the audio band. To activate this you select View – Signal Browser from the menu.

<LOG> - Don't forget to add <LOG> to your QSO final over macro to automatically save a log entry at the end of the QSO.

Ham Radio Deluxe – DM780

Web Link: http://www.hrdsoftwarellc.com/
Support Forum: http://forums.hrdsoftwarellc.com/

Originally created by Simon Brown, G4ELI/HB9DRV, the software (screen layout shown in **Fig 8.2**) is now looked after by HRD Software LLC. HRD is a very comprehensive rig control program that includes the powerful DM780 data modes software that I'm covering here.

Installation

Follow the link and menu to get to the Download section, where you can access the current or earlier versions. The download is 95MB, so it may take some time, depending on your Internet speed. Once downloaded, double click on the .exe file to run the installer. For a standard installation you can accept all the default options. You may see a message about installing the Microsoft C++ 2010 redistributable. This is a set of software libraries that are required to run the program, so you should agree to the installation. If this fails (as it did for me) this is often because you have a later version of the re-distributable files already installed. In this case you will need to download the files separately from Microsoft. After the HRD installation has completed, open your browser and Google 'Microsoft C++ 2010 redistributable', then choose the Microsoft link to download the library. Double-click on the .exe to complete the installation.

Configuration

When installation is complete and you run HRD, you will be presented with a small connection configuration screen where you can enter details of your rig. If you have a rig control interface you should enter the appropriate details here. If you don't have rig control and just want to use the DM780, choose Dem-o-Matic as the company and any rig you fancy from the list. Before leaving this screen tick the box marked Start DM780 and then press the connect button at the bottom left. When the full HRD opens you will be presented with a 'Getting Started' screen where you enter your station details for inclusion in macros and also select your soundcard and radio interface details. The Getting Started page covers this extremely well, so I won't repeat it here. Once you've completed the configuration you can close the Getting Started tab. If you need to return

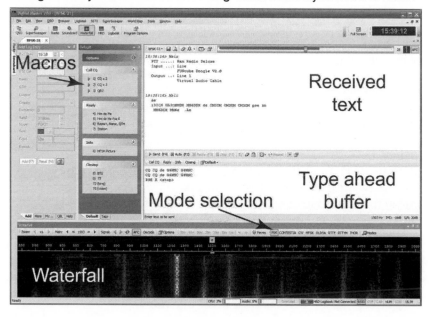

Fig 8.2: Screen layout for DM780 software.

to this section, it can be found via the menu system – Tools – Program Options where you'll find the Getting Started button at the bottom left. Before you finish configuration, I find it useful to have the modes showing in the Waterfall toolbar. This is activated by clicking the Modes icon and ticking the box at the top labelled "Show modes in waterfall toolbar". You can then choose to display all your favourite modes using the tick boxes adjacent to each mode.

Operation

In addition to using the menu immediately above the waterfall display, you can also select the operating mode using the drop-down menu at the top of the TX/RX text box. Once the desired mode and frequency has been selected, any activity will be shown on the main waterfall display. Tuning to a station is simply a question of clicking the mouse in the centre of the signal. The bandwidth of the signal is shown by the highlighted bar that follows the mouse click. Received text appears in the top text box, as does the transmitted text (after it has been sent). The lower text box is the transmit type ahead buffer, where you can prepare messages ready for transmission. The combination of DM780 with HRD and its logging and control functions make for a very powerful and sophisticated setup that is beyond the scope of this simple introduction.

MixW

Web Link: http://www.mixw.net
Support Site: http://groups.yahoo.com/group/RealmixW/

Shown in **Fig 8.3**, MixW is a commercial data modes program written by Nick Fedoseev, UT2UZ and Denis Nechitailov, UU9JDR. Two versions are available; MixW v2.2 and v3. The main difference between the two versions is the addition of more comprehensive networking facilities, so you can automatically link with DXclusters and store logs on remote servers. Although both versions are paid-for software they are available on a fully functional 15-day trial, so you can check that the software is right for you before you buy.

Installation

Navigate to the Download page and choose the latest MixW full version. The download is under 8MB, so should be fairly quick. At the time of writing the download comprised a zip file with a single .exe file inside. When the download is complete, extract and run the .exe file to start the installation. Follow the default settings in the installer for a normal installation.

Configuration

When you run MixW for the first time you will be presented with the

Personal Data panel, where you should enter your call sign and station details for automatic inclusion in macros and logs. The next step is to make sure the correct sound card or interface has been selected. To do this, choose Configure – Sound Device Settings from the Menu bar and use the drop-down selection to choose the correct sound card. If you are using a proprietary interface it's worth using the separate Interface wizard to help complete the configuration. The wizard can be found via the menu at Configure – Interface Setup Wizard. Immediately below the menu bar you will find a set of Macro buttons that can be configured using a right-click.

Operation

MixW is very easy to use and, like most of the programs here, uses a waterfall display to show activity and aid tuning. To receive a new station you simply click the mouse on the waterfall trace and decoding will start immediately. MixW also makes use of your Internet connection to automatically look-up received call signs, report their location and even tell you whether or not you've worked them before. Double clicking on a call sign in the received text box will automatically transfer that call to the electronic log and the stored call will also be used in the macros. If you get in a muddle, the Escape key causes an immediate switch back to receive.

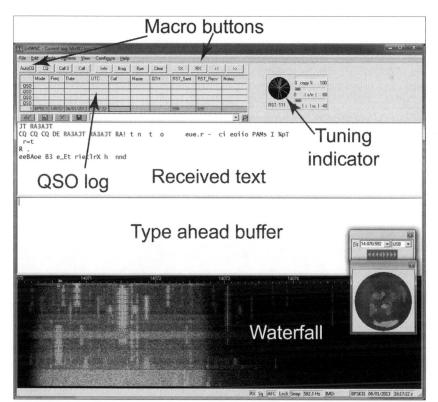

Fig 8.3: Screen layout for MixW.

WinWarbler

WebLink: http://www.dxlabsuite.com/winwarbler/
Support Site: http://groups.yahoo.com/group/dxlab

WinWarbler (**Fig 8.4**) is a free program that supports CW, PSK and RTTY communications at a variety of speeds and has proven to be very popular, due to its ease of use.

Installation
WinWarbler is part of the DXLab Suite of programs, so the first stage in the installation is to install the DXLab Launcher application. Full instructions for this are well documented on the DXLab Suite web site. Once the launcher is installed and running you can start the WinWarbler installation by clicking the ww button in the launcher. If you accept all the default settings during the installation, WinWarbler will be installed in c:\DXLab.

Configuration
As with most of the software described here, WinWarbler supports the use of transmit macros and a certain amount of automation of the log keeping process. One of the first requirements is to populate the software with your call sign and you may find that you are prompted for this when the program starts for the first time. To update that information, click the Config button in the top right-hand section of the main screen. When the Configuration screen opens you will find the call sign entry on the General tab. You should use the Soundcard tab to select the appro-

Fig 8.4: Screen layout for WinWarbler.

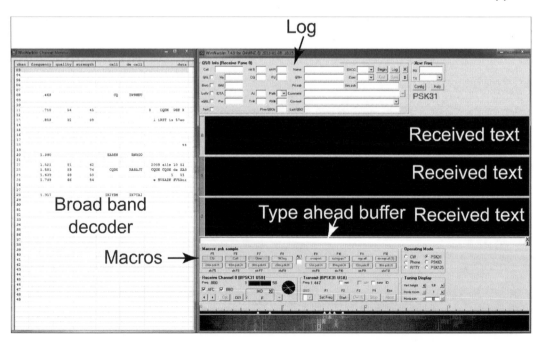

priate sound card. The Configuration screen also provides access to a wide range of customisation controls, including logging and contest operation. A selection of example transmit macros are provided in the macro section, which is located just below the text screens. The stored macro is displayed when you hover the mouse over the button and a right-click provides access to the macro editing screen, where all the macros can be customised.

Operation

Many operators find the WinWarbler channel monitor particularly helpful, as the software can decode more than 40 channels of PSK simultaneously. This is a very effective way to assess band activity. Each decoded signal is supplemented by a signal strength and quality measurement. Activating the Broad Band Decoder (BBD) is simply a case of ticking the BBD box at the bottom left of the main screen. In addition to showing the decoded output in the Channel Monitor screen, you will notice a number of small white triangles in the spectrum display. These are channel indicators for the stations that are currently being processed by the Channel Monitor.

HamScope

WebLink: http://www.qsl.net/hamscope/
Support Site: http://groups.yahoo.com/group/hamscope/

HamScope is another free decoding programs that supports PSK31 modes, along with RTTY, ASCII, MFSK16, Packet and CW. However, support for RTTY requires the download of the MMTTY Engine and Packet requires the AGWPE engine.

Installation

Start by downloading the latest HamScope zip file from the Internet site (v1.56 at the time of writing). The resultant zip file can then be extracted to a location of your choice. A separate directory on the C drive is probably best. The next step is to download and install the help file using the same process. Make sure you put the help file in the same directory as the HamScope extracted file. If you want to be able to use HamScope for RTTY/ASCII you need to download the MMTTY engine using the links on the HamScope site and then copy the mmtty.exe file to the HamScope directory. For Packet you need to download the AGWPE engine from: http://www.elcom.gr/sv2agw/ and copy the installed files to the HamScope directory. For a more detailed description of using Packet with HamScope, take a look at the tutorial on: http://www.soundcardpacket.info/

　　　Windows 8 compatibility: I encountered a compatibility problem when running Hamscope under Windows 8 that caused my ATI graphics

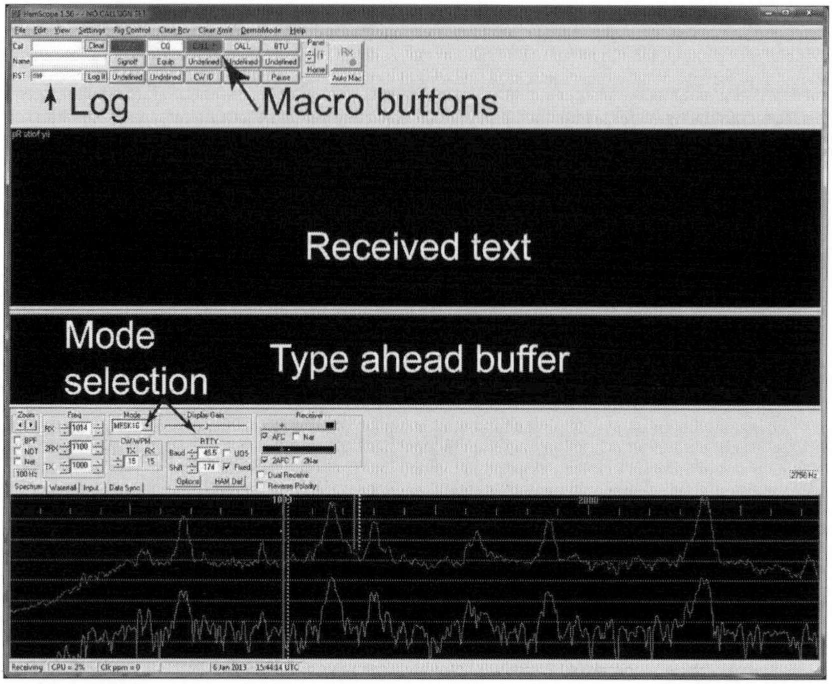

Fig 8.5: Layout of the HamScope screen.

card driver to consume approximately 90% of the processor capacity. This resulted in a very sluggish response on the Hamscope spectrum display. None of the usual compatibility settings resolved the issue.

Configuration

The first step is to open the Settings menu – General Setup and make sure the appropriate sound card has been selected for send and receive. If you have a transceiver interface lead you can also enter the details on the screen, to allow HamScope to control your rig. The next step is to customise the macros. These are to be found in the centre of the screen, immediately below the menu bar. A few of the macros are predefined, but you will need to customise them for your QSO preferences. To edit a macro you simply right-click on the button to open-up the macro edit screen. Here you can change the macro and use keywords to create more complex macros with automatic Tx/Rx switching.

Operation

One important point to note is that the screen of HamScope (see **Fig 8.5**) doesn't automatically re-size in quite the same way as many modern Windows programs, so you need to expand the window to make sure you are seeing all the controls. The next step is to select the required operating mode. This is done via the Mode selection box that's located in the central panel between the upper text boxes and the lower spectrum displays. This section also carries all the other adjustments that are appropriate for the mode, i.e. speed, shift, etc. As with most of the programs here, HamScope uses a type-ahead buffer so that text can be prepared prior to transmission. As an indicator of transmission progress the type-ahead text is displayed in red prior to transmission but turns green when sent. The bottom window of the display provides a very useful spectrum display, so you can easily find stations and then tune with a single mouse click. To abort transmission at any time, press the Escape key on your keyboard.

MultiPSK

WebLink: http://f6cte.free.fr/index_anglais.htm
Support Site: http://groups.yahoo.com/group/multipsk/

MultiPSK (see **Fig 8.6**) is free software written by French amateur Patrick Lindecker, F6CTE. It features an extremely wide range of modes that include BPSK/QPSK, CW, Packet, PACTOR 1, AMTOR, ASCII, MFSK8, MFSK16, Olivia, Contestia, Throb, Domino, PAX, ALE, JT65, FELD-HELL, HF-FAX and SSTV. In addition, MultiPSK includes receive only capability for a number of commercial modes. The inclusion of so many modes and options has made the interface extremely crowded, which can be confusing for the inexperienced operator. However, the software performance is very good, hence its inclusion here.

Installation
The software is supplied in a zip file that can be extracted to a directory of your choice. Once extracted, the software can be run from that directory by double-clicking on the MULTIPSK.exe file.

Configuration
The initial screen shown at start-up is the configuration panel and the first

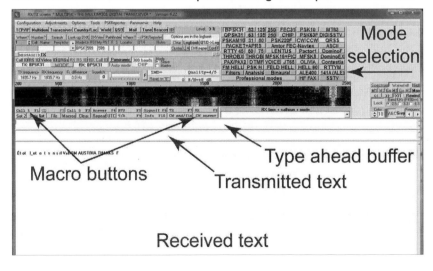

Fig 8.6: Layout of the MiltiPSK screen.

Mode selection

Type ahead buffer

Macro buttons

Transmitted text

Received text

task is to run through the top menu and set the Sound Card (Input) and Sound Card (Output). To get to the main operational screen of MultiPSK, press the large RX/TX Screen button towards the bottom left of the configuration screen. Macros are located just below the waterfall display and are edited via a right-click of the mouse.

Operation

In addition to a busy interface, general operation of this software is slightly quirky. To tune to a RTTY or similar signal you must click on the right-hand peak rather than the centre. The text screen layout is also different, with the received text occupying the lower section while the type-ahead buffer uses the upper text box. The central text box is used to show text after it has been transmitted. MultiPSK retains the use of the Escape key to abort transmission.

Specialist Modes Software

WSJT

WebLink: http://physics.princeton.edu/pulsar/K1JT/
Support Site: http://groups.yahoo.com/group/wsjtgroup/

The WSJT suite of programs (see **Fig 8.7**) by Joe Taylor, K1JT have been developed for use with difficult signal paths such as Earth-Moon-Earth (moon-bounce), ionospheric scatter, etc. As such they are mainly con-cerned with the task of establishing whether or not basic communications have been established, rather than the conversational style of other amateur data modes. Joe Taylor has provided excellent PDF manuals for all the software in the WSJT suite, so I would strongly recommend using those to help you get going. The following text is intended to provide a brief run through the installation and setup. Most of the WSJT modes rely on accurate timing between the transmit and receive sites, so it is vital that the accuracy of your PC clock is maintained. For most applications the Windows Internet Time service is adequate, but if you want improved accuracy you can install specialist time synchronisation software such as Dimension 4, Socket Watch or NetTime.

WSJT: This program specialises in the reception of extremely short duration signals such as those from a meteor scatter or an ionised meteor trail. The software can also deal with more conventional, steady state signals that are 10dB below the audible threshold.

MAP65: This software provides a 90kHz wideband receiver for WSJT65 signals and displays a band map showing all the decodable signals within the band.

WSPR: (Weak Signal Propagation Reporter) is designed as a propagation reporting tool for the MF and HF bands. Live propagation results can be seen on wsprnet.org.

Installation – WSJT

WSJT installation is very simple and starts by downloading the latest WSJT Windows executable which is about 11MB. Double-click the .exe file to install it. I suggest installing somewhere other than the Program Files directory, because some users have experienced runtime errors when installing in the normal Program Files. This may be due to permission problems, which can be avoided if the software is installed outside the Program Files directory.

Configuration – WSJT

To run the software successfully for the first time you may need to run it with Administrator authority. To do this right-click, choose Run as Administrator and click 'yes' to the prompt that follows. The next step is to choose Options from the Setup menu item, so you can enter your call sign, grid locator and select the appropriate soundcard and interface connection. Soundcard selection is a little unusual, as you need to enter the device numbers and these are shown on the Console Window that should have opened when the program started. The next step is to adjust the input and output audio levels, which can be done via the soundcard mixer or interface level controls. The input level should be adjusted so to show around 0dB on the bar graph at the bottom rights of the Spectrum screen. Once the configuration is complete you can use the Mode menu item to select the appropriate mode for the band you're using.

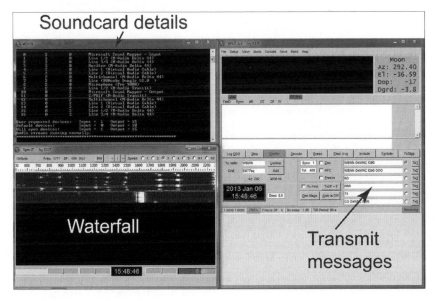

Fig 8.7: Screen layout for WSJT in JT65 mode.

Operation – WSJT

Operating these weak signals modes is very different to most other data modes, as there is no real conversational mode. Instead, exchanges follow a formal protocol that's designed to confirm little more than the fact a two-way contact has taken place. Rather than describe the process here I suggest you refer to the excellent tutorials on Joe Taylor's web site.

Installation – MAP65

The software can be downloaded via the WSJT site and installed by double-clicking on the downloaded .exe file. Following the installation the software will optimise the FFT (Fast Fourier Transforms) for your PC. This can take a little while, so you need to be patient whilst this stage completes.

Configuration – MAP65

This software provides a wideband receive function, so it can only operate with certain wideband SDR receivers. The most popular choices are the FUNcube Dongle (original v1.0) or the SoftRock series of receivers. MAP65 includes frequency control tools for the FUNcube Dongle (c1.0) and the SoftRock that can be accessed via the Setup menu item.

Operation – MAP65

If you're using a SoftRock receiver with a Si570 series local oscillator you can adjust the centre frequency of the MAP65 receiver by typing the frequency in SetRxFrequency box in the lower right of the waterfall display. For FUNcube Dongle users, frequency adjustment is performed via the Setup menu under FUNcube Dongle Settings. In addition to being able to change the Dongle frequency, this panel gives you access to all the dongle settings.

Installation – WSPR

Its very simple to install this tool – download the Windows exe file and double-click to install. Follow the default prompts and you will find the software in the Program Files directory.

Configuration – WSPR

As with the other software in this series you need to enter your call sign and soundcard details. This is done via the Setup menu, then choosing Station Parameters. The soundcard selection is somewhat easier with this software, as the devices are all listed by name rather than just the device number. As a final part of the configuration make sure you tick the upload spots box just below the waterfall display, as this will enable your spots to be added to the central database.

Operation

As WSPR is a propagation reporting tool your station is really being used as part of the overall network of WSPR stations and contributing to the pool of propagation information. Once everything is setup and your transmit and receive levels adjusted, you can leave the software running. To see how well your signal is propagating, log on to the wsprnet.org site, select Database from the menu and if you choose Specify query parameters and enter your call sign you will see a list of reports from all the stations that heard your last call. The system operates in real-time, so it provides a very useful indicator of propagation from your station.

ROS

WebLink: http://rosmodem.wordpress.com/
Support Site: http://groups.yahoo.com/group/RosMode/

Controversial when first introduced, but now gaining wider acceptance, ROS uses Multiple Frequency Shift Keying (MFSK) along with sophisticated encoding techniques to provide a very robust data mode that's ideally suited for use under poor conditions.

Installation
Download and extract the zip file to a location of your choice. Once the file has been extracted, double-click on the Install.exe file to complete the installation process. Unlike conventional Windows programs the installation routine does not put an entry in the Programs list, but the program can be run by double-clicking the ROS v...exe file in the extracted directory. You can create a desktop item by right-clicking on the .exe file and choosing Send to Desktop.

Configuring
The first step is to open the Configure menu item and choose Operator to enter your station information. This is followed by the rig setup, where you can choose the type of rig control you want to use and select your rig. ROS makes this process very easy as it automatically scans the COM ports to locate your rig and automatically configures the data rate, etc. The final step is to select the appropriate soundcard for input and output. In the central area, just above the type-ahead buffer, you will find the macro buttons that are pre-configured with a selection of useful texts. These can be edited by right-clicking over any of these buttons.

Operation
The author has made ROS extremely easy to operate, especially if you are able to link ROS with your rig. As **Fig 8.8** shows, at the top right of the screen you will see the band and channel information. You can use these controls to select your operating frequency. To the left of that panel you will find the activity reporter that uses your Internet link to flag-up other ROS activity across the bands. The central area also contains a

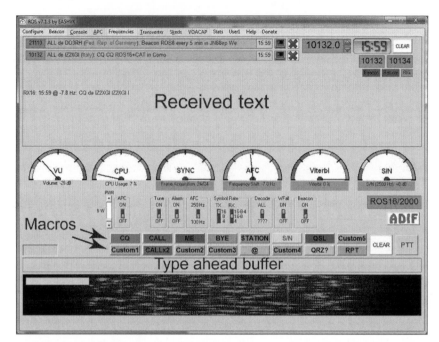

Fig 8.8: Screen layout for ROS modem.

dashboard of indicators that may at first look a little daunting. These are simply gauges that show the quality of the received signal – the more greens you get the better the signal. You will also note that ROS provides a measured signal-to-noise ratio. It s customary to use this as the signal report, rather than the subjective RST system. It is also important to note that ROS is a very robust system with built-in error correction, so you don't need to repeat key information such as name, QTH etc.

V4Chat

WebLink: http://www.winlink.org/node/501
Support Site: http://groups.yahoo.com/group/V4Protocol

This new mode was developed by Rick Muething, KN6KB and provides a fully error corrected keyboard QSO mode. V4Chat is an extension to the WINMOR protocol that was originally developed as an alternative to PACTOR for amateur HF e-mail systems. WINMOR operates using a new soundcard based Terminal Node Controller (TNC). Both the WINMOR TNC and V4Chat are free of charge.

Installation
The program installation file can be found in the Files section of the Yahoo! support site. Download and unzip the file, then start the installation by double-clicking on the V4ChatSetup.exe file. On completion of the installation you will find a desktop icon available to run the program.

Configuration

When you run the program for the first time you will be presented with a registration reminder. You can either choose 'remind me later' or click on the web link to register. The registration process takes you to a site where you can make a voluntary registration donation of $25 to support the Amateur Radio Safety Foundation. When the program starts you will see two windows, one of which shows the V4 Sound card TNC and the other is the V4Chat program. In V4Chat choose File – Setup and enter your call sign, locator and select the appropriate V4 Capture and Playback devices (sound cards). In the lower right of the setup screen choose Radio Setup to configure your rig control. When this is completed don't forget to hit Save Settings and then Update on the following screen to ensure all your settings are saved. The final stage in the configuration is to adjust the audio drive so that the transceiver is operating in its linear region. To help with this V4Chat includes a two-tone test signal that can be sent via the Test menu on the TNC panel. One final point to note is that this mode requires rapid switching from transmit to receive and rarely works with systems using VOX for TX/RX switching. You will need to use CAT or PTT line switching.

Operation

V4Chat (**Fig 8.9**) has two operational modes which are ARQ (Automatic

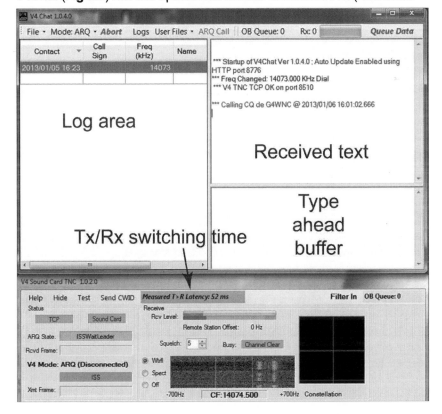

Fig 8.9: V4Chat screen layout.

Repeat reQuest) or FEC (Forward Error Correction). The most common operational mode is ARQ, which provides a fully error-corrected link between two stations. Common calling frequencies are 3.635, 7.073, 14.073 and 21.073MHz. V4Chat includes an automated CQ call for the main ARQ mode, which is activated via the ARQ call item on the main menu. This same button also provides the facility to answer a CQ call from another station by entering the call in the Target call sign box. V4Chat operates by breaking the message into smaller groups of characters that are sent and then checked for error-free reception, before moving on to the next groups of characters. The result is a very robust link, but it is important to avoid adding repeats in your message as the system automatically repeats any damaged parts of the message.

The V4Chat screen is split into three sections, with a QSO log on the left, status messages and received text at the top right, and a type-ahead buffer at the bottom right. Once a link has been established between two stations text is usually sent from the transmit buffer every time a CR is encountered. However, this can be changed to force transmit on the following conditions: Ctrl + CR, CR, CR/double space, end of each word.

At the time of writing V4Chat does not include conventional macros, but it does have the facility to insert pre-compiled text messages that have been created using Windows Notepad or similar. Once a QSO has been established, the two stations are effectively locked together and will continue until an operator forces a close using the Abort button.

MMVARI

WebLink: http://hamsoft.ca/pages/mmvari.php
Support Group: http://groups.yahoo.com/group/MMVARI/

Shown in **Fig 8.10**, MMVARI is a multi-mode package written by Makoto Mori, JE3HHT, who also developed the well-known MMTTY RTTY software, so it has a good pedigree.

Installation
The software downloads as an EXE file so can be run immediately to start the setup. Installation is menu driven and if you accept the default optionsthe software will be installed in C:\Ham\MMVARI.

Configuration
The first time the program is started you will be prompted to enter your callsign, which will then be used in MMVARI's macros. The next step is to select the appropriate soundcard. This is done via the Options – Setup MMVARI menu item. Select the Misc tab of the setup panel and you will find the Sound card section at the top left. You can then use the drop-down selection box to choose the appropriate card. If you

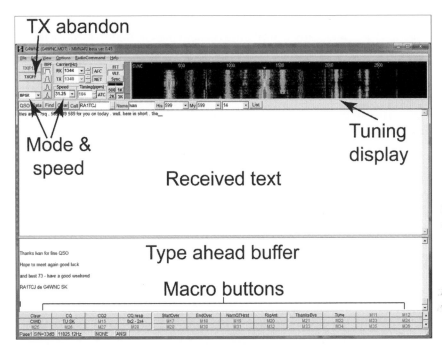

TX abandon

Mode &
speed

Tuning
display

Received text

**Fig 8.10: MMVARI
screen layout.**

Type ahead buffer

Macro buttons

want to use rig control MMVARI can supply basic rig control commands, but you need to select the rig in the Options – Radio Command menu item. Here you can select the COM port, radio and other parameters. One point to note is that Baud rate is limited to a top speed of 19200, so you may need to change your rig settings to match this. MMVARI has lots of macro buttons and each can be programmed by right-clicking on the appropriate button, which will open the macro editor window. This gives access to a very wide range of macro commands that include a simple programming language,, so you can make interactive macros.

One other task that is not essential but can lead to improved decoding is to calibrate your sound card using the Options – Calibrating the SoundCard menu item. When opened, you will see a screen with instructions that are very slowly scrolling down the screen. The first step is to tune your receiver to a standard frequency transmission; RWM on 9.996Mhz being a good choice in the UK. When you are tuned-in, note the audio frequency of the beeps as shown in the display at the top of the screen and enter that into the Tone box at the bottom of the screen. The display will then change to show a new pattern of colour blocks. Let this run for about 10 or 15 minutes and you should have a screen full of this pattern, which will probably be slanting slightly to one side or the other. The slant is caused by inaccuracy in your sound card's sampling clock and the next step measures and corrects that. Now click on the bottom left of one the colour blocks and move the cursor to the top of that block so that the line produced by the cursor matches the slant of the signal and click again. That completes the measurement and calibration. Pressing the OK button to store the correction completes the process.

Operation

MMVARI is very simple to operate, but has some sophisticated features hidden under the bonnet. The main tuning display can be seen at the top right of the display and this can be set to display a waterfall, spectrum or a synchronisation display. The bandwidth of the display can be altered by the adjacent buttons. MMVARI also includes variable Band Pass Filters (BPF) that can be very helpful when the band is very busy or noisy. One particularly useful feature of MMVARI is its sub-channels decoders that can be set to monitor different frequencies and modes within the audio passband. The Sub Channels are activated via the View – Sub Channels menu item and appear as small, separate decoding windows. The windows respond to tuning by mouse click and the mode can be changed by clicking on the mode window for that channel.

MMVARI is one of the few programs that don't use the Escape key to abandon a transmission, so you have to remember press the TXOFF button on the main panel for this. If you double-click on a callsign in the received screen it will automatically pop into Call box on the log and be ready for use in macros. You can also gather other station details quickly by clicking on the received text, whereby you will be presented with a menu where you can choose how to use the information.

Table 8.2: Multi-mode software comparison table.

	FLDIGI	DM780	MixW	Win Warbler	Ham-scope	Multi PSK	MMVARI
PSK	Y	Y	Y	Y	Y	Y	Y
QPSK	Y	Y	Y		Y	Y	Y
RTTY	Y	Y	Y	Y	Y	Y	Y
CW	Y	Y	Y	Y	Y	Y	
Packet			Y		Y	Y	
Pactor 1			Y			Y	
Contestia	Y	Y				Y	
Olivia	Y	Y				Y	
Domino	Y	Y				Y	
Hell	Y	Y	Y			Y	
MFSK	Y	Y	Y		Y	Y	Y
MT63	Y	Y	Y			Y	
Olivia	Y	Y				Y	
Thor	Y	Y					
Throb	Y	Y	Y			Y	
WEFAX	Y		Y			Y	
NAVTEX	Y		Y			Y	
WWV	Y						

9.
Slow Scan Television

by Paul Young, G0HWC

Analogue SSTV

Analogue SSTV was invented by Copthorne Macdonald in 1957 and the first SSTV image was sent across the Atlantic Ocean from WA2BCW to G3AST on 20 December 1959. It has come a long way from the early days of using vidicon tubes to display images such as **Fig 9.1** shows. In 1970 the first commercial system arrived on the scene from Robot, with the Robot 70 monitor and Robot 80 camera, then onto the better-known Robot 1200 in 1984. At this time the first computer based systems arrived and these have got better as years passed up to present-day software like MMSSTV and DM780.

Fig 9.1: The first ever SSTV picture transmitted across the Atlantic.

Software
MMSSTV is by Makoto Mori, JE3HHT. The latest version is 1.11G, final release. The software is a standalone package and includes all the regular modes plus many obscure modes.

DM780 by Simon Brown, HB9DRV, is part of Ham Radio Deluxe and within DM780 is an SSTV module. DM780 is an ongoing develop-ment, but as it is now it covers most of the regular used modes. More will be added over the course of its development. The advantage of DM780 is that it also caters for other modes such as PSK and CW.

Software Set-ups
Don't skip the setting-up step in any analogue SSTV program, because all analogue software requires slant adjustment to be undertaken. The reason for this is that programs use the clock on the soundcard for

Fig 9.2: A slightly slanted SSTV image.

Fig 9.2: A slightly slanted SSTV image.

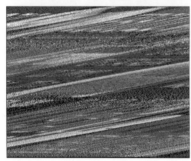

Fig 9.3: A badly slanted SSTV image.

timing and this is not 100% accurate. To overcome the offset, all SSTV programs have an option to calibrate the soundcard, effectively compensating for it. Every SSTV program has its own setup for this and if you skip it your transmitted images will be slanted. See examples of a slight slant in **Fig 9.2** and bad slant in **Fig 9.3**. Transmit badly slanted images and you will not get any replies. All software has a facility called 'auto slant', but this only works in receive mode and is there to correct slight slant errors.

In the early days of SSTV there was no auto slant and everyone did their best to keep their transmitted images straight, but since the introduction of auto slant many are getting lazy, thinking that it will fix badly transmitted images. Unfortunately, if your slant is too far off, it won't. Get it adjusted as per your software instructions or do an Internet search for 'SSTV slant' and re-check it from time to time.

MMSSTV and DM780 have built-in template makers for your CQ, reply and information texts, ready for sending. Some of the templates that may be used in a QSO are shown in **Figs 9.4 -9.6**.

Most SSTV programs use macros that automatically fill in from a receive log or user filled-in screen. Things like the callsign of the station you are working and their signal report would all use macros, so you will not need to make a new template for every QSO. Remember to keep the text size large if you are sending on HF, as QRM can make small text difficult to read. On VHF you will often get away with smaller text, if needed.

Analogue Modes
There are many SSTV modes, from the early Robot-8 (8 second black & white + grey scale) up to things like Scottie-DX (268 seconds RGB). There are some obscure

Figs 9.4 to 9.6: Examples of templates used in SSTV QSOs.

modes that can take even longer to send. A breakdown of some of the more commonly used modes is shown in **Table 9.1**.

Mode	Type	Time (sec)	Scan Lines	VIS
Martin 1	RGB	114	240	44
Martin 2	RGB	58	240	40
Scottie 1	RGB	110	240	60
Scottie2	RGB	71	240	56
Robot 8	BW	8	120	2
Robot 12	BW	12	120	6
Robot 24	BW	24	240	10
Robot 36	BW	36	240	14
Robot 36	YC	36	240	8
Robot 72	YC	72	240	12

Digital SSTV

Digital image programs are a relatively new thing and there is one program that has taken the lead called EasyPal. Incidentally, the 'Pal' in the name does not imply the use of the Phase Alternate Line TV standard.

Table 9.1: SSTV analogue modes. The Vertical Interval Signalling (VIS) code is detailed later in the chapter.

Digital File Transfer History

In about 2001 Barry Sanderson, KB9VAK, created the RDFT (Redundant File Transfer) programs for DOS.

In mid 2002 the first GUI for RDFT – DIGSSTV – came from VK4AES. The latest version is from May 2005, but it is still an ongoing development.

In December 2002 the first version of DIGTRX from PY4ZBZ was used, initially only by a few Brazilian operators. It was totally in Portuguese. Then he received many requests to translate it into English.

He created DIGTRX mainly to offer all radio amateurs a friendly interface for the fantastic RDFT programs from KB9VAK, but also to learn to program in Delphi, to study Fast Fourier Transform and new digital modes.

In February 2005 he also included the new HamDRM mode in DIGTRX, an adaptation of the Digital Radio Mondiale (in English, Digital World Radio) mode for digital broadcasting below 30MHz, done by Cesco, HB9TLK, based on another fantastic program from Volker Fisher and Alexander Kurpiers of the Darmstadt University of Technology in Germany. Several months later, VK4AES included the HamDRM mode in EasyPal, using the same hamdrm.dll originally made by HB9TLK for DIGTRX.

DRM Digital SSTV

This is not SSTV as in slow scan television, but file transfer with error correction.

EasyPal by Erik Sundstrup, VK4AES, is an ongoing development, with regular updates of enhancements and fixes. Incidentally, most radio amateurs start with analogue and move onto digital, but you can use the same interface for both.

EasyPal is a complex program, with many configurations required before you start to transmit an image. You can be up and running in receive mode very quickly though; just install the program, setup the audio path in the software, what sound card your radio is connected to and adjust the audio level. The best places to listen are either 14.233MHz or 3.733MHz and wait until you start to receive DRM. You will know when the signal is DRM, as you will see the vertical Sync bar change from all red to green. Not until all green is lit up to the top will the program be decoding the signal. In **Fig 9.7** you can see the EasyPal screen.

In the box at the top left is the callsign of the station being received. Just under the callsign, 'RX -13Hz' indicates that his transmission is 13Hz low. This could be adjusted from the radio, but the software is doing this for us. Under this, 'SNR 8dB' indicates how good the signal to noise ratio is. In this case it's not very good, at only 8dB.

Fig 9.7: EasyPal screen layout.

The next item down is 'Total 245'. This is the total number of data segments needed to fully display the image. 'OK Segs 60' indicates how many segments have been received OK. 'Position 139' is the last segment received and '185 missed segments' is the number of segments needed to finish the image. The first vertical box to the right of the callsign box shows your settings for transmit and the settings that the received station is sending, in this case mode B, as the sending station is on 20m, width 2.4 (this is used 99% of the time), ErrFix is set to high and should always be set to this. Regarding QAM, this is 16 (which is used most of the time on 20m) but QAM 4 could be used if the signal is not 'making the trip'. Finally, 'LeadIn'. 24/lng is the default and should always be used.

Under the control buttons is a spectrum display window that displays the receive audio. Under this is a waterfall display. In it you can see that three vertical lines stand out. These are in line with three small markers at the top of the waterfall. They stand out because they have higher gain, transmitted at twice the power and are used to calculate the initial coarse frequency offset of the received DRM signal. At the bottom left of the screen is the receive progression line. The size of this is set by the size of the file being received, the red part being missing data and the green being received data. The right of the window shows the last received image. The program has been configured to append some data about each received image to the top corner of it – the callsign of the sending station, date and time received, and the mode it was received in. This is handy to append to the image if you decide to FTP your received images to your website.

Some time needs to be spent in fully understanding Easypal and setting it up. A good place, with all the help files you should ever need, can be found at: www.g4rob.co.uk/easypalhelp/

The DRM mode is a modern digital transmission mode for HF, based on DRM. In some aspects it is similar to RDFT, but in others very different. Both use many carriers: RDFT (W11 to W14) uses 8, and EasyPal uses from 45 to 51 carriers. Both also use the Reed Solomon code for Forward Error Correction. The RDFT carriers are modulated in phase with 9 different phases, and they are fully separated in the frequency domain.

The HamDRM/EasyPal carriers use Orthogonal Frequency Division Multiplex (OFDM). The modulated carriers are overlapping in the frequency domain and are modulated in QAM (quadrature amplitude and phase). The transmission of a file requires three separate operations; coding, recording (of the transmission) and decoding, which increases the total time of transmitting/receiving.

In HamDRM/EasyPal a file is codified and transmitted simultaneously. Also, it is decoded at the same time that it is received. There is only a small delay between the end of the transmission and the reception (some seconds). Mode A is faster than Mode B, but Mode A doesn't tolerate the negative effects caused by multi-path propagation, so Mode B is more robust. Mode E is the slowest, which helps in bad conditions.

The QAM modulation can be in 4, 16 or 64 vectors or symbols. 64 QAM is much faster, but needs a very good Signal-to-Noise Ratio (SNR) or a high quality channel. 4 QAM is the slowest, but supports more noise or a smaller SNR. On the VHF/UHF bands you will often be able to use 64 QAM, but on HF you will struggle with this, so 4 or 16 QAM is usually called for.

Interleaving consists of changing the natural symbols sequence. If long (2 seconds), it allows better error correction with slow fading, but it causes a little larger delay in the reception. Short interleaving is 400ms.

In Easypal the occupied bandwidth for the DRM signal can be set to 2.2 or 2.4kHz. The smaller is a little slower and should be used if the SSB TX/RX equipment's filters are too narrow or do not have a flat transfer function.

The DC frequency simply refers to the inferior limit of BW, and also should be chosen to agree with the equipment's filters.

Interfacing

Setting-up your computer to run analogue or digital SSTV is very easy. You could be up and running, receiving images from around the world within half an hour. If you want to transmit as well, you will need to ether build a simple interface or buy one. If you want to build one, the parts should cost you around £15. Ready built ones start from around £25 (see http://www.m0aqc.co.uk), up to about £100 for an interface with built-in sound card.

Looking at what a simple interface will do, you could just connect your RX and TX audio to your computer sound card, but this is not a good approach as you could have a potential difference between the computer and the transceiver, so it is good practice to use isolating transformers. A 'get you going on the air system' could just use two isolating transformers and turn your VOX on. Most basic interfaces also have transmit switching, controlled by the software.

Care for your radio

SSTV is a 100% duty cycle mode, so it can damage your radio. Always watch your ALC and note that it's not a good idea to run at full output of most radios. Most modern radios are not rated at full power for long periods, so you would be advised to run at a maximum of 50% of maximum power. Please check the user manual that came with your radio. Incidentally, you should never use speech compression/ processing when transmitting SSTV.

Finding activity

When you have set up some basic templates you can start monitoring. The main place to find SSTV is on 20m. The main frequency is 14.230MHz, and sometimes 14.227MHz. Note the 3kHz spacing; any less would result in QRM. When you start hearing sounds, look at the panoramic display. If you are receiving SSTV you should see something like the image shown in **Fig 9.8.** Note the spike on the left. This shows the line synchronization pulses that tell the software to go to the next line of the image. This should always be centred on 1200Hz. If it is not, you need to make fine tuning adjustments on your radio. The wide peak on the right between 1500Hz and 2300Hz is the image information. When receiving a monochrome image, 1500Hz is black and 2300Hz is white, with the part in between being the grey scale.

When receiving a colour image it is more complex. The sync

Fig 9.8: The spectrum of a typical SSTV signal.

pulse still works in the same way, but depending on the mode in use the part between 1500Hz and 2300Hz works in different ways. Pictures are either sent as RGB (Red, Green and Blue, separately) or YC (Luminance and Chrominance). All software will send a Vertical Interval Signalling (VIS) code at the beginning of an image. See **Fig 9.9**. It consists of bits of 30 milliseconds in length. The code starts with a start bit at 1200Hz, followed by 7 data bits. An even parity bit fol-lows, then a stop bit at 1200Hz. The VIS code is decoded by the receiving software and sets it into the same mode as the transmitting station. Then the image is sent. At the end, most software will then send a Frequency Shift Keying Indent (FSKID) code at 1900Hz and 2100Hz at 45.45 Baud. This contains the callsign of the sending station and when decoded will display the callsign within the software. More comprehensive programs like DM780 will add this into the log and even send an eQSL card if wanted.

1200 Hz	d_0	d_1	d_2	d_3	d_4	d_5	d_6	even	1200 Hz

Fig 9.9: Makeup of the VIS code.

When starting out it is good to watch for a while, to see how QSOs work and also to get some ideas on templates that others use in their CQ calls etc. Before you transmit you need to pick a mode. If sending a reply to someone, you would be best to reply in the same mode as you received the image from the other station. If you make a CQ call, try either Scottie2 or Martin2. With luck you will get a reply and have your first analogue QSO. Over time you will hopefully make new templates and obtain new images to send. It is good to con-tinuously get new images to send, using either your digital camera, a webcam, or even the Internet, be-cause there is nothing worse than seeing the same images from a station over and over again. If you become a regular SSTV user you will soon know what is meant.

Fig 9.10: An analogue SSTV image received on 20m.

Many SSTV users have websites where the images they have received are uploaded and can be viewed. Some sites have pages that display the latest received images from sites all round the world. Take a look at http://www.g0hwc.com as an exam-ple. **Figs 9.10-9.13** show some images received on 20m.

SSTV and the Internet

A lot of radio amateurs now have websites that include pages to display station details etc. Many of those who are SSTV enthusiasts are now adding a page to display their received images, because many SSTV programs have File Transfer Protocol (FTP) for uploading images built in. For programs that don't, John Benedict, KE5RS, has a free program called FTP Widget. Whether you use a built-in FTP or the external program, once the programs are setup, the process is fully automated. If you want a free website, just go to www.qsl.net and sign up for a free one. You will get www.qsl.net/yourcall The service is free to all amateur radio operators, but you are asked to donate towards the upkeep. It's your choice, but remember that if no one donates the service is either likely to close or end up having a fixed charge. You could just put on one page to display your analogue or digital images and at a later date build on it.

For those that do not understand how to make a web page, some 'get you started' templates can be found at: www.g0hwc.com/sstv.html These can be used for any SSTV images.

To make your own web pages you will need a program like Microsoft Front Page and as you get to understand HyperText Markup Language (HTML) you can add to them.

Once you have your basic page on the Internet you will want to get your images onto the page. To that end there follows the setting-up of DM780, MMSSTV and EasyPal.

Fig 9.14: DM780 FTP setup.

DM780

All you need is built in. On the menu bar click 'SSTV' then go down to 'FTP' and then 'FTP settings'. You will now see the window shown in **Fig 9.14**. This has a part for both TX and RX images to be completed. Just fill them in as shown, but with your supplied password from qsl.net Your user name will always be your callsign. When you are done you will need to turn FTP on. You need to decide if you want to send just your received images to your site or both transmitted and received. It's your choice and the templates that you will have downloaded and put on your site will either be able to display just your received images or both. If you want to turn on the FTP for received images only, just click on the FTP button just under the left side of your RX window. If you want both, click on the SSTV pull-down from the top menu bar, then 'FTP' and highlight both TX and RX icons. You can test the FTP from the FTP set-up page or from the main screen above your saved images by clicking 'FTP all'. This will upload your latest images to your site and fill your page.

MMSSTV

You will need the external program FTP Widget installed. This is a small, very stable program that will do all the work for you.

Before you set up FTP widget you need to configure MMSSTV to send the received images to a specific folder on your PC. You can make this any place you want. Personally, I use a folder called 'mmsstvfiles' off the root of C:. When you have made the folder, go to MMSSTV and click on the 'History' tab above the RX window. Now right click on the image and from the menu click on 'Assign another folder name'. In here you need to put the full path to the folder you have made. On mine it looks like this: c:\mmsstvfiles You must use the full path and drive letter. When you have done that, right click again on the history image and click on 'Auto copy to another folder name'. This will turn on the service and from this point onwards any images you receive will also be sent to your new folder for FTP Widget to use. As a final check, right click in your history image again and check that you have a tick next to 'Auto copy to the another folder' and 'Copy as JPEG format'. Now you need to run FTP Widget. Click on 'File' and then 'Properties'. This will open the set-up window shown in **Fig 9.15**. Just fill it in as shown, but add your callsign and password. The most common mistake is incorrect setting-up of the 'Local Drive and Directory Path'. To confirm, double click on the drive at the top. This will show the folders under the drive. Double click on 'mmsstvfiles', so it changes to blue and then click the 'Save' button. The final thing you need to do is click the 'file' button and then click 'Scanning'. The program is now waiting for an image to arrive in the 'mmsstvfiles' folder to do its work. To check that it is working you will need to wait until you receive an image. Each image you receive will move all the images down by one, until your page is full. Until your screen is full, when the program finds an image and sends it to your site you will see errors on the details window of FTP Widget, as it tries to renumber image files on your site. Do not worry about this.

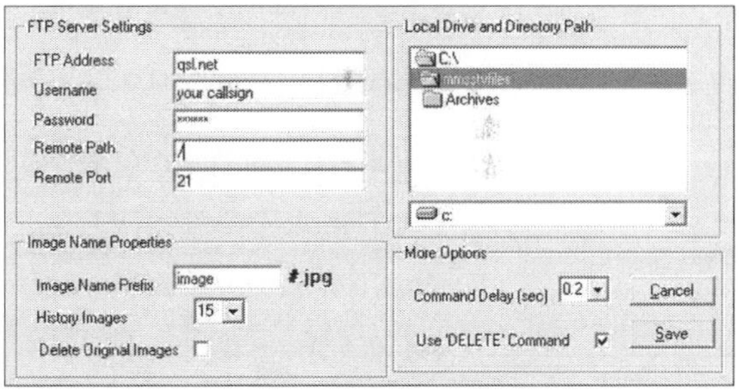

Fig 9.15: MMSSTV FTP setup.

Errors will stop when you have a full set of images (set at 15 within the set-up screen).

Fig 9.16: EasyPal FTP setup.

EasyPal

This has FTP built in. Click the 'FTP' button from the menu bar then click 'Allow FTP Auto-Upload of your received pictures'. This will bring up the window shown in **Fig 9.16**.

Fill in the details as shown, but with your callsign and password. Click the 'Upload as image1' and press 'FTP on' and that's your set-up done. While here you can do a few things. Click the FTP button again from the menu bar and make sure the second item on the list 'Tag FTP received pics uploads with callsign, date, SNR, mode, band' has a tick next to it and further down the list 'Do not allow my TX pictures to be uploaded by other stations' is *not* ticked. You can ether wait until you receive an image to get images to your site or you can force a bunch up from stored images. Click the 'View' tab and you will see your recent RX images along the top of the screen. Hold down the Ctrl key on your keyboard and while holding the key, click on some of your RX images. This will highlight them with a red box. Now release the Ctrl key and click 'To Web' on the bottom right of the screen. This will FTP the selected images to your site.

Useful links

MMSSTV*: http://mmhamsoft.amateur-radio.ca/pages/mmsstv.php

Ham Radio Deluxe (DM780)*: http://www.ham-radio-deluxe.com

EasyPal: http://vk4aes.com/

EasyPal help files: http://www.g4rob.co.uk/easypalhelp/

DigTRX311: http://www.qsl.net/py4zbz/hdsstv/HamDRM.htm#downl

FTP Widget: http://ke5rs.com/john/software/widget/

G0HWC pages, showing received analogue and digital images plus pages showing latest images from hundreds of other ham sites round the world with links: http://www.g0hwc.com

2D0DRM was the first to build a page showing live feeds from EasyPal sites all round the world: www.2d0drm.co.uk/cams.html

Cheap, well-built interfaces, ready-wired for your radio: www.m0aqc.co.uk

* Included on the CD that accompanes this book

10.
Internet Remote Operation

by Wojtek (Berni) Bernasinski, G0IDA, SP5GU, and Steve White, G3ZVW

The technological advances in computing and microcontrollers that have taken place in the last few years have resulted in it being easier than it has ever been to set up and operate a remote station. This practice would appeal mainly to those who have limited real estate at home to put up a good antenna, or indeed for those who live in a flat where a garden is not available.

For people without the ability to erect antennas, a remote station can literally transform their enjoyment of amateur radio. It can be installed far away in the countryside, or at a friend's property where ample antenna space is available.

Basic Overview

The first part of this chapter is based around the RRC-1258 MkII from Microbit. It comes in two parts; one for the remote end and one for the home end. The remote unit controls Voice Over IP and serial data to the rig and is connected to a router via a Local Area Network hub, which in turn is connected to the Internet and a Web Switch for switching relays (which will switch the power supply on and off as well as the remote controller and the rig). The home end comprises a PC with Windows XP running Ham Radio Deluxe, a Virtual Comm Port Emulator (for the Microham unit) and the RRC-1258 MkII controller, which is connected directly to the router at home via an Ethernet cable. Headphones, iambic key, foot switch and microphone all connect to the control box.

When complete, the Internet will carry signals between home and the remote station, and here lies the essence of using a remote station which could be located anywhere in the world.

Advantages

A clear advantage of operating remotely is that the station can be connected to a large antenna, perhaps a full sized dipole on 160m, a beverage or a tower with a beam on it. Other advantages may include a reduced level of noise, a problem which most of us who live in a town or city would undoubtedly suffer from.

For those who like to experiment, gain knowledge, enjoy 'fiddling and tweaking' and having the satisfaction of a remote station working reasonably well (and I'll get back to why it doesn't work well all the time) then it is all worth the time and expense.

Disadvantages

Cost

For a start the Remote Control units I will be describing are not cheap and are priced at around £400. The Web Switch, described later, costs around £160. Assuming you already have a transceiver, a power supply, antenna system and a free place with free Internet and mains, then your basic cost at the time of writing has already mounted up to £560, the price of a small but adequate HF rig!

Latency

Delays in the Internet may cause problems and there will certainly be a delay between talking at the home end and what is actually transmitted. I measured mine using 'traceroute' command and found 15 hops (routers) between my home and the remote site and a latency of 60-90ms. This changes a bit every time I connect to the remote station, as different routes are used through different routers on the Internet.

Legality

A remote station needs to conform to current radio licensing regulations, the most important one being for the radio to go back to receive should the transmitter get stuck. Some modern radios include in their menu a setup for timeout. I have set mine to five minutes, in the hope that none of my transmissions will be any longer than that.

Our licence states that our messages 'must be adequately secure' from one end to the other, but do not mention what is meant by the word 'secure'. I am happy with the idea that my signal going into the Internet and out into my radio is secure, as 'Joe Public' is unable to intecept the data easily. There isn't much we can do about data between the time that it leaves our router and arrives at the remote end anyway.

Security

Security of equipment can be of concern if it is hosted on a remote site, for example in a shed in the middle of a field. These are just the basic

disadvantages but they could be enough to put you off such a project.

I have been very lucky at the remote end, as I have free Internet access, free mains and good security for the equipment, hence this project has been worthwhile.

Fig 10.1: Front view of the RRC-1258 MkII.

Hardware Requirements

The project revolves around the remote control units RRC-1258 MKII, as seen in **Fig 10.1**, produced by Microbit of Sweden.

On the left hand side you can see the controller which connects to the radio at the remote end, while the controller on the right connects to the PC and router at the home end. They look almost identical, except for a CW speed control on the right hand unit.

The small USB format sockets on the far left are used to program the initial IP address of the units via a utility program which can be downloaded from the SM20 website www.remoterig.com Alternatively, a serial connection can be used on Com 1 for the same purpose. The next socket, AUX/MIC, is where the microphone and PTT are connected via a network type plug. Here I just made patch leads to plug into my head set and PTT footswitch. My speaker plugs directly onto the socket marked 'SP'. At the remote end, microphone and PTT leads are connected from this socket to the transceiver. A lead (grey) is connected from the speaker socket of the transceiver to the back of the controller, into the microphone input socket, as seen in **Fig 10.2**, as well as a serial cable which controls the rig, the 12V DC cable and the network cable.

The lowest band-

Fig 10.2: RRC-1258 MKII back view.

width which the audio channel uses is approximately 85kbps using mode '0' and the codec G711 at a sampling rate of 8KHz. Other rates are available and used to suit your needs.

The control channel uses far less bandwidth and is not specified at the time of writing.

Setting up the Controllers

Setting up the controllers is relatively straightforward. Detailed information can be found on the manufacturers web site.

First of all there are five jumper leads inside to configure in each controller. Four positions will depend on the make of your radio and the fifth is to provide power to your microphone. After this you need to set up the IP addresses for each unit. I used 192.168.2.200 and 201 for each controller.

The controllers each have a built-in web server, so having assigned them their own IP addresses and using port 80, log into them and configure a few basic options like the FQDN (Fully Qualified Domain Name) and the audio quality. There are more advanced options, but they do not need to be set to get you going. Configuring the controller at the remote end to have port 8091 for web operation is ideal as the Web Switch will be configured for port 8090. As you will see later, it too has a web server running for remote set up. The Web Servers in both units have username and password control, so the units are relatively safe from an outside attack.

Having set up the basics (by referring to the web site), the router at the remote end needs to have its ports opened to enable the two units to communicate and for you to be able to administer the controller and the Web Switch.

The ports which need to be opened and the protocol used are:

8090 - Web administration of the Web Switch (TCP)
8091 - Web administration of the remote controller (TCP)
5060 - SIP in/out port (UDP)
11000 - Audio in/out port (UDP)
12000 - Command in/out port (UDP)

There is no need to open any ports on your router at home, as all traffic is initiated by the controller in the shack, which then opens outbound ports automatically in your router; it's just inbound ports which need to be opened at the remote end. You can now type an FQDN like http://remote.dyndyns-net.org:8091 in your web browser and be presented with the controller's administration page.

Web Switch

The clever little Web Switch 1216H from the same manufacturer can be seen in **Fig 10.3**. I say 'clever', as it can not only switch five relays at 240VAC 5A, it can also read temperature (rig or ambient) on two of its inputs if Dallas DS18B20 sensors are attached.

The Web Switch is an item of equipment that needs to be powered on all the time, as it provides the FQDN to the Internet where you can log in and switch relays on and off or read the current temperature.

On the left side of Fig 9.3 is the network cable which is connected to the hub, and then to the router. On the bottom right side is a 9V DC supply and the twisted wire is connected to Relay 2, the cable which when shorted switches the K3 on. Relay 1 is used to switch the mains side of the PSU, but is not shown in the photo. In **Fig 10.4** you can see that the PSU and the radio are on.

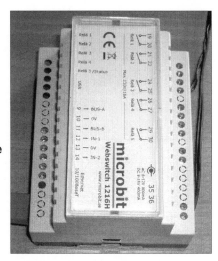

Fig 10.3: The Microbit 1216H Web Switch.

Setting up the Web Switch

The Web Switch is set up in the same way as the controllers, via the mini USB port at the side of the unit. All that is required is an IP address to get you started. I used 192.168.2.202.

Once connected, using your web browser on port 80 through your Local Area Network, you then need to change the port number to 8090 for remote administration. At the same time a username and password should be added. The menus are found on the left hand side.

The home end needs to know the IP address of the remote end, so a FQDN needs to be inserted into one of the setup fields. You can make one up from the web site www.dyndns.com It will look something like 'remote.dyndyns-net.org' where, when you type this into your browser, this address will find the remote station on the Internet.

The Web Switch will then send every 30 minutes (this is configurable) to the web site www.dyndns.com a request, and the web site will then do a reverse lookup on the remote end IP address and resolve the FQDN 'remote.dyndyns-net.org' to numbers

WEB Switch 1216H - 1216H Web Switch			
microbit			
WEB Switch 1216H	Relay 1:	ON OFF	PSU on
System Info	Relay 2:	ON OFF	Radio on
Set relays	Relay 3:	ON OFF	
Inputs			
Temperature	Relay 4:	ON OFF	
IP settings	Relay 5:	ON OFF	
Relay settings			
Serial settings			
Advanced settings			
DynDNS settings			
Application upgrade			
Bootloader upgrade			
Restart device			

Fig 10.4: Web Switch relay status page.

which the Internet and routers understand. You can now type your own FQDN with port 8090 in your web browser and you should be presented with the Web Switch administration page.

Radio Equipment

You need to do a bit of investigating before you decide on which radio you wish to use. You may not want to put your pride and joy in a field in the middle of nowhere but one issue I came across was how to turn a modern radio on and off. In the shack we just push the ON/OFF switch, but how do we do that remotely?

Not all radios have a method for switching on and off remotely, but luckily the K3 has, whereby pulling pin 8 of the Accessory connector low switches the radio on. To turn the radio off, pin 8 must be high and the command 'PS0' issued from the K3 Utility Software. Only then can the power supply be turned off. Older equipment may work by just turning on the mains using a relay in the Web Switch.

Make sure also that all the functions you wish to use via your favourite radio interface like Ham Radio Deluxe are available.

Software Requirements

There are three software packages required for the operation, all of which I have running on my Linux machine in a virtual environment hosting a Windows XP Operating System guest. The OS needs to be able to work with the following software:

1) A software package of your choice, which will control your radio remotely. I am currently using Ham Radio Delux, as it fulfils my requirements.
2) Software which specifically controls hidden functions, updates etc. For the K3 I use 'K3_EX', as Ham Radio Deluxe does not have these functions built in.
3) Software from Microbit to configure the controllers and Web Server via mini USB.

I also have microHam Virtual Comm Software running, as I have no serial ports on my modern PC and a microHam unit which converts USB to serial. This is then plugged into the back of the shack controller, as seen in Fig 10.2.

Configuring Ham Radio Deluxe is very easy, with just the selection of the type of radio you are interfacing with and the Com port required for control. Tuning up and down the band is done by using the slider, and frequency change appears to be instant. **Fig 10.5** shows my setup.

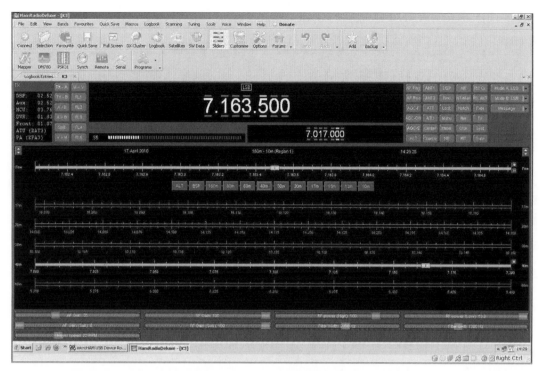

Fig 10.5: Ham Radio Deluxe.

Using the utility K3_EZ I have access to various menus and functions which Ham Radio Delux does not offer. Your radio of choice may need such software. One smart function this offers is to see the SWR over a range on a band. **Fig 10.6** shows a graph of the SWR on 40m.

I also use K3 utility software for uploading any firmware changes and many other functions. The last most useful function is the one to turn the radio off. Using the CMD Utility I issue the command 'PS0;' and the rig switches off.

The Remote Station

The remote station with all its connecting cables is shown in **Fig 10.7** (overleaf). From top to bottom and left to right we have the rig controller and next to it a Netgear Hub. The hub is not usually necessary, but with only one port available on my friend's router I employed a hub

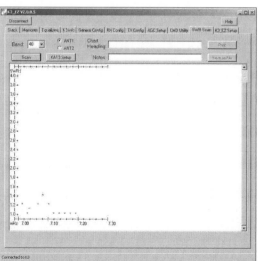

Fig 10.6: Measured SWR on 40m.

Computers in Amateur Radio

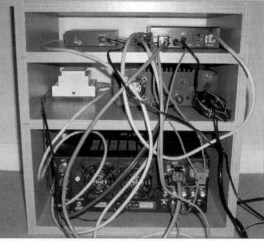

Fig 10.7 (top left): Remote station, front view.

Fig 10.8 (top right): Remote station, rear view.

Fig 10.9 (right): Home end block diagram.

Fig 10.10 (below): Remote end block diagram.

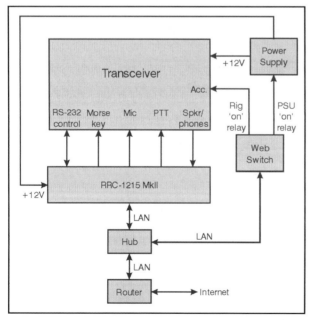

which connects the Web Switch and the controller to the Router. On the middle shelf is an Alinco 30-amp Switched Mode power supply and next to it the Web Switch. On the bottom shelf is the Elecraft K3 transceiver.

Fig 10.8 shows the back of the setup. As you can see, I made no effort to tidy the wiring up. The mains cable was connected to the Web Switch at the remote site.

The shelf unit was home made, with material bought from a DIY store where they kindly cut it into pieces of the required lengths. All that was left for me to do was to measure out at home where the shelves should be positioned and fit them, which made a sturdy cabinet.

100m of Westflex coax connects the transceiver to a trapped dipole on a 30ft mast in a very large and open field, with no QRM! A diagram of the layout of the home end is shown in **Fig 10.9** and the remote end in **Fig 10.10**.

On Air Results

On air results on HF have been remarkable, where reports of good quality audio have been reported and operators have said that they would have never known that I was using remote equipment. A latency of 60-80ms is not noticeable. Even on CW there is no issue, as you hear the sidetone generated by the controller at the home end. The usual band noise of 80m and 40m covers up the slight hiss that is heard in the headphones when no signal is present, but overall very impressive audio can be heard.

For home users the Internet is not perfect and I think for what I'm trying to do a lot of improvement is possible, because from time to time I get dropouts, that is to say that the audio stops and I am unable to control the rig. I have noticed this more in peak usage times of the Internet. I am still trying discover the root cause of this problem, because these dropouts last anything from 5-30 seconds and can be very frustrating if one occurs in mid QSO.

Conclusion

Like for like, the price of the project wouldremain roughly the same if one were to use a dedicated computer at the remote end. However, the the simplicity of setting up the RRC-1258 MKII is of great benefit. Also, it is certainly smaller than any laptop to date. Being a dedicated unit for remote control it has numerous features built in, one of which will automatically reconnect the controllers if the link drops.

Internet bandwidth can be controlled quite well and power consumption is certainly lower than a PC.

Icom

Introduced in 2012, the Icom RS-BA1 offers the owners of selected Icom transceivers the ability to operate remotely. The package comprises the RS-BA1 remote control software and the RC-28 USB encoder. The software will work with modern Icom HF radios, but not older models.

There are two major selling points of the package:

1. Low voice latency.
This results in the same operating experience of having the radio in the same room as the operator.

2. Familiar user 'feel'.
The remote control USB encoder utilises the same tuning knob and

Fig 10.11: The RC-28 uses the same encoder as Icom radios.

shaft encoder (**Fig 10.11**) used on many Icom HF radios, providing the same 'feel' to the user.

Configuration

The majority of the Instruction Manual is devoted to configuring the system. The process is beyond the scope of this book, as it depends on the Operating System(s), whether access to the transceiver is via a Local Area Network or the Internet and the setting of audio levels. It also involves changing Firewall settings. These settings will be user specific, but it is certainly worth taking an overview of the system as a whole.

Two personal computers are required, one at the transceiver (local) end of the proceedings and one at the operator (remote) end. **Fig 10.12** shows that there are tthree connections between the transceiver and the local computer; one for transmit audio, one for receive audio and one for transceiver control. Depending on the model of transceiver in use, the control cable will beither be USB, RS232 plus an S/P DIF cables or an RS232 cable plus a CT-17 CI-V level converter.

The local computer links to the remote computer via routers and
Fig 10.12: Icom the Internet.
remote system At the remote end a microphone, headphones and the RC-28
layout. remote controller are connected to the computer.

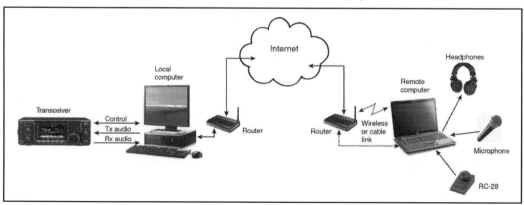

The RS-BA1 software itself consists of two component applications; system configuration software and remote control software. The system configuration software sets up IP address, audio sampling rate and other settings. The remote control software provides a user interface that is similar to the radio's front panel (**Fig 10.13**), and allows control of the radio from a remote location.

The RC-28 includes a PTT button and two user-programmable function keys. Most functions and modes of the transceiver, including interference rejection functions and IF filter settings, can be controlled remotely. Also, the S-meter and SWR can be observed. A voice recording function is also included.

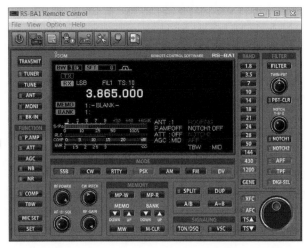

Fig 10.13: The RS-BA1 graphical user interface.

11.
D-Star

by Dave Thomas, MW0RUH

Contrary to widespread belief, Digital Smart Technologies for Amateur Radio (D-Star) is a communications standard, not a brand name. Moreover, it is not limited to one manufacturer. It was released in 2001, having been developed and funded by the Japanese Ministry of Post and Telecommunications, who were tasked to investigate digital technologies for amateur radio. The committee included representatives of the Japanese amateur radio manufacturers, including Icom, plus other observers.

The standard is published by JARL, but it is an open system, which means that any equipment complying with the standard can use it. It is a two part communications system, the first being formed by radio-to-radio transmissions - either direct or via a standalone repeater - and the second deemed to be the 'spine' (or backbone) of the system is by integrating with the Internet via 'gateways' to the wider amateur community. The D-Star standard also controls the way in which the signal is relayed, by converting voice to and from digital format. This digital exchange takes place by the use of the AMBE (Advanced Multiple Band Encoding) codec ('codec' being short for **co**ding/**dec**oding).

The early days

Initially you were only able to operate on D-Star (simplex range excepted) by purchasing Icom factory-built repeaters, but since then many new ways of entering and using the system have surfaced.

To encourage people to adopt D-Star, Icom offered discounted deals on the purchase of a repeater if a number of radios were bought, which allowed clubs and individuals to enter into negotiation with those in a locality to take up the offer. Today, however, there are many more ways of joining the network. These will be discussed further on in the chapter, but now include the DV Node Adaptor, DV Dongle and DV Access Point to name but a few.

D-Star modes

D-Star carries digitized voice and digital data, but it does the job in two different ways, there being a combined voice and data mode (DV) and a high speed data only stream (DD).

Although data and voice are carried at different rates and are managed in different ways, they are transmitted as packets. The D-Star protocol is therefore similar in some ways to the Packet Radio (AX.25) protocol that allows the exchange of data between Terminal Node Controllers (TNCs) or the Ethernet protocol used by home and business computers.

The AMBE codec was mentioned earlier. It can digitise voice at several different rates. D-Star uses 2.4kbps (bits per second). In addition, AMBE adds information to the voice data that allows the codec at the receiving end to correct errors in the transmitted stream. The result of the overhead is that the digitized voice stream carries data at a rate of 3.6kbps.

Simultaneously to the digitised voice, DV Mode (low speed data mode) can also carry 8-bit digital data at 1200bps. This data is un-modified when transmitted, so it is up to the operator's software to manage the flow of data whilst it is being exchanged.

When operating in DD Mode (high speed data mode), the voice signal is unused and all packets are dedicated to the use of digital data. Transmitted data is sent as raw data at a rate of 128kbps. Like DV mode, this is transmitted with no modification, the flow control being undertaken by the software package chosen by the user. In DD mode the net data rate is comparable to or better than a high-speed dial-up Internet connection.

How D-Star works

Being a packet based protocol, D-Star data is processed and packaged using the required data and additional information. Packets are sent in their entirety and are processed as a group by the receiving station.

An important difference between AX.25 Packet Radio and D-Star is that AX.25 requires an acknowledgement and the TNC at the

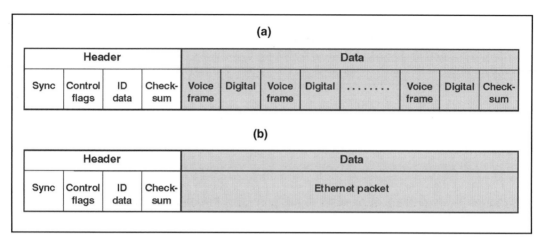

Fig 11.1: (a) Structure of DV mode, and (b) structure of DD mode.

receive end can request retransmission if a packet is received with errors, whereas D-Star is a one-way protocol, so no response is required from the receiver to acknowledge that a packet has been received. The reason D-Star does not require acknowledgements is because, as previously stated, it has error detection and correction built into the datastream.

The structure of the DV and DD modes are illustrated in **Fig 11.1**. Each consists of a header and data segment.

D-Star utilises a common method of using one protocol to send data formatted according to another protocol. In the DV packet, voice data is contained in short segments (frames) which are formatted according to the AMBE protocol. In the DD packet, the data is formatted using the Ethernet protocol. This process of putting data from one protocol 'inside' another is called encapsulation.

The illustration of the packet structure is broken down in **Fig 11.2** as follows:

Sync frame
Bit Sync is a standard pattern for GMSK 1010 modulation used by D-Star.

Frame Sync is '1110110010100000' - a unique bit pattern in D-Star packets.

Control flags
Control flags are used to direct the processing of the packet.

Flag 1   Indicates whether the data is control data or user data, whether communication is simplex, repeater, set priority, etc.

Flag 2   Reserved for future use as identification data

Flag 3   Used to identify the version of D-Star protocol being used, so that as new functions are added the receiver can apply them

Sync		Control			Identification					Error
Bit sync	Frame sync	Flag 1	Flag 2	Flag 3	Received Repeater Callsign	Sent Repeater Callsign	Counterpart Callsign	Own Callsign 1	Own Callsign 2	P-FCS

Fig 11.2: D-Star packet structure.

Identification Data

Received Repeater Callsign   Callsign of the repeater that is to receive the packet

Send Repeater Callsign   Callsign of the repeater sending the packet

Counterpart Callsign   Callsign of station that is to receive the data

Own Callsign 1   Callsign of the station that created the data

Own Callsign 2   Callsign suffix information

P-FCS Checksum

A checksum is used to detect errors. The P-FCS checksum ID is computed from the flag and ID data.

How D-Star corrects errors in digital voices

D-Star uses two methods of combating transmission errors:

1. **Error Detection codes** are used to detect errors. These codes only tell the receiver that the data is damaged or corrupted, not how corruption came about. D-Star checksums follow the CRC-CCITT Standard.

2. **Error correcting codes** contain information about the data. Because the codes are sent with the data (to enable correction at the receive end), they are called Forward Error Correcting or FEC codes. FEC codes contain enough information for the receiver to repair most damage.

Both the DV and DD data packets in Fig 11.1 use the P-FCS checksum in the header, but the DD packet also contains the Ethernet data packet checksum at the very end.

With the DV packet data segment, each AMBE digitised voice frame contains its own FEC code to allow the receiver to repair errors. DV Digital data frames are not protected, relying on the applications to detect and correct errors.

D-Star system layout

Fig 11.3: Icom D-Star Repeater.

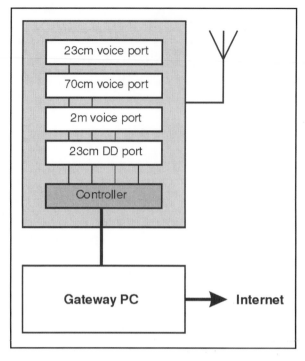

We will begin with the D-Star repeater. Unlike an analogue repeater which operates on a particular band with an individual callsign such as GB3QQ, a D-Star repeater can be built according to the keeper's requirements and be active on several bands with the same callsign. GB7CD will be used as an example. At present it only has the 70cm (B port), but **Fig 11.3** illustrates a full repeater stack setup.

As you can see from the illustration, a fully loaded D-Star repeater can be constructed with four ports. It can also be built with any combination of the four ports. Funding, the frequencies available to the builder and any licencing restrictions in his or her particular area will determine how complete a D-Star repeater is.

Fig 11.4: Satoshi node adaptor board.

Assuming a complete setup, a user would be free to access the system on any of the bands available within the repeater. Across the world it has been decided that wherever possible the 'A' port will carry 23cm (1.2GHz) voice traffic, the 'B' port 70cm (430-440MHz) voice and slow data, the 'C' port 2m (144-146MHz) voice and slow data, and the D port 23cm (1.2GHz) high speed data .

For the system to be able to take advantage of the capabilities of D-Star, the repeater requires a broadband connection to the Internet to 'Gateway' the completed project. It should also be mentioned that a gateway connection requires specific Linux software to allow full operation on an Icom factory built system. A server-based PC would give the system the best results, although a good spec PC will work well.

Several homebrew options are now currently available in simplex (licenced in the UK as MB6xx callsigns) and in full repeater mode (GB7xx callsigns). These use either Satoshi Yasuda's DV Node Adaptors (see **Fig 11.4).** Satoshi, 7M3TJZ/ AD6GZ, was a member of the original committee that designed D-Star. Alternatively, by the use of other node adaptor boards listed as mini hotspots (or not so mini hotspots) and manufactured in the US and Netherlands by other enthusiastic hams looking to develop the hobby.

Fig 11.5: The DV Dongle.

Any one of these boards can be connected to an analogue radio with a 9600 packet data port to create a passage for the packet to be passed via the adaptor to the system. You will, however, still require a D-star radio to access these nodes, as they do not provide a platform for an analogue radio to enter the system (which some believe they do). There are also several software applica-tions around to operate these nodes, either via Windows or Linux platforms. Some amateurs have coupled these hotspot adaptors to dummy loads, to provide an access point solely for their use at home. This enables access with a D-Star handheld on very low power.

Fig 11.6: DV Access Point (DVAP).

For those with property or antenna restrictions, or if travelling regularly, a DV Dongle - **Fig 11.5** - is the best choice for operation. This is a device with the AMBE codec installed and works in a similar way to Voice over Internet Protocol (VoIP).

Any PC running the DV tool software along with the DV Dongle and a suitable headset can access D-Star from anywhere they can get their PC / Laptop / Netbook to operate using WiFi or fixed broadband connections. They have even been heard mobile via a laptop and a mobile phone in a vehicle. This DV Dongle method is the preferred option for those who have no local D-Star equipment.

The latest piece of equipment to hit the market - shown in **Fig 11.6** - is the DV Access Point (DVAP). It transmits 10mW of RF on the 2m

Sync		Control			Identification					Error
Bit sync	Frame sync	Flag 1	Flag 2	Flag 3	Received Repeater Callsign	Sent Repeater Callsign	Counterpart Callsign	Own Callsign 1	Own Callsign 2	P-FCS

Fig 11.7: D-Star header.

band (frequency of your choice) and is connected (similarly to the DV Dongle) to a PC and dedicated software, which then permits the use of a D-Star radio to access the network anywhere within range of the DVAP, via the PC's Internet connection. These have been in used in hotel rooms by amateurs on business or on holiday, and have been reported as invaluable around the home. External antennas have been known to increase the distance from the DVAP and people have been heard in the locality using these.

Operating D-Star

So far the emphasis has been on the theory behind D-Star, how it is put together and methods of accessing the network, but for someone who has never operated on D-Star before, how do you get up and running?

Most of the problems for new users seem to be assocated with correctly configuring their radio to operate the mode. This because, unlike analogue where you switch on your radio and tune to a specific frequency and begin to operate, D-Star is menu driven and its main requirement is to ensure that certain information is included in the header (**Fig 11.7**) to guarantee that your conversation is heard and routed to where you want it to go.

D-Star has a more complicated configuration prior to making that all important first contact. The operator is required to input information into their radio to correspond with the identification section of the header. It's this information that determines success or failure. This part of the radio configuration, shown in **Fig 11.8**, is sometimes described as the 'Ohm's Law' of D-Star. It contains four fields of information corresponding to the identification contained within the header. All D-Star radios require this information set in an exact manner to make it work (simplex excluded, where only CQCQCQ [UR] and your callsign [MY] is required).

Fig 11.8: These four fields are sometimes known as the 'Ohms Law' of D-Star.

UR	Sets who you send to
RPT1	Sets the local repeater call and band
RPT2	Sets call routing - Local or Distant
MY	Who *you* are

To get to grips with these four fields of information we are going to set some information into the menus, with an explanation of some likely information that must be contained in it to make that all-important QSO.

Note:
As with an analogue repeater, your radio would need to be pro-grammed with the frequency of GB7xx. The output frequency would have to be set and the 'shift' set to the designated split, so that it transmits and receives on the appropriate frequencies. There is no CTCSS used in D-star. In the setup shown in **Fig 11.9**;

UR=CQCQCQ allows the general call to be placed. It is also the most used field in the identification process and can be varied according to where and who you want to speak to.

RPT1 setting selects **GB7xx** and port **B** (could be A,C or D, if available) as the part of the repeater you wish to communicate through.

RPT2=NOT USE tells the controller *not* to route the call to the Internet, but to remain in the local vicinity.

Fig 11.9: Typical information set in radio menu fields.

MY: Is your own callsign and identifies you as the user.

A note about the setup in Fig 11.9. When **RPT2=** is set to 'NOT USE' or is blank, if the repeater is 'Gateway' connected to the network (linked) any user on the wider system will not hear the station who has RPT2= set this way. For those who appear to listen to one sided conversations on D-Star, it is the RPT2= setting that is responsible for this.

There is one more rule that needs to be applied which has not been mentioned so far and that is D-Star commands.

For the network to recognise that a stream wishes to pass, it must receive a com-mand to execute what is required by the user.

We have seen that GB7xx is required and we have selected port B, but for the system to accept this command of using port B the 'B' itself must be in the 8th character position when programming **RPT1**.

UR=CQCQCQ
Tells the gateway not to route your call to any particular repeater or station. A general CQ to all stations.
RPT1=GB7xx-B
Indicates that you wish to communi-cate using the repeater GB7xx and on port B (generally 70cm)
RPT2=NOT USE
Prevents your call from being routed to the internet. (What goes on here stays here)
MY=
Your callsign

This 8th position is going to come up throughout the rest of this chapter, as it is the basis for all Linking and Unlinking (see **Fig 11.10**).

Character position	1st	2nd	3rd	4th	5th	6th	7th	8th
Callsign setup	G	B	7	X	X	Blank space	Blank space	B

Fig 11.10: Menu set with the important 8th character (RPT1).

So to 'Gateway' to the Internet, the only change required is to change RPT2 from 'NOT USE' to the callsign of the repeater in use, adding a 'G' (Gateway) to the callsign. As shown in **Fig 11.11**. With this, plus the **UR, RPT1, RPT2** and **MY** callsign data in place, you should successfully be in position to undertake that all-important first QSO on D-Star.

Fig 11.11: Menu set with the important 8th character (RPT2).

Character position	1st	2nd	3rd	4th	5th	6th	7th	8th
Callsign setup	G	B	7	X	X	Blank space	Blank space	G

Wider System Operation

Fig 11.12: Reflector 5 Dashboard.

The wider operation of the D-Star network relies on use of the Internet and the network connections within it. Any D-Star user must register their callsign on the system to link or unlink to the available connections within D-Star. Registration is normally done with the user's local D-Star repeater. This enables the local repeater keeper/group to verify the identity of a user (who they may already know).

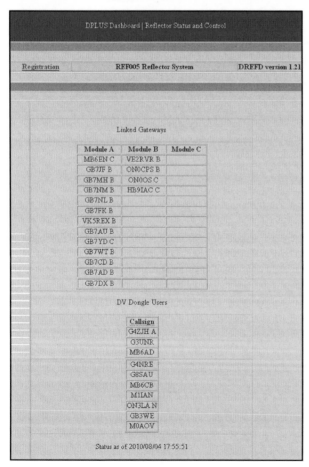

Reflectors

A reflector is a 'hub' or conference room where users congregate. There are many of these across the world. The most up-to-date list can be found on the Internet at www.dstarinfo.com

As has already been explained, D-Star repeaters may have A, B, C and D ports. Reflectors normally have three possible connections (modules). There is no strict rule as to which of the three modules (A, B or C) is used for any specific use, it is the decision of the reflector owner.

Fig 11.12 shows the Dashboard of Reflector 5, the London-based main UK reflector and the connections made on some of the modules.

DV Dongles and some simplex

gateways/hotspot users and non-Icom repeaters will also be shown within the DV Dongle section on the dashboard page. As can be seen at the time of capture, Reflector 5A appears to be the busiest module. Reflector 5B is generally in use by European repeaters, although this screenshot also shows a Canadian repeater connected. It carries multiple language transmissions, whereas Reflector 5A is English speaking.

Having established that the wider network involves the use of reflectors, it is now useful to explain further how to do this connecting and disconnecting of repeaters to reflectors - something that an analogue system does using a DTMF code to connect or disconnect to IRLP or Echolink nodes. D-Star uses the identification portion of the header to do this and it is done by changing the **UR:** from '**CQCQCQ**' to '**REF005AL**'. The command 'L' (Link) is again in the 8th position, as shown in **Fig 11.13**. All other menus remain as previously set, **RPT1:**

Character position	1st	2nd	3rd	4th	5th	6th	7th	8th
Callsign setup	R	E	F	0	0	5	A	L

Fig 11.13: Change UR menu to connect to Reflector 5A.

with your local repeater and port setting, your **RPT2:** with your local repeater and 'G' Gateway setting and the **MY:** your own callsign set.

Once connected, the **UR:** menu needs to be switched back to 'CQCQCQ', to undertake your QSO whilst connected to your now chosen reflector.

Once your conversation is completed you may wish to disconnect your local repeater. To do this you use the unlink command, simply a 'U' for unlink. See **Fig 11.14**.

This will bring your local repeater into Standalone mode for local use (remember again to switch the **UR:** menu back to 'CQCQCQ').

Some repeater keepers auto link their gateways in a semi-permanent way. This is to encourage users to use the network by keeping traffic on their gateway. Many users feel obliged to leave them in their semi-permanent location, but I am not aware of any keeper who restricts the movement from this semi permanent setting, so feel free to disconnect and move to wherever you wish.

Those repeaters with semi permanent connections have default scripts installed which automatically disconnect after a period of inactivity. This brings them 'home' to their semi-permanent location.

Character position	1st	2nd	3rd	4th	5th	6th	7th	8th
Callsign setup	Blank space	Blank space	Blank space	Blank space	Blank space	Blank space	Blank space	U

Fig 11.14: Change UR menu to unlink from the system.

It is good practice to drop the link to the system when you wish to speak locally with a station on the same repeater, because it frees the reflector for other users.

There are other ways of using the D-Star network (repeater to repeater, direct callsign routing). The **UR:** menu is key to these operations. Once the **RPT1:** and **RPT2:** fields are set to your local gateway and stored in a memory in your radio (along with your own callsign), it is just the **UR:** field that will determine the success of your routing and use of the network. Once you become accustomed to the methods described here of connecting to the network, the rest should come easily at a later stage.

Other uses of D-Star

So far we have concentrated on the use of D-Star for voice and the principles of connecting and disconnecting using the menu settings, as this is the starting point to effectively use the mode, but D-Star can do other things.

D-Star can simultaneously send data whilst streaming voice, so you can talk to other users whilst typing messages to them via the keyboard of your PC. The only additional requirement to carry out this activity is the use of an interface lead to/from the radio.

Radio amateurs across the globe have become involved with the provision of software applications to exploit this data capability and it is widely used by radio emergency teams (especially in the USA) for weather nets and so forth.

Some software packages allow low speed file transfer, picture exchange and e-mail capability. Examples of these are D-Rats, D-Chat, D-Star TV and D-Star Comms, to name but a few of the many packages out there on the World Wide Web. Conduct a D-Star search and you may be amazed at how much there is.

D-Star can transfer your GPS position to servers such as APRS.fi, it can help you locate another user on GPS, tell you which direction you need to travel and how far away that station is, then effectively home you into them by following the direction arrow on your radio's front panel to their beaconing signal. Imagine this in an emergency situation, where medical care maybe urgently required! Even their latitude and longitude is displayed on your radio. The 23cm DD mode in particular has endless possibilities.

Computer connection

D-Star radios are quite complex and it is well worth investing the extra money to purchase the necessary interface lead and software dedicated to the transceiver of your choice.

Programming can be quite tedious and a long process to learn, but many local D-Star groups have ready-made files that can be dropped into the radio via the software, saving many hours of hard work. Looking through these files on your PC will also give you a better understanding of how the mode really works.

Future Development

As D-Star is an emerging technology it is continuously developing. Since the first edition of this book D-Star has moved forward considerably in the homebrew development aspect of the mode.

Although when the first edition was written a secondary network existed, there was little known about. The users and developers were seen as rebels and were frowned upon by the main D-star network, which was created by Icom and is operated by the US Trust.

The US Trust developed and utilises a network known as 'G2', which was a follow-on from the original 'G1' network developed by the JARL in its early stages and which to this day remains in use in Japan. The G2 network is primarily run using Icom equipment, with only a handful of homebrewed equipment (which was rigorously tested), but it has proved difficult for this equipment to remain on its network.

This US Trust system is a production network which discourages any experimentation. D-Plus was added to the G2 system by Robin Cutshaw, AA4RC, as a transport mechanism for an operator's callsign information to be distributed across all of the connections to the system and allowed for direct routing to users by replacing the normal 'CQCQCQ' in the UR: menu to the callsign of the person you wished to make contact with. The problem with this was that if the station was mobile and travelling across several nodes, the information was slow in being spread across the network by D-Plus. This often led to failed attempts to hold a successful QSO, because by the time the routing information had been propagated the user had switched to another connection so the call was being routed to the wrong node. Improvements have now been made to improve the speed in which the information is relayed across D-Plus.

The secondary network began to experiment and improve the way in which D-star was being utilised. This was being led by the amateurs in Germany, but the biggest changes to the way things were being influenced came about from Jonathan Naylor, G4KLX, who started in 2009 with repeater software development (soundcard based for D-Star and FM) purely because there was no home-brewing going on. His work began to revolutionise how the network could be accessed. He approached the US Trust and Robin Cutshaw to assist in developing their network, but was rejected.

The German amateurs made use of Internet Relay Chat (IRC), which is used by millions of people and thousands of organisations to communicate, share, play and work with each other on IRC networks around the world. IRC was utilised to manage the database that pushes operators' callsigns in a similar way to which D-Plus was, the difference being that it was almost instantaneous so it cut down on the time it took to move the data across the nodes around the world. This transport mechanism was named as ircDDB (Internet Relay Chat Database).

Jonathan worked by the request of the German team on this method of transportation and developed a program called ircDDB Gateway, which was open source software. The first release of this was in September 2010 and it very quickly became adopted for a number of repeaters. GB3IN was the first to use this repeater software and also the first one introduced to ircDDB. This allowed access to this new network and it started a rapid trend for homebrew and experimental equipment to be used on this separate network from the US Trust production network. Although the US Trust had an experimental server on its network, the restrictions on experimentation discouraged many from utilising this and many felt that they were not welcome, hence the breakaway to the secondary network.

IrcDDB has always encouraged openness, whilst most other groups do not. It is this openness that has made this network the success it is today, because - after all - this is what our hobby was intended to be about, self-learning and experimentation.

In the spirit of amateur radio, those frequenting the developing secondary network (which was named the X-reflector network) began to share ideas and with the developers. Buoyed by enthusiasm and spurred on by the flood of requests for improvements, this network began to move forward. Not only was Jonathan developing the ircDDB Gateway software, but also Digital Voice and PC repeater software. As this is being written it is still developing and is now opening-up to include other protocols like DMR, P25, etc. Some of this software is compatible for use on analogue as well as digital repeaters and networks. Again, Jonathan's other projects are also open source. The name has recently changed to OpenDV (Open Digital Voice) and the project is available at http://opendv.berlios.de

In relation to D-Star, due to this open source approach, some variations of the original software began appearing in other parts of the world. In Canada Ramesh Dhami, VA3UV, formed the FREE STAR* system, which appears to utilise this software. There was another developer also active in the early days that developed software; Scott, KI4LKF. I have no knowledge of his involvement and cannot add his account, but I mention him so as not to exclude his input as I am aware he was also involved in some development outside of the US Trust.

So the X-reflector system began to flourish, with all the individual experimenters doing their thing. 'Dextra' reflectors were added to this secondary network, although for what purpose I cannot say. It appeared to just spread the network and give more choice, but made it slightly more difficult to get people together as the users spread across the network. The same could be said with the US Trust system, which was also growing to some extent.

In the meantime more hardware was becoming available, with PCBs and manufactured boards from the US, Holland and Poland entering the fray; but with Jonathan's software rapidly progressing the need for a board was becoming redundant as his software required little more than a soundcard and a PTT circuit to add to a compatible analogue radio to access the network as a simple node, either as a personal hotspot or as a licensed simplex gateway. As I write this, this soundcard and a rather 'over the top for the purpose' Vellman board is my hardware set up on MB6BA.

Meanwhile the German amateurs decided to progress with a 'DV-RPTR' board and their own gateway software, which is getting rave reviews as a solid and reliable piece of hardware for D-Star. This DV-RPTR board offers future add-ons for more functionality and is still developing.

In early 2012 there was a further breakthrough, with a re-writing of the protocol coding. As mentioned in an earlier part of the chapter, D-Star was prone to dropouts, termed 'the D-Star black hole', and the robotic break-up of audio, termed 'R2D2'. This was prevalent on the G2 network and was off-putting to most. Some even sold their equipment, as it was too annoying, but the rest of us tolerated it as it was the best we could get. However the re-coding changed the way in which the header information and packet data was read. This changed D-Star for the better and as a result a DCS reflector was introduced and branded the second generation of D-Star repeaters. Now users could experience far less in the way of dropouts and a reduction in R2D2. Any person who did drop out due to fringe coverage on a node miraculously came back mid over, which was never possible prior to DCS.

DCS reflectors became the 'in' thing and users migrated in their droves to join in this new breed of usable system. In the UK many repeater keepers added IRCddb to their repeaters, although some still resist.

What's the difference to those who utilise IRCddb nodes over Non IRCddb systems?

The users on the G2 network have just that - G2 connected Nodes. Users of the ircDDB network have access to the second generation

DCS reflectors, X-Reflectors and Dextra reflectors (although these may soon be phased out due to the success of DCS), plus they also have the ability to link to all the connections on the G2 network. This is something it's users cannot do without ircDDB, so with this development in early 2012, DCS is expanding at breakneck speed. Where G2 has up to five connections per reflector, DCS has 26 per reflector, so there is plenty of room for expansion.

The introduction of DCS reflectors also did what D-Plus said couldn't be done, which is the ability to utilise DTMF (Dual Tone Multi Frequency) tones. The introduction of this has simplified the way in which D-Star can be accessed and makes it easier for the user. Please remember though that (at the time of writing) if the Gateway you are accessing doesn't have ircDDB, DTMF is not possible.

So how does DTMF make this simpler? Using the system as described earlier in the chapter, D-Star makes use of the 'UR: menu' in your radio. I mentioned the use of the 8th command position to carry out your instruction to link / unlink etc, and that the easiest way to do this was to program each of these commands for each repeater you want to use into the radio's memory channels and banks. IrcDDB-configured gateways have this information stored at the gateway, so by using the pre-determined DTMF codes for your wanted connection it puts you where you want to be. Consequently your radio only needs the repeater callsign and module letter in RPT1 and RPT2 set to your local gateway, plus your callsign (as previously mentioned) in the MY: menu, and the UR: menu set to CQCQCQ. By simply pressing the PTT on your radio and utilising a DTMF microphone you key in the module number and you will be automatically disconnected from the repeater's current connection and reconnected to your chosen link. This includes connecting to G2 based systems too. It's pretty clever and more user friendly, so no more programming files to fill your radio to the brim, just one for each ircDDB-configured repeater. Once again, non-ircDDB repeaters will still need individual memories to access each connection on the G2 network and you will not be able to access DCS / X-Reflector or Dextra from a G2-only system.

The great thing about DCS is that there are up to 26 available connections per reflector. This gives reflector owners more scope to provide *you*, the user, with more choice. Take the UK reflector DCS005 for example. The main module of choice (determined by it's owner) for UK wide contacts is DCS005 'B' module.

A protocol seems to have been agreed for each DCS reflector to allocate the 'A' module for worldwide contacts, therefore all DCS reflector 'A' modules are linked together. Regardless of whether you go to DCS001'A', 002'A' or 013'A', you will be linked to the same connection. Another neat thing with DCS is that (in most cases) module owners have allocated dedicated chat channels; so if you make contact, say, on the UK national module of DCS005'B' and you

	Last Update (UTC):	Registered:	Activated:	Online:	Onl/Reg:	%total:
ircDDB:	2012/08/23 12:33	951	946	598	62.9%	69.1%
US-Trust:	2012/08/23 12:02	847	842	531	62.7%	61.4%
Common:	2012/08/23 12:02	412	410	264	64.1%	30.5%
ircDDB only:	2012/08/23 12:33	539	536	334	62.0%	38.6%
no ircDDB:	2012/08/23 12:02	435	432	267	61.4%	30.9%
Total:	2012/08/23 12:02	1386	1378	865	62.4%	

Fig 11.15: Gateway utilisations statistics.

would like a long ragchew with your mates, you can QSY to modules DCS005'O', 'P', 'Q' or 'R'. You can also visit the London area on DCS005'L' or the Midlands on the 'M' module, or maybe in the evenings Wales and the West on DCS005'W', or switch to other areas of the world such as USA (DCS006) or Australia (DCS014). Many European countries also have their own reflectors, so if you are proficient at a foreign language you can communicate or practice your skills in these areas of the network.

At the time of writing, ircDDB had overtaken the US Trust in terms of network provision, so from being a secondary network it has now become the primary one. Statistics from August 2012 are shown in **Fig 11.15**.

With this new network comes new ways of following the data and **Fig 11.16** shows the live feature page which can be accessed at www.ircddb.net Here systems that utilise ircDDB have data that corresponds with each PTT on the network and offers the users a location to see where activity is.

All active connections to each of the available DCS reflectors can be found on dedicated Internet pages, which identify where and how long each connection has been linked. It also shows the last user of

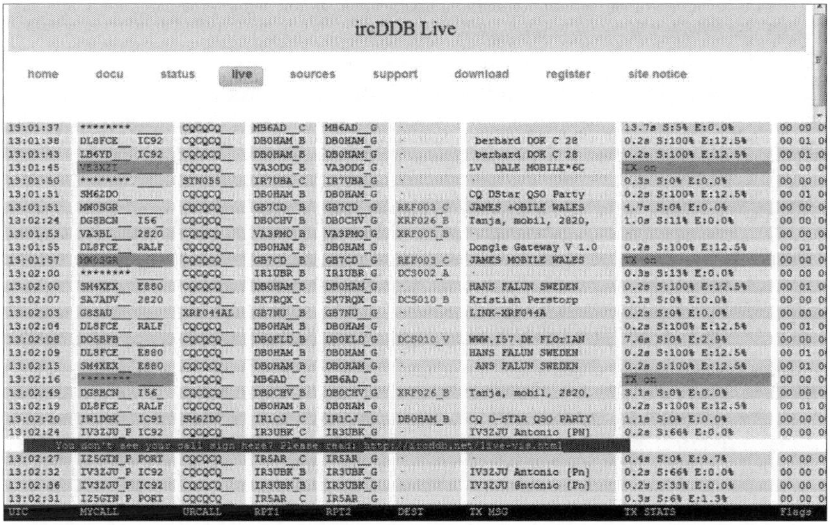

Fig 11.16: ircDDB Live.

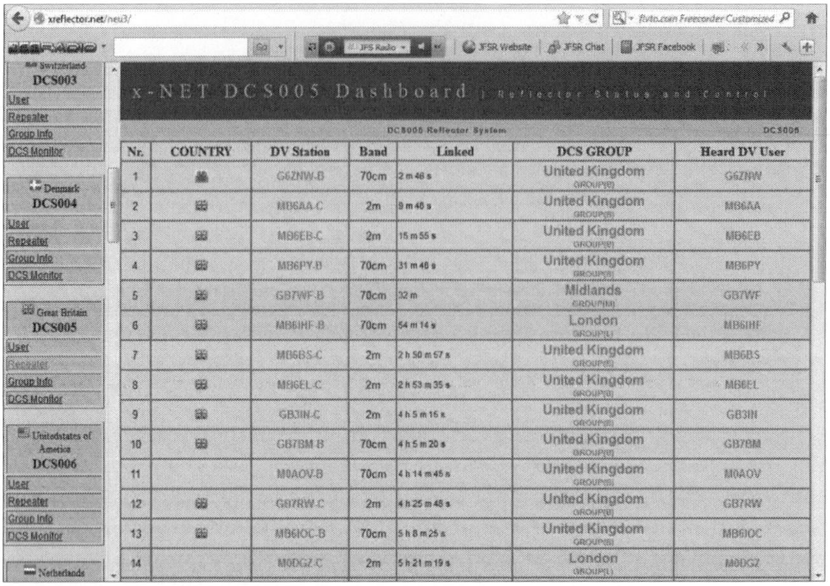

Fig 11.17: DCS5
active
connections
dashboard.

that connection (see **Fig 11.17**).

A further Internet dashboard shows the different parts of that country that can be accessed on each of the modules, including it's DTMF and radio programming code for the UR menu. It also shows how many repeaters / connections are made on the module (**Fig 11.18**).

StarNet Digital Services

Further to the introduction of DCS and ircDDB, StarNet Digital (developed by John Hays, K7VE, and implemented by Jonathan Naylor, G4KLX) has been introduced to the network. Although frowned upon by some (primarily from the G2 network side), Starnet Digital has the ability for user groups to be formed under a dedicated Starnet user Callsign, normally listed as 'STN' followed by the group number. This STN group can be joined by changing your UR:menu from CQCQCQ to the STN group callsign. A quick PTT logs you into the group and this then follows you across the network, like callsign routing. It just requires a quick PTT on each repeater you move to. This could become a valuable tool for emergency responders such as RAYNET / ARES etc, as all logged-in users will be alerted if contacted by their respective net controllers, plus the net controller can also see who is logged into the group. All that is needed to update their status to the net controller is a quick PTT.

StarNet Digital can be used by all amateurs to set up specific interest groups, such as HF contests, satellite users, SOTA groups etc.

Further developments from around June 2012 saw the arrival of the

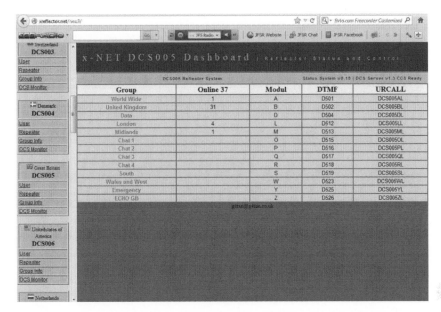

Fig 11.18: Area Allocations dashboard and codes for use.

Raspberry Pi computer, which has further whetted the appetite of experimenters. These have successfully been introduced as the gateway repeater for some systems. The beauty of this little gem is that it's cheap, consumes little power and is extremely small, so coupled with the other bits and pieces it doesn't take up too much space.

Ability to add third party software

One of the other beauties of D-Star is that software developers can create third party software. Jon, G4TSN currently has some neat software that integrates with Jonathan Naylor's ircDDB Gateway software to add additional flexibility in connecting and managing the gateway, such as timed switching from/to various connections and the ability to program your favourite links for easy access via the software.

Where do we go from here?

There is no doubt that D-Star will continue to push the boundaries as a mode. As this is being written (late 2012) Icom are promoting two new radios - a new dual-band handheld and an all-new all-mode multi-band mobile which covers from 160m to 70cm including 4m. It has the ability to operate D-star across the HF bands as well as VHF-UHF and is the first amateur transceiver to feature touch-screen technology.

D-Star is definitely here to stay and exciting times are ahead as we continue to experiment and push the frontiers.

12.
Automatic Packet/Position Reporting System

by Chris Dunn, G4KVI

Automatic Packet/Position Reporting System (APRS), developed by Bob Bruninga, WB4APR (www.aprs.org), is a lightweight system that allows users to transmit location and other data in single data packets.

Normally, stations being tracked use GPS receivers to provide real time tracking data.

APRS uses existing packet Terminal Node Controllers (TNCs), which are small, low-cost micro-controller driven units containing modems to transmit standard AX.25 packets on a frequency of 144.800MHz at 1200 baud, but APRS can also be used over HF and satellite links.

APRS is intended as a short-range tactical system, but it can also be viewed over broad areas using Internet gateways. Such gateways can be run on low-cost computers and can relay the transmission of packets to and from the international Automatic Packet/Position Reporting System - Internet Server (APRS-IS).

As a multi-user data network, it is different from conventional packet radio in four main ways.

1. By the integration of maps and other data displays to organize and display data.
2. By using a one-to-many protocol, updating everyone in real time.
3. By using generic digipeating, so that prior knowledge of the network is not required.
4. Since 1997, a worldwide transparent Internet backbone, linking everyone worldwide.

Consequently, APRS turns packet radio into a real-time tactical communications and display system. Normal packet radio is useful in passing bulk message traffic (e-mail) from point-to-point, but it does not do well at real-time events where information has a very short lifespan and needs to get to everyone quickly.

Although APRS is mainly intended to be used locally, the Internet monitors APRS worldwide, but this is not the primary objective. However, like our other radios, how we use APRS in an emergency or special event is what drives the design of the APRS protocol. Although APRS is used the vast majority of the time over great distances and benign conditions, the protocol is designed to be optimized for short distance real-time crisis operations using RF.

APRS provides universal connectivity to all stations by avoiding the complexity and limitations of a connected network. It permits any number of stations to exchange data, just like voice users would on a voice net. Any station that has information to contribute simply sends it, and all stations receive it and log it.

How APRS works

As **Fig 12.1** shows, an APRS station broadcasts (beacons) a single packet of information to all stations in range, which in this case is one other car and Digpeater B. This packet usually contains GPS coordinates and other information. The packet may be received and decoded by any station that can hear it and has suitable software or hardware. Digipeater (Digital Repeater) stations can also hear the packet and rebroadcast it based on rules in the digipeater software and commands that are integral to the packet. Packets that need to travel long distances can also be routed across the internet.

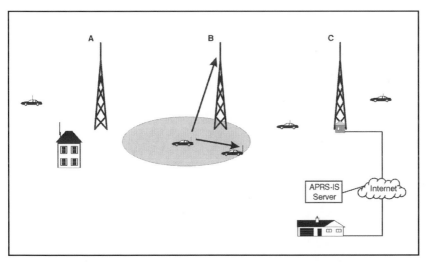

Fig 12.1: APRS station (in car) sends a beacon, which is heard by every other APRS station in direct range.

What happens next is that the packet is re-transmitted by every digi than can hear it, including any Internet Gateway (iGate). This is

Fig 12.2: The
packet is then
re-transmitted by
every digi that
can hear it,
including any
Internet Gateway
(iGate).

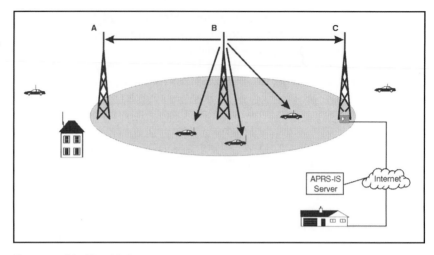

illustrated in **Fig 12.2**.

Fig 12.3 shows how the packet is then re-transmitted by every digi that heard the first digi. The packet is heard by every APRS station in direct range of this second set of digis, including the first one.

The final step of the process, shown in **Fig 12.4**, is that the packet is again rebroadcast by every digipeater in direct range of the second set of digis, including the original digipeater. Correct setting of the Unproto command is essential to control this and prevent channel overloading.

The fundamental principles of APRS, as described by Bob Bruninga, are:

• The system should provide reliable, real time, tactical digital communications.
• Use a 1200 baud network system operating as an Aloha random access channel (see below).
• You should hear everything nearby or within one digipeater within ten minutes.

Fig 12.3: The
packet is then
re-transmitted by
every digi that
heard the first
digi, including the
original.

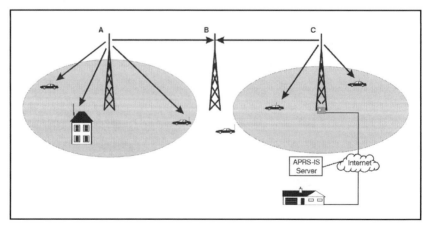

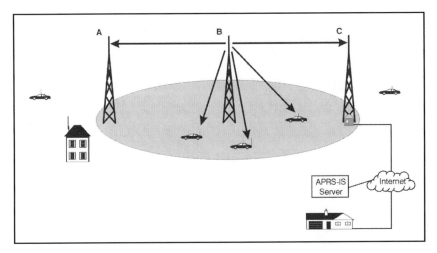

Fig 12.4: The packet is rebroadcast again by every digipeater in direct range of the second set of digis, including the original digipeater.

- You should hear everything within your Aloha circle within 30 minutes.

An ALOHA channel provides access to a common communication channel from multiple independent packet transmitters by the simplest of all mechanisms. When each transmitter is ready to transmit its packet, it simply transmits the packet burst without any coordination with other transmitters using the shared channel. If each user of the ALOHA channel is required to have a low duty cycle, the probability of a packet from one user overlapping and thus interfering with a packet from another user is small as long as the total number of users on the shared ALOHA channel is not too large. As the number of users on the shared ALOHA channel increases, the number of packet overlaps increase and the probability that a packet will be lost due to an overlap with another packet on the same channel also increases.

Practical uses

It is possible to configure and use APRS in a number of ways, but before we discuss them there are a number of things that is is useful to know.

Hardware

Terminal Node Controller
A Terminal Node Controller (TNC) is a basically a packet modem. One end connects to a radio, the other to a computer or GPS receiver. A Windows software package called AGWPE can replicate the functions of a TNC, reducing the cost of a such a system.

There are also some dedicated low cost devices that can take the

Fig 12.5: The TinkTrak4 from Byonics interfaces between a GPS and transceiver.

place of TNCs. These include the TinyTrak (shown in **Fig 12.5**) and the OpenTracker. These devices are attached to a GPS receiver and are only capable of transmitting location data.

The Kantronics KPC-3+ (**Fig 12.6**) and the older, obsolete KPC-3 have built in APRS functions. However, the 3+ unit can connect to a computer and a GPS receiver at the same time.

Fig 12.6: The Kantronics KPC3 can interface between a GPS, computer and transceiver.

GPS Receiver

There are many GPS receivers to choose from. They come in many shapes and sizes, some being more practical than others for specific applications.

Any GPS receiver used for APRS must have a data connection and must output NMEA format data. Consider whether you want to have your GPS receiver powered via external power or internal batteries.

Radio

Whether you use a mobile or handheld depends on how mobile you will want to be. In most urban areas handhelds/low powered trackers are sufficient for general use.

Kenwood have the THD-7E (**Fig 12.7**), which can be used as a standalone APRS transceiver. For a more permanent mobile solution, the Kenwood TM-D700 and TM-D710 are ideal transceivers. D-Star radios are also capable of transmitting positioning data to the APRS network. Whichever solution is used, care must be taken with the cabling, as most radios have totally different connection methods.

Computer

You only need a computer if you want to see other stations or you want to run an Internet gateway or smart digipeater. Older laptops are ideal to use with APRS, as it is a small program. Also, newer laptops may not have RS-232 ports, which you will need to connect to a TNC. If your laptop has USB ports only, you can buy a USB to serial adapter which should do the job.

Fig 12.7: The Kenwood THD-7E handheld transceiver can be used as a standalone APRS radio.

If you want to run really portable, consider using a palm device or a pocket PC. These are really good if you want to be pedestrian portable. It is now even possible to run an APRS tracker on the latest Android smartphones, indeed the author successfully runs an APRS tracker using exactly this method.

Connecting a TNC to a radio

TNC-to-radio connections are custom, depending on the TNC and radio in use, so care must be taken when making connections.

Connecting a GPS to a TNC

Most GPS receivers that are useable for APRS use an RS-232 connection. You will need to connect at least three wires between your GPS equipment and your APRS station; TX, RX and Ground. See your GPS manual (or maybe download one from the Internet).

The connector at the GPS receiver is often proprietary, forcing you to buy one from the manufacturer or a specialist supplier. The connector at the computer or TNC end is usually a DE-9 9-pin or a DB-25 25-pin, although other connectors are possible (e.g. a miniature stereo plug is used by the Kenwood TM-D700).

You can test your GPS by plugging it into your computer's RS-232 port and configuring a terminal program (such as Hyperterminal) to look directly at the comm port, rather than a modem.

The common data configuration for GPS is 4800 baud, 8 bits, 1 stop bit, no parity. The most common data standard that your GPS should be configured for is NMEA (maybe NMEA OUT /NMEA IN). NMEA stands for National Marine Electronics Association, and is a standard that defines all sorts of connection standards for shipboard navigation equipment.

The most common datum that your receiver should be configured for is WGS-84.

APRS Software

If you want to see APRS stations, you'll need some software. There are software packages for most operating systems. Once you have decided on your hardware there are also some basic software settings you will need to know.

Secondary Station IDentification (SSID)

In the early days of APRS, the SSID was used to identify the 'type' of the station for display purposes (its symbol). Nowadays, as almost all APRS devices are capable of having a symbol configured and included as part of the beacon, this is no longer required, though this convention is still supported and mostly followed (i.e. -4 signifies a bicycle, -9 a car, -10 a motorcycle, -12 a jeep). A list of currently used symbols can be found at: http://wa8lmf.net/miscinfo/APRS_Symbol_Chart.pdf

Latitude and Longitude

This will need to be inputted in a format required by the selected software.

Unproto Address

There was a huge debate as to what address should be used, with a consensus being reached as to what the paths should be and how digipeaters should be configured.

A fixed station should use WIDE2-2. This should get your packet one hop through the nearest digipeater and onto the nearest Internet gateway.

Mobile station WIDE1-1, WIDE2-2. This will ensure your packet gets to any digi, including 'fill-ins' and then in to a wider network.

Some examples of raw packets are shown in **Fig 12.8**.

Fig 12.8: Some examples of what raw APRS looks like.

Packet of a fixed internet station with weather data
2011-01-04 13:20:18 UTC:
g4kvi>APRS,TCPIP*,qAC,CWOP-3:@041321z5116.99N/00229.66W_135/
002g005t041r001P005h87b10031eCumulusEW

Packet of a fixed RF station with weather data showing it's route to the Internet
2011-01-04 18:49:28 UTC: G4KVI>APU25N,MB7UC*,WIDE2,qAR,G3PWJ-
3:@041850z5117.00N/00229.40W_270/
002g004t042r000p...P005h96b09996 running 1w {UIV32N}

Packet of Smartphone running APRSDroid
2011-01-03 15:27:43 UTC: G4KVI-7>APAND1,TCPIP*,qAU,jFindU-JS:!5122.89N/
00223.74W>042/011/A=000241 Chris,running Aprsdroid

Beacon Comment
This can be any text, such as a frequency that you monitor.

Status Text
This can be transmitted alongside the beacon and can include the status of your station, e.g. On Duty, On Station, En Route, Committed, Emergency.

APRS in practice

I hope you now have a broad understanding of the basic hardware and software equipments for an APRS station. That being the case, we are now ready to see what APRS can do. You will first need a suitable program. These are available for most platforms. One of the most popular in use is UIView (http://www.ui-view.org/). You will also need a suitable TNC. If you have an old packet radio setup, this is ideal for APRS. All APRS traffic in the UK uses a single frequency of 144.800MHz. Once you have the station set up, you should see a screen like the one shown **Fig 12.9**. In it you will see that there are different symbols on the map. These indicate what information each station is transmitting. It is udeful to go through the most common ones and explain how they are generated.

Base stations
The illustration in **Fig 12.10** shows a typical station's information. The Beacon and Status text can be changed to suit individual circum-

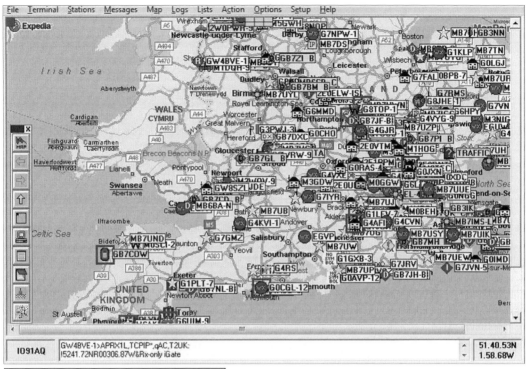

IO91AQ | GW4BVE-1>APRX1L,TCPIP*,qAC,T2UK: | 51.40.53N
!5241.72NR00306.87W&Rx-only iGate | 1.58.68W

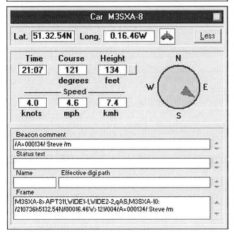

Fig 12.9: A
Typical UIView
screen shot from
a station
connected to an
Internet server.

stances. The 'Effective digi
path' field shows the path that
te packet has taken. A blank
field shows the packet has
been received directly. The
'Frame' field shows the raw
packet. Please note the
'WIDE2-2'. You may also
notice that some station labels
are different colours. Yellow
shows the station is using
UIView, whereas the ones in
white are using another form of
APRS. They do, however, all
conform to at least the basic
APRS principles.

Fig 12.10: A
typical base
station's
information.

Mobile stations

As you can see from **Fig
12.11**, we can now use APRS
as a tracker, as course, speed
and height are displayed. Note
the 'WIDE1-1', 'WIDE2-2'
setting. This will ensure the

Fig 12.11: A
typical mobile
station's
information.

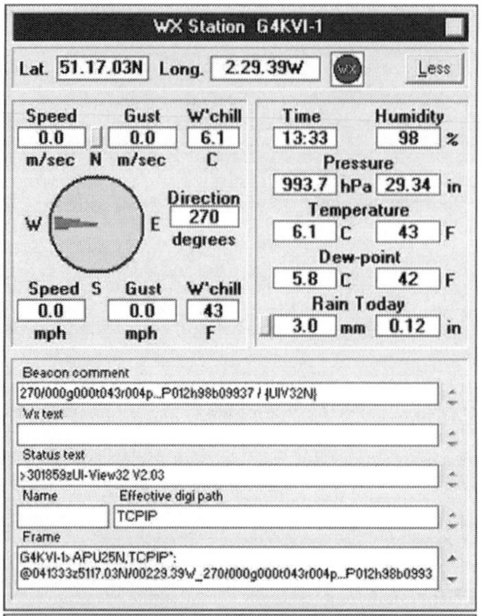

**Fig 12.12:
Display
of a weather
station.**

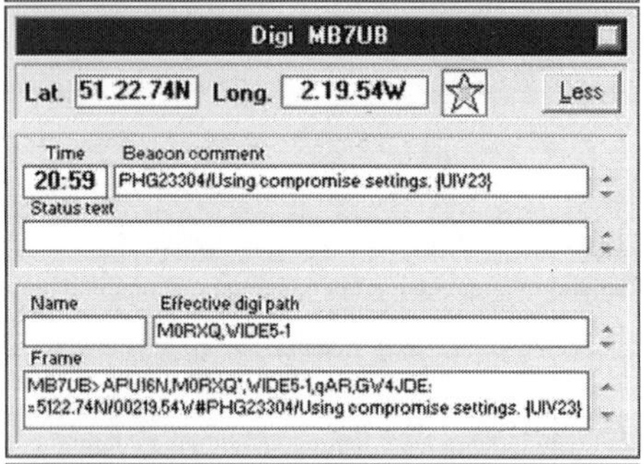

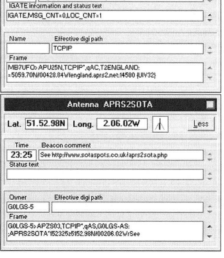

**Fig 12.13:
Display
of a Digital
Repeater.**

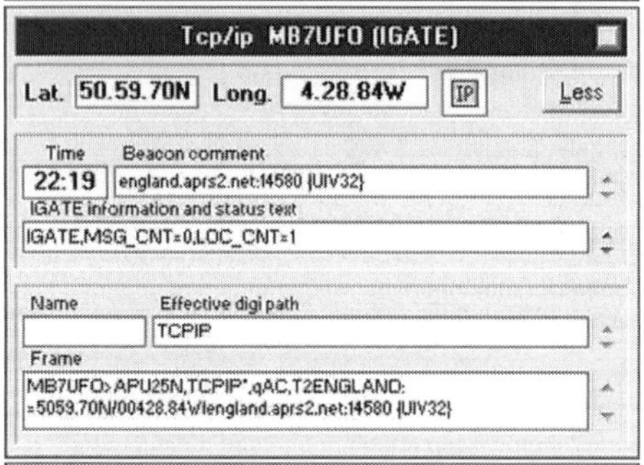

**Fig 12.14:
Display of an
Interget
Gateway.**

**Fig 12.15:
Display of an Info
Kiosk.**

packet will be received by any Digi, including 'fill in'. Mobile setups vary, but some common setups are shown below.

Weather Station
Most APRS programs are able to take data from commercially available weather stations and output it as shown in **Fig 12.12**.

Digis (Digital Repeaters)
These stations, usually identified by an MB7 callsign prefix, are set up in a favourable location. They receive APRS signals, relay them on to other Digis and also on to an Internet gateway. You may also find individual stations setting up as a 'fill in' Digi, but these will normally be as a result of local requirements. See **Fig 12.13**.

Igate (Internet Gateway)
These stations will take any packet they receive on RF and relay it onto one of the many APRS Internet Servers, enabling a low power APRS station to have worldwide coverage. **Fig 12.14** shows the typical display from an Igate.

Info Kiosk
This feature in UIView, shown in **Fig 12.15**, is a very easy and simple way to display local information on items such as a rally or road information. They can also be used to display the status of a local repeater.

Mobile Phones

In recent years the use and availability of smartphones has exploded, the most popular being the iPhone and those running the Android software. There are several applications available which enable these devices to run APRS. These use the signal from the 3G / WiFi network and the inbuilt GPS to send location information to an APRS Internet server, such as APRS.fi The most popular are APRSDroid (https://github.com/ ge0rg/aprsdroid/wiki/) and U2APRS (http://aobajoke.no-ip.org/~ja7ude/ japanese/U2APRS10/indexe.html) for Android phones and iBCNU for the iPhone. These applications enable the device to be used as a full feature APRS tracker. Although this may be seen by some as not amateur radio this is an exciting development enabling realtime tracking without the use of an expensive radio or computer. One again it shows how amateur radio can evolve and embrace new technologies.

Practical applications

To what practical application can APRS be put? The most obvious is realtime tracking. This can simply be an amateur using an APRS enabled transceiver or mobile phone to show their position on UIView maps. It is also widely used by RAYNET groups during events, to keep track of vehicles. An example would be to place APRS trackers in St John Ambulance or Red Cross vehicles. The ability to 'see' where vehicles are is a valuable tool when responding to an incident. It can also be helpful to 'see' in realtime where the 'lead' and 'tail' vehicles are, for example on a marathon event. The messaging facility is also very useful. The ability to send a message to a number of stations in realtime has endless possibilities.

Another exciting use for APRS is as a propagation indicator. Over the course of time you will come to know which stations you normally receive directly. As conditions change due to a 'lift', you will notice more stations appear on the map in the direction of the enhanced propagation. This feature can also be useful when installing a new aerial system.

Mention has been made of Internet servers. The information from these is collected and displayed on APRS.fi. This website shows a large amount of data from APRS stations, including tracks of mobile stations.

APRS can be a valuable and interesting addition to any radio amateur's inventory. I hope this has wetted your appetite and that you will give the mode a try. There is a vast amount of information available and I encourage you to seek it out.

13.
Electromagnetic Compatibility

by John Pink, G8MM, and Steve White, G3ZVW

Whilst the use of a computer in the shack has been shown as necessary for the implementation of many amateur radio facilities, such as logging or PSK operating modes, great care is required to avoid interference with the main purpose of radio communication. In a nutshell, the computer and all of its associated peripherals and interfaces must be electro-magnetically compatible. That is, the computer must not interfere with radio communication, and it must be immune to interference from the transmitters in the shack. This requires considerable care and consideration by the operator.

Equipment Issues

All items of electrical equipment are manufactured and tested to comply with international standards, which gives some degree of protection to the radio spectrum, and an assurance that devices/apparatus will be reasonably immune to interference from other apparatus.

The Standard CISPR 22 (55022) requires that any equipment shall not emit signals above limits that give general protection to radio services. In practical terms this means that emissions shall not mask broadcast radio services.

Many situations are catered for in the standards, but the following tables most closely typify the issues which are to be found in the average home and therefore radio shack.

Firstly, below 30MHz, all limits are specified by reference to 'conducted disturbances'. This is because of the difficulty of making radiated measurements in this frequency range. It can be seen in **Table 13.1** that

Frequency range	Limits dB(uV)	
	Quasi-peak	Average
0.15 to 0.50MHz	66 to 56	56 to 46
0.50 to 5MHz	56	46
5 to 30MHz	60	50
Note 1: The lower limit shall apply at the transition frequencies.		
Note 2: The limit decreases linearly with the logarithm of the frequency in the range 0.15 to 0.5MHz.		

Table 13.1:
Limits for conducted disturbance at the mains ports of class B ITE.

quite a large signal in terms of dB(μV) is permissible. Note that 60dB above 1μV = 1 Volt. These signals do of course radiate!

Table 13.2 covers all connections to/from equipment, such as peripherals, interfaces and any type of data connection – all generally referred to as telecommunication ports.

This specifies the limits on 'common mode' signals on these ports. The use of the expression 'common mode' may not be generally understood, but it is an important concept in the context of interference. (See explanation box below). Once again it can be seen that the interference signal can be very large.

Frequency range	Voltage limits dB(uV)		Current limits dB(uA)	
	Quasi-peak	Average	Quasi-peak	Average
0.15 to 0.5MHz	84-74	74-64	40-30	30-20
0.5 to 30MHz	74	64	30	20
Note 1: The limits decrease linearly with the logarithm of the frequency in the range 0.15MHz to 0.5MHz.				
Note 2: The current and voltage disturbance limits are derived for use with an impedance stabilization network (ISN) which presents a common mode (asymmetric mode) impedance of 150$\grave{U}$ to the telecommunication port under test (conversion factor is 20 log10 150 / I = 44dB).				

Table 13.2:
Limits of conducted common mode (asymmetric mode) disturbance at telecommunication ports in the frequency range 0.15MHz to 30MHz for class B equipment.

Finally we get to the situation above 30MHz, where radiated measurements are used, and the distance between the interfering source, and the 'victim' is set at 10m. In **Table 13.3** the signal strength is given in dB(μV)/metre.

Frequency range	Quasi-peak limits dB(uV/m)
30 to 230MHz	30
230 to 1,000MHz	37
Note 1: The lower limit shall apply at the transition frequency.	
Note 2: Additional provisions may be required for cases where interference occurs.	

Table 13.3:
Limits for radiated disturbance of class B ITE at a measuring distance of 10m.

Having established what is in the 'Standards', consider the practical situation that radio amateurs face when operating on the bands. Even the average HF communication receiver is able to discern signals down to a few microvolts, and at VHF/UHF signals down to 0.1μV are several dB above the noise and therefore quite readable.

Choosing the Right Hardware

Power Supplies/Motherboards/Cables

Possibly the best advice on choosing a computer for the shack is to spend as much as you can possibly afford. There is no doubt that the EMC effectiveness is clearly reflected by the quality of the product. There is no need for the latest and fastest, with super graphics perform-ance. Moderate performance will be satisfactory, unless of course you intend to use the machine for other purposes – but do think about what you will do with the machine and purchase accordingly.

Tower vs. Laptop Computers

Tower PSUs

Probably the biggest contributor to RFI is the power supply. These days all computer power supplies are Switched Mode units. These are notorious for radiating unwanted emissions. Even when they use 'best practice' they can be detected somewhere in the HF spectrum.

The biggest single offence that manufacturers commit is to omit the mains input filter components. **Fig 13.1** shows an example of a power supply where the filter has been omitted at the manufacturing stage. Without opening the case it is difficult to determine whether these components have been fitted. However, it is possible with an optic-scope to take a peep inside through the rear fan opening. In any event, the absence of the filter parts will be obvious on an HF receiver when the computer is turned on. See the recommendations that follow!

Fig 13.2 gives typical plots of a second power supply (see **Fig 13.3**), showing the emissions when in 'stand-by' mode, and when

Fig 13.1: Purchased from a High Street vendor – showing how the power line filter components were omitted in manufacture to save cost. This unit failed to meet the limits by more than 20dB.

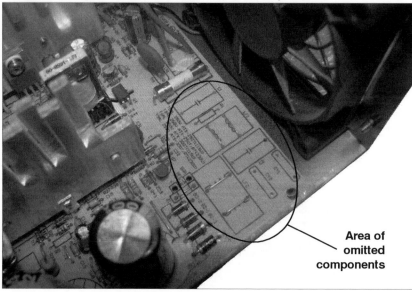

Area of omitted components

loaded with a nominal operating current. In this case the load was a passive resistance, avoiding any possibility of other emissions. The limit lines indicate the Class B standard limits.

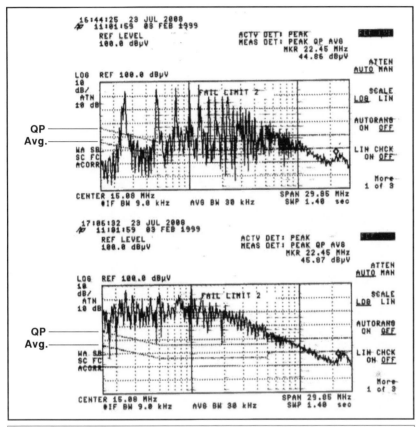

Fig 13.2: Plots of the emissions from an unscreened power supply (a) in standby, (b) operating with a 60 watt load on +12V.

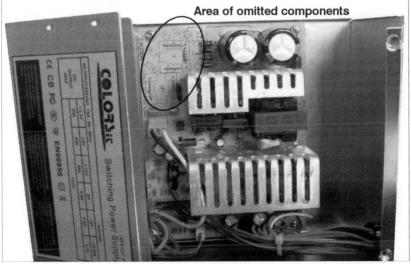

Area of omitted components

Fig 13.3: Another power supply in which the power line filter components were omitted in manufacture.

Cases and Cabinets

Build it yourself vs. a branded model

There are as many cases available on the market as there are power supplies and the quality issues are exactly the same. These cases are turned out in the thousands by 'job-shop sheet metal workers' who have little or no knowledge of the issues of EMC. In all probability they have copied a case design and missed the important aspects of ensuring that all gaps close and all parts make good electrical contact when screwed together.

Many cases use fingering along closing edges to make contact with an opposing part, but frequently the fingering is found to be flattened, in which case it does not contribute to electrical connection.

Purchasing a cheap case with a power supply already installed almost certainly means that the power supply is cheap. Such a purchase is best avoided.

There is certainly no guarantee that a branded model will have good EMC characteristics, but it does reduce the risk of EMC problems. Major manufacturers have a great deal of reputation to lose, even with just a few complaints. What can be more certain is that the case and power supply will have been built up to a quality, all of which will have been through a rigorous EMC assessment routine.

As with any product, maintenance is important if the best performance is critical, and this goes with computers and peripherals. Ensure all screws are kept tight on covers, especially if they have previously been removed. Make sure that the finger-stock which ensures RF shielding is clean and in good contact. Finger tightening may not have the desired effect, as shown in **Fig 13.4**.

Fig 13.4: The bonding resistance of supply line filters.

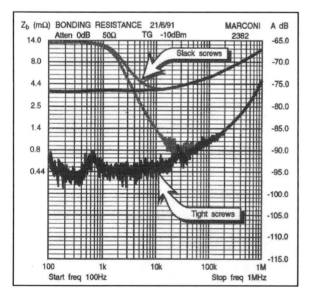

Make sure that screws on D-type connectors are tight. It is surprising how often these screws are not properly tightened by interface board manufacturers, and they only hold in place by friction or because somebody has applied a dab of Loctite. They often unscrew when a cable is removed.

All screws should be tight and if they help to perform an earth connection you should ensure that there is no paint or other insulator under the parts.

Don't entrust the tightening of screws, closing of gaps and installation of clip-on ferrites – check them yourself!

Laptop/Portable

There are some advantages for the use of laptop computers in the radio shack, and especially on the field portable site. Size is sometimes an important consideration, where the shack is in a very confined space.

From the point of view of EMC, laptops perform quite well. Because of the compact nature, radiation from the computer unit is quite well controlled, and this speaks well for the direct ingress of RF.

However, all modern laptops have an external, in-cable, power supply, and these are a potential source of RFI. Even the more expensive laptops use PSU's 'Made in China', and whilst some of these are built to a very tightly controlled specification, there is evidence that others are not.

Unfortunately, this is one of the areas where reading the specification is not a good indicator of EMC performance that will be good enough in the radio shack.

Possibly the biggest disadvantage of using a laptop is that the I/O ports may be quite constrictive. Many now have only USB and/or Firewire ports, which means that all level conversion for RS232 or TTL must be achieved outside of the unit. Unfortunately these products are not well screened, often being housed in plastic cases. It is important to examine the quality of items like USB/serial convertors, and USB port extenders. Look for products in metal cases!

Fig 13.5: A power line filter recovered from a large-screen plasma TV. The filter components are across the top half of the PCB.

Mitigation Measures

However good the filtering, it should be remembered that it was provided at a price and the manufacturer will have been cost-conscious. Some additional mains filtering could prove valuable, both by providing a reduction in the leakage signals, but also by breaking the common mode impedance between the computer and its associated hardware, and the elements of the radio station itself.

A typical common mode filter looks like a low-pass filter, usually with two inductive elements, which are common mode chokes, and three stages of capacitive decoupling, perhaps using Y-capacitors. A very good source of these materials is old computer power supplies, or if you find somebody dismantling a defunct large screen plasma TV they have excellent filtering on the mains. **Fig 13.5** shows a unit recovered from an old Sony plasma, which also contains low voltage controlled power on/off switching, and as can be

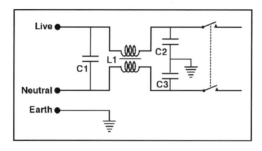

Fig 13.6: Circuit of a typical common-mode supply-line filter. The common-mode choke (L1) is wound with the live and neutral in counter phase on the same toroid, so that the currents cancel but the winding still provides effective in-line (common) impedance.

seen a good measure of additional screening.

The circuit diagram of a typical common-mode supply-line filter can be seen in **Fig 13.6**, with its performance depicted in **Fig 13.7**.

Whole Station Filtering

The advent of digital processing and more and more electronic devices in the home has resulted in what can best be described as 'radio fog'. Whilst the measures set-out in this chapter apply particularly to computers in the shack, it is worth remembering that a lot of 'rubbish' may be arriving into the shack via the mains supply. To this end the installation of a filter for the whole shack; indeed even the whole household, may be beneficial.

For the shack, which may consume up to 2kW, the installation of a filter is quite straightforward. A filter such as the one recovered from the plasma television will be quite suitable for loads up to 1.5kW. There are just one or two safety issues to remember – the capacitors and inductors must be suitable for purpose. The capacitors in particular must be X2 type across the supply and suitable Y types from Live and Neutral to ground. The inductors must have good insulation resistance and the whole assembly should be flash

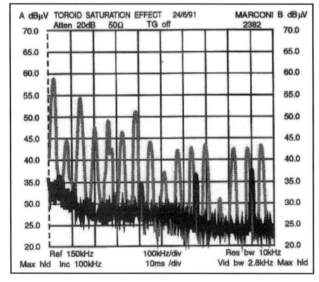

Fig 13.7: Performance of a typical common-mode supply-line filter. The plot shows the effect of saturation caused by not having the windings in counter-phase (in grey).

tested with a Megger before use. Your local electrical installer may be able to help do this.

The installation of a filter for the whole household requires the help of a qualified electrician, since it may mean dealing with the incoming mains supply current of 60A or more. Components are readily available from electrical suppliers, with suitable safety housings, but since this is work identified under the Wiring Regulations, it does require certification.

It may be worth considering this if you believe the mains supply is noisy as a result of industrial activity nearby, or even a neighbour with an engineering workshop in the garden shed.

Motherboards/Processors

Higher clock frequencies present less of a problem on HF, but are potentially more noticeable on VHF. However, most motherboards and I/O boards, have clock dividers/multipliers which result in a myriad of frequencies that could result in 'birdies' within the usable radio spectrum.

Most motherboards are very well manufactured from the point of view of RFI. They are built on multi-layer PCBs, with the outer planes often being ground or power supply rails. All of the active tracks are buried well away, inside the board. This is done, not only to control RFI, but more particularly so that the impedance of the tracks can be closely controlled. Many of the signal paths will be carrying bit rates well up into the 1GB/s region, so impedance control becomes critical.

All motherboards will have an array of clock oscillators and multipliers/dividers. It is therefore inevitable that some 'birdies' will be heard somewhere within the radio spectrum. The choice of a motherboard will come down to preference of a particular chip-set (Intel/AMD) and the user interfaces available, although these are becoming more standardised.

Cables and Interfaces

The interconnection of a motherboard and its many peripherals is important from the point of view of RFI. The quality of these cables has a significant bearing on the leakage of radiation. Better quality cables and the associated connectors will be less likely to cause a problem. Look particularly at the grounding of a plug into a socket, especially if it uses screws. Make sure that these fit well and are of course properly tightened/locked. Not only will this reduce the possibility of egress of interfering signal, it may also have an impact on ingress of RF into the computer.

In recent times there has been a tendency to migrate to serial interfaces for disk drives (SATA), which provides some advantage. SATA cables are run in a small screened bundle of uniform twisted pairs (UTP), which reduces/controls radiation.

Wherever a cable leaves a computer it is important to stop any common-mode signals from leaving the unit. This is usually achieved by clip-on ferrite chokes. Whilst these look ugly, the bigger they are the better they are at stopping the egress of RFI. In choosing a computer, make sure that all cables leaving the main computer unit, and at the input/output of all peripherals are fitted with ferrite chokes. If you are building your own machine, be liberal with 'common-mode' stoppers.

The tendency towards USB for all I/O devices connected to modern computers has led to the need for convertors, for example for serial or parallel devices. There are still very many of these around, especially in the Radio Shack. Many transceivers and TNC modems use RS232, and a number of antenna rotator controllers use parallel port connection.

If possible, these convertors are best housed *within* the tower cabinet. The USB port connections can be found on the motherboard and routed to the convertor, and its serial/parallel output routed to the rear panel. A good idea is to find the finger-plates from old unused interface cards – these will have standard RS-232 connector or parallel connector cut-outs and can be adapted to carry the connections to the outside world. Often these will have fully screen connectors with built in capacitors, so do not throw away the original connectors. It is a truism that some of yesterday's products were better built than todays!

A big advantage of putting all the hardware inside the computer case is that it is all connected to a common earth, thereby reducing the possibility of ground loops.

Of course it is still possible to purchase motherboards with at least two serial ports and there are suitable PCI - I/O cards which can add more serial and/or parallel ports. These, however, are not the norm.

Monitors

There is no doubt that the monitor of choice for the radio shack are flat-screen solid-state LCD models. Perhaps this will change in the future, with the rapid introduction ontp the market of Organic LED (OLED) monitors.

Very few RFI problems have been identified with LED monitors, but once again you should look to the interface cable as a potential source. Make sure that the screws are properly tightened and keep the cable away from live RF circuits.

Many monitors are independently supplied by small, Switched Mode power units. These are notoriously bad sources of RFI. The manufacturer may have fitted clip-on or moulded-on ferrites, but these are often insufficient to stop radiation at higher frequencies. It is advisable to fit additional ferrites on the power cord, and on the output cable of the supply. Trying another PSU, of suitable voltage and current rating may also help – quite often the switching frequency will be different, and a spurious signal may be moved away/outside of frequencies of interest. You may even find an old linear power supply of suitable size and ratings.

There is also the issue of various clock oscillators within the Monitor. The wise and additional precaution here is to fit clip-on ferrites to both the signal cable coming from the computer, place this as close as possible to the connector on the monitor, and once again on the cable leading to the PSU. Finally, do not leave cables sprawled around behind the monitor/computer. It is best to coil them up, not only to make them look neat and tidy, but more particularly to minimise radiation and pick-up of RF in the shack.

External Hardware

Already mentioned is the issue of common-mode signals andhow they can be prevented, but it is worth emphasising the need to connect all parts of the system to one common earth point and ensure that any cables do not carry common mode signals by the generous use of clip-on common-mode ferrite chokes.

Connections to/from transceiver(s) require special attention. Most CAT interfaces use the RS232 interface standard, although some (notably Icom) have adopted a TTL interface.

Whichever is used, it is good practice to use an optically isolated interface on data and control lines. This may either be built within a purchased interface adapter or with a home-brew adapter built to one of the many published designs.

TNCs and issues connected with these are somewhat similar to the CAT interface, except that the modulation signals need to be considered. In practice, by far the best way of dealing with low frequency audio circuits is by the use of 1:1 isolation transformers. Although these are getting a little harder to source, they can be found in older surplus modem interface cards. See the chapter on Interfacing and Interfaces.

The more expensive solution for those who do not have an aptitude for construction is one of the ready-made multi-mode interface units, which handle keying, data-mode modulation schemes as well as the essentials of the CAT interface.

For the homebrew constructor wishing to deal with sound card input/outputs, there are a number of published circuit configurations, the simplest involving small audio transformers to achieve physical isolation, and thereby ground loop problems which may result in RFI/EMC problems.

When tracking-down RFI it is important not to forget direct radiation from interface devices. TNCs, multimode adapters, bridges/routers and the like that will contain microprocessors clocked at frequencies up to or even greater than 24MHz. Once again these may be divided or multiplied, thus providing a spectrum full of birdies.

When investigating these problems, start with everything turned off except for the station receiver. Turn things on one at a time, investigating at each stage what unwanted signals have appeared. You should certainly find some signals and you will have to assess whether they warrant tracking down.

Most computer clocks can be identified. Being crystal oscillators thay are reasonably stable, if not a little raucous in tone. However, in recent years there has been a tendency towards the use of 'dithered' clock oscillators. These are quite difficult to identify and sound more like a noise source. The only way of being certain that they are a source of interference is to turn them off.

The technique of dithering a clock oscillator spreads the spectrum created, thus reducing the Power Spectral Density. Since EMC measurements are made with defined bandwidth filters, spreading the signals across the spectrum reduces the peak level, making it easier for a manufacturer to meet the limits in the standard.

Positioning of Equipment and Cables

The concept of a single earth, both to avoid ground loops and also RFI/EMC problems, is difficult within the entirety of a radio shack. However, every effort must be made to achieve the very minimum number of earth connections between the computer and associate peripherals, and the radio equipment proper. If connections have to be made it is advisable to break-up the common impedance with the ubiquitous CM choking – a clip-on ferrite or several turns through a ferrite ring.

Separating data cables from RF signal circuits is an important objective, which might mean positioning the computer and all peripherals at one end of the shack bench and taking all live RF circuits to the other end. This requires some careful planning, but separation may pay dividends in the long run. Most importantly it reduces the possibility of magnetic field coupling between the computer system and the radio. Whilst it may be easier to deal with near field magnetic coupling by moving things further apart, the real issue which will confront radio amateurs, most of the time, will be the far-field electric field, which does not decay quickly with separation distance.

Many radio amateurs will wish to be connected to the Internet when operating, for the many reasons given elsewhere. Best practice suggests that a wireless system is safest in the shack.

It avoids the issues of coupling of RF along networking cables, although many prefer this type of system because of the security it affords. When RF is coupled into UTP wiring it inevitably gets into the home hub or router and seriously reduces data rates or disconnect from the remote server.

It almost goes without saying, but must be said – whatever you use, avoid PLT or any similar power line communications products at all cost.

Finally, when you think you have paid attention to all of the potential problems, there will be others! However, most problems have a solution. It may take a little experimenting, but that is what rmateur radio is all about.

Telephones

In the days of landline telephones with mechanical dials, they contained little in the way of electronics and were not particularly susceptible to interference from nearby transmitters. These days its a different story, because practically all landline telephones on the market contain electronics. Cordless domestic telephones invariably contain a lot of electronics.

It is the active, amplifying elements of modern telephones - corded or cordless - that lead to interference being caused so readily to them, but fortunately there are a number of steps that can be taken to reduce or eliminate it.

Today, probably the easiest and simplest thing to try and remedy a landline telephone that is suffering breakthrough is a line filter used for ADSL (Asymmetric Digital Subscriber Line). ADSL filters are readily available and plug directly into telephone sockets. A Speedtouch ADSL filter is shown in **Fig 13.8**. Other makes and models are also available.

An ADSL filter will have two sockets on it - one for a telephone and the second for an ADSL modem. As **Fig 13.9** shows, the circuitry inside an ADSL line filter consists of a low pass filter to remove the higher frequencies used by the ADSL signal from the telephone socket. The signal from the incoming line passes straight through to the ADSL output socket, with no filtering.

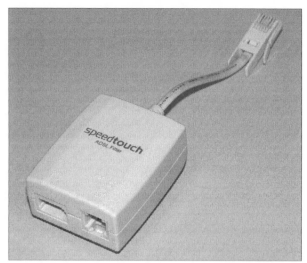

Fig 13.8: An ADSL line filter, which can be used to filter the line for a telephone which is suffering RF breakthrough.

ADSL

At the present time, the most popular way of accessing the Internet from home is by ADSL, which uses frequencies up to about 1MHz, these signals being passed along a standard 2-wire telephone line. Amateur radio transmissions of 1.8MHz and up in frequency should not affect it, but unfortunately it is not uncommon to hear of ADSL lockups occurring when transmissions are made on the 1.8 or 3.5MHz bands. Naturally it depends on how close the transmitting antenna is to the telephone wiring and how good the telephone wiring is, but sometimes it only requires a few watts of RF to cause a problem.

Plug-in ADSL line filters are good at what they do, but as already stated they do not filter the ADSL signal. Enter a second problem. A lot of domestic telephone wiring is based on a wiring plan which inherently unbalances what should be a balanced circuit - the telephone line itself. This is because a lot of master sockets contain circuitry to extract the ringing signal from the incoming line and send it along a third wire within the home. Although the telephone line is now unlananced, it does not usually affect ADSL performace adversely... until RF is radiated nearby. It is also worth noting that ADSL line filters do not pass the 'ringer' signal through, because modern telephones don't need it.

As standard, the incoming telephone line will be connected through to pins 2 and 5 of the telephone socket, with the circuitry in the master socket extracting the ringer signal and passing it

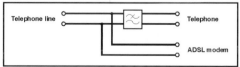

Fig 13.9: Internal arrangements of an ADSL line filter.

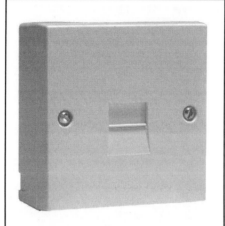

Fig 13.10: Old style telephone socket. Master and extension sockets look the same externally, but there are three extra components inside a master socket.

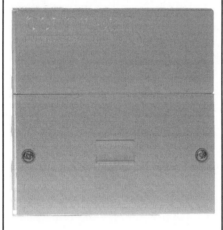

Fig 13.11: Standard BT type NTE5 master socket.

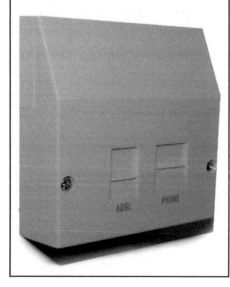

Fig 13.12: NTE5 master socket with replacement faceplate that has a built-in ADSL line filter.

through to pin 3. If you can extract the ADSL signal before the master socket, any unbalanced part of the system will be 'downstream' and should no longer cause a problem.

If your master socket looks like the one shown in **Fig 13.10** it is the old style and your best option is to plug an ADSL line filter into it and position your ADSL modem close to it. If you can gain access to the telephone line where it enters the house, it could be worthwhile adding a clip-on ferrite ahead of the master socket.

If your master socket looks like the one shown in **Fig 13.11** overleaf (note the fact that the screws are near the bottom and there is a dividing line just over half way up) it is a new style master socket (NTE5) and more possibilities for interference reduction exist.

Whilst you are still not entitled to make any modifications to the line or the master socket itself, the master socket is in fact hidden inside and it is possible to replace the faceplate with one that has an ADSL line filter built into it. This results in a master socket that looks like the one shown in **Fig 13.12**.

This type of arrangement has two distinct advantages:

1. The filter for all the telephones is built into the master socket, so there is no need to use an ADSL line filter for any of the individual telephones.

2. As **Fig 13.13** shows, the ADSL signal also appears on the connections inside the faceplate, so if you do not wish to locate your ADSL modem near the master socket you can add a twsired pair to conduct the signal away to where you want it.

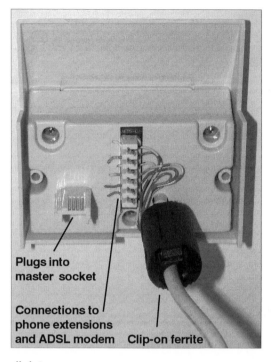

Fig 13.13: Inside a faceplate that has a built-in ADSL line filter. Extension telephones and a remote ADSL modem are connected via the cable.

Plugs into master socket

Connections to phone extensions and ADSL modem **Clip-on ferrite**

If required, further filtering can be added to the separated ADSL signal, by fitting a suitable low pass filter. The design shown in **Fig 13.14** is attributed to OZ7C. Standard value components can be placed in series and/or parallel, to acheive the required values. It is stated as having a 1dB ripple up to its cutoff frequency of 1MHz and offering 40dB of attenuation at 1.8MHz (see **Fig 13.15**).

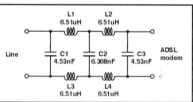

Fig 13.14: ADSL filter attributed to OZ7C.

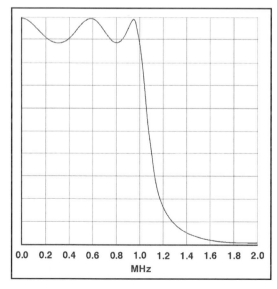

ADSL2

Depending on the distance of the access multiplexer from the subscriber's premises, ADSL 2+ can theoretically acheive download speeds of 24Mbit/sec and upload speeds of 3.5Mbit/sec. Using the trading name BT Infinity, BT is actively rolling it out across the UK. Early experience is good, although there have been reports of interfer-

Fig 13.15: Performance of OZ7C's ADSL filter.

ence with 160m (Top Band), causing broadband to drop out. The simple cure is to get the modem to train-up in the presence of the amateur transmission. Be aware that if the modem retrains at another time (for example after it has been power cycled), it will need to be trained again in the presence of the amateur signal.

Instances of interference have been rare, which is as a result of the very good balance of the network cables and wiring, right up to the modem. BT do not use stub connections within their network, which might otherwise cause imbalance and radiation. An important point to remember here is that the 'good practice' BT adheres to should be maintained right throughout the wiring. By choice, the modem will be as close as practical to the master socket. All in-house wiring beyond the modem should at the very least comply with the CAT5 or - even better - CAT6 standard. Maplin and other suppliers stock suitable cable with 5 Uniform Twisted Pairs (UTP), and connector boxes.

The filter shown in Fig 12.14 is not suitable for homes served with ADSL2, since it cuts-off at too low a frequency. For ADSL2 frequencies up to 2.2MHz are employed.

If you have issues the best you can do for yourself is fit a Service Specific Faceplate (SSFP) fitted to eliminate the internal wiring, since (a) internal wiring acts as a significant antenna system to pick up interfering signals, and (b) the SSPF will eliminate the additional unbalance that this 3-wire network can create. If a SSFP is not suitable because you require the flexibility provided by plug-in micro-filters, the BT Broadband Accelerator plate (www.bt.com/accelerator) may help improve things, although this is only suitable for ADSL and ADSL2+. This however does not matter since BT Infinity is currently installed with a SSFP only. BT also has a common mode filter, the BT80A-RF3 (an example can be seen on www.kitz.co.uk/adsl/btsockets.htm), that engineers will fit if they suspect noise issues (for example from SMPSUs), but I don't know how you would go about requesting this item from BT.

Sites like Kitz (www.kitz.co.uk) provide a lot of very useful information on broadband and how it works, issues etc, with the section at www.kitz.co.uk/adsl/rein.htm dealing with interference from faulty power supplies (what BT call REIN).

If you suspect your broadband service is being interfered with by REIN (it could be a regular pattern every evening or at a particular time of day and fine at all other times), try listening on a battery powered Medium Wave radio tuned off station when you are experiencing broadband problems. You may hear a horrible buzzing noise, especially if the radio is placed near the telecom network cable. If you do hear this, turn off your mains power. If the noise disappears the source is almost certainly within your own home and you should trace it by turning circuit breakers off one at a time and isolating individual items of equipment. (Note that faulty power supplies can also be incredibly hot to the touch!). If you turn all the power off and the buzzing does not disappear the problem is likely to be within another property in the neighbourhood, in which case you could talk to your neighbours to see if they have similar issues at the same times and perhaps get them to do the same power down of their property.

Finally, if there is excessive RF around the shack (or household), the use of clip-on ferrites may eliminate RFI on the phone connections, especially if the in-house network is old and runs alongside mains cabling.

14.
Internet Linking

by Steve White, G3ZVW (with information from other sources)

These days there are several ways in which radio amateurs can communicate without the straightforward use of a transceiver. Some Internet-linked systems don't involve radio at all, but of those that do, not all methods offer the same facilities.

IRLP

The Internet Repeater Linking Project (IRLP) began in 1997, initially just as an attempt to use the Internet to link radio systems across Canada. Early trials were fraught with difficulties, but the developers found that by using computers running Linux instead of Windows, not only was the system more stable, but it was easier to program for this OS.

IRLP uses Voice over Internet Protocol (VoIP) with custom software and hardware to link amateur radio systems without the use of an RF link. The software used by IRLP has a name – Speak Freely – and a purpose built hardware board (see **Fig 14.1**).

Fig 14.1: The IRLP control board.

Referring to **Fig 14.2**, IRLP works like this:

At the local host, audio is sampled by the A/D converter in a standard PC sound card. A 16-bit stream of monaural

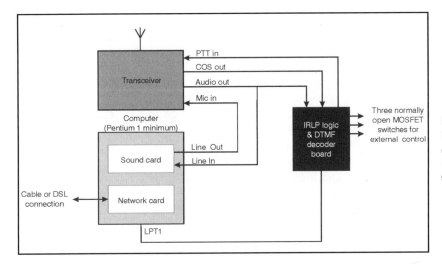

Fig 14.2: How the IRLP board connects with a PC and a transceiver.

audio at 120kb/sec is compressed down to 32kb/sec, split into packets and transmitted via the Internet to the remote host. At the remote host the audio is decompressed back to a 16-bit stream and played through the sound card. The software controls the stream using Carrier Operated Squelch (COS) or Continuous Tone Coded Subaudible Squelch (CTCSS) to start and stop the stream. When COS is present, the computer detects it through the IRLP interface board. The PTT line to the radio is controlled by the buffer that joins the audio packets back together. While there are packets in the buffer the IRLP interface board receives a 'transmit' signal from the computer, and an 'unkey' command when the buffer is empty.

Radio amateurs communicate over the IRLP network by interfacing to the IRLP computer at a local node, using Dual Tone Multi Frequency (DTMF) signals sent over their radio. DTMF sequences are programmable and can used to accomplish almost any function. The DTMF signals are detected on the IRLP interface board and sent directly to the computer in binary, where they are converted into numbers. The commands associated with these numbers are what start and stop Speak Freely, basically establishing and breaking the link.

IRLP does not support access direct from the Internet; all QSOs are via RF at each end. See: http://status.irlp.net/ for a list of nodes.

Echolink (from *QST*, February 2003)

EchoLink was developed by Jonathan Taylor, K1RFD, in early 2002. In an astonishingly short period of time, it became one of the dominant amateur radio VoIP systems, with more than 30,000 users worldwide. The free EchoLink software for Windows can be downloaded at www.echolink.org

When you start the EchoLink software, your computer taps the Internet to connect to an EchoLink server. Before you can make your first connection to the network, your callsign must be verified with the information in the FCC database. This can take minutes or hours, depending on the state of the system, but it helps reduce the chances of 'nonhams' entering the EchoLink network.

Once you're validated (you only do this once), the rest is easy. The EchoLink server acts like a telephone switchboard in cyberspace. It maintains a directory of everyone who is connected at any moment. After browsing the directory, you can request a connection between your computer and that of another amateur.

Here's where it becomes interesting. The amateur on the EchoLink receiving end may be sitting in front of his computer with a headset and microphone. Alternatively he may have his computer connected to a radio at his station that is acting as an RF relay to a handheld transceiver or mobile rig. Or the destination station may be part of a repeater system. In any case, once the connection is established, anything you say will wind up being heard in the other amateur's headset or transmitted over the air.

At your end of the EchoLink connection, you may be the one wearing the headset, or using a simplex connection to your base radio, or using a repeater. When you connect to an individual station, the custom is to call in the same fashion as you would during a traditional on-air conversation. If you are connecting to a distant repeater system, you need to hesitate for about two seconds before speaking, to compensate for the delay.

The EchoLink servers also support conferencing, where several amateurs can converse in a roundtable fashion. There are even EchoLink nets that meet within these conference areas on a scheduled basis.

Table 14.1: Echolink commnads.

Command	Description	DTMF Code
Connect	Connects to a station on the internet, based on its node number. The node numbers can be 4, 5 or 6 digits.	nnnnnn
Random Node	Selects an available node (of any type) at random, tries to connect to it.	00
Random Link	Selects an available link or repeater (-L or -R) at random and tries to connect to it.	01
Random Conf	Selects a conference server at random and tried to connect to it.	02
Random User	Selects an available single-user station at random and tries to connect to it. .	03
Status	Announces the callsign of each station currently connected.	08
Reconnect	Reconnects to the station that was most recently disconnected.	09
Disconnect	Disconnects the station that is currently connected. If more than one station is connected, disconnects only the most-recently-connected station.	#
Play Information	Plays a brief ID message.	*

If you plan to connect a radio to your computer so that you can use EchoLink over an RF link, you will need an interface. The strong enthusiasm for EchoLink is driven by the fact that it does not require a specialized hardware interface for connections to transceivers. All timing functions and DTMF decoding take place within the EchoLink software. This means that you can enjoy EchoLink with the radio of your choice by using common sound card interfaces such as those sold by West Mountain Radio (the RIGblaster folks), MFJ, TigerTronics and others. If you are already operating PSK31, RTTY, SSTV or similar modes with a sound card interface, you can become an EchoLink operator by simply downloading and installing the software, but there are also hardware interfaces specifically designed with VoIP in mind.

Echolink commands can be seen in **Table 14.1**.

eQSO (from *QST*, February 2003)

eQSO, created by Paul Davies, M0ZPD, was designed to operate like a worldwide amateur radio net. It is based around dedicated servers and can be used from a personal computer or through a radio link (known on eQSO as an 'RF gateway').

The eQSO software for Windows is available for free downloading on the Internet at www.eqso.net, with on-line support available at www.eqso.org A linking version of the software offers courtesy tones and a CW ID, and uses the computer's COM port for keying the transmitter and reading the receiver's squelch status. If a squelch line is not available, eQSO has an internal VOX function that can be selected.

eQSO works with all the usual PC-to-radio interface boards, such as the SignaLink SL-1 (see **Fig 14.3**).

Fig 14.3: The SignaLink SL-1+ interface.

Because there is no callsign validation, eQSO has security features that can be activated by administrators, who can mute or even block people who don't operate according to licence conditions.

Short Wave Listeners are also encouraged to use eQSO, and they are trusted not to talk in 'rooms' containing radio links. Those who do are muted or banned. However, SWLs can talk with hams in 'off-air' rooms and many consider this as an encouragement to gain a licence. Operators of RF gateways should avoid connecting their stations to these 'off-air' rooms.

WIRES-II (from *QST*, February 2003)

WIRES-II – Wide-coverage Internet Repeater Enhancement System –
is a VoIP network created by Yaesu that is similar in function to IRLP,
except that the WIRES-II node software runs under Windows. Like
IRLP, WIRES-II is entirely radio based; you cannot access a WIRES-II

node directly from the
Internet. A WIRES- II host
server maintains a
continuously updated
list of all active nodes.
The hardware

**Fig 14.4: The
Yaesu HRI-100
interface.**

portion of WIRES-II is the HRI-100 interface (see **Fig 14.4**). It connects to
a PC, which in turn is connected to the Internet. **Fig 14.5** shows the
layout. The HRI-100 also acts as the interface between the node radio
and the computer. Even though the HRI-100 is manufactured by Yaesu,
it is designed to work with any transceiver.

There are two WIRES-II operating modes:

The SRG (Sister Repeater Group) mode allows users to connect
to any other WIRES-II node (up to ten repeaters or base stations)
within a group specified by the node operator. As with IRLP, DTMF
tones are used to control access. Depending on how the node operator has configured his system, you may need to send a single DTMF
tone before each transmission, or just at the beginning and end of
your contact.

The FRG (Friends' Repeater Group) operating mode allows you to
connect to any other WIRES-II node in the world. The FRG mode also
allows group calling of up to ten nodes, a kind of conferencing function. To make a regular FRG call, you press #, then five more DTMF
digits depending on the ID number of the WIRES- II node you are
attempting to access.

**Fig 14.5:
Connections of
the Yaesu HRI-
100 interface.**

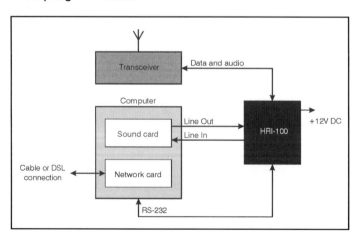

CQ100 (from *RadCom* May 2008)

If you believe in the traditional definition of radio as communication using electromagnetic waves, this new wonder-rig - the internet-based CQ100 - is not a radio all. But if your pleasure comes from rag-chews with fellow amateurs all over the world on technical matters of mutual interest, this radio may well be the one for you.

The virtual ionosphere and CQ100 are the brainchild of Canadian radio amateur Doug McCormack, VE3EFC, whose vision is a virtual ionosphere 'QSONET'. CQ100 is the first of what might be a family of transceivers using this virtual ionosphere.

Getting started with CQ100 couldn't be easier. You simply register your name, callsign and a password of your choice on the parent website (qsonet.com/programs.html), after which you'll be required to provide evidence that you are indeed a licensed radio amateur. The simplest procedure here is to scan your Ofcom licence and e-mail it as an attachment. The whole procedure can take up to 24 hours, but it's usually much faster.

Fig 14.6: The CQ100 virtual transceiver that works with a virtual ionosphere.

Once the licence has been verified, you'll be able to install the software for a 90-day free trial (US$32 per year thereafter), a painless procedure as CQ100 is reported to work happily with any Windows operating system from 95 to Vista. A reliable Internet connection is required with a speed of at least 33.6k dialup. There is no Mac version of the program, though there have been reports of successful operation using Windows emulators on Mac computers.

The 'transceiver', as it appears on the computer screen (**Fig 14.6**), will be familiar to anyone who has used a modern rig. It covers six simulated amateur bands: 3.500-3.800; 7.000-7.299; 14.000-14.350; 21.000-21.450; 28.000-28.999 and 29.000-29.700MHz. Apart from the last, all have designated CW portions as in conventional amateur radio. The large central spectrum display shows transmitting stations as small vertical blips on their chosen 'frequency'. To tune into that station, there are various options: manually click and drag the tuning knob to rotate it; click on the blip; or press Ctrl + left or right arrow. When a station is tuned in, its callsign is automatically displayed, together with the user's name and location. A click on the callsign automatically links to the station's details on www.qrz.com

As with a normal radio, there are various (simulated) transmission modes. Speech can be by push-to talk or VOX, the latter being controlled via traditional 'Level' and Dwell' controls. For CW, the simplest option is to use a code practice oscillator connected to your computer's line input socket. Alternatively, the rig's built-in keyer automatically converts typed messages into CW at user-chosen speeds ranging from 10 to 35WPM and at adjustable pitch from 400 to 650Hz. A novel feature is optional background noise, which disappears when a station is tuned in and which can be removed between stations by means of a Squelch button. It's a useful facility that provides reassurance that the receiver is actually working! An authentic-looking S-meter shows modulation depth on both transmit and receive.

The relative newness of CQ100 means that activity level is still building, but it is rare to make contact with anyone who is less than enthusiastic about its potential. Unlike the real ionosphere, it's possible to monitor activity via an automatic server activity graph helpfully provided on the QSONET home page. Activity peaks seem usually to occur mid-afternoon and in the early hours of the morning UTC. The number of nets and skeds is increasing. A particularly interesting example is WA5QPZ's Sunday afternoon Flex Radio net (14.239MHz, 19.00UTC) which runs both on HF and as a simulcast on CQ100. Anyone struggling with 'real' ionospheric reception problems can turn seamlessly to the virtual ionosphere backup; a good example of the two technologies working together, rather than in opposition.

The software appears to be remarkably bug-free and it is certainly user-friendly and instinctive. Any perceived deficiencies – and there are a few - are largely down to factors outside the control of the system's designers. Speech quality is variable, simply because the quality of computer sound cards is variable. Computer-type microphones also often leave a lot to be desired. Another occasional problem is sound break-up because of Internet congestion.

When working well, CQ100 is very impressive indeed; and at a time of indifferent band conditions the idea of having noise-free and QSB-free contacts with stations all over the world will be attractive to many radio amateurs, particularly those who live in a flat or similar accommodation where antennas are a non-starter, or travel the world with their laptops and can be 'on the air' in seconds wherever there is a broadband facility. Another more incidental attraction is that CQ100 can also reach stations that cannot be contacted by conventional radio, like Iraq during part of 2007 where radio transmissions were banned but where computer links survived.

The most recent add-on is 'Dahdidah', which enables the CQ100 to be used for CW via a key connected to the computer's serial port. Some work has been done on a logging program and a picture sharing add-on.

As for future developments, the CQ100 Forum has produced a number of fanciful ideas including the possibility of introducing simulated 'bad band conditions' and QRM.

15.
Interfacing and Interfaces

by Steve White, G3ZVW

There are numerous commercially-made items of equipment that will interface between a computer and a radio. Some are complex and some are so simple that those with basic knowledge of electronics should be able to build them. In this chapter you will find information on commercial and make-at-home interfaces.

Build Yourself

Non-isolated

The simplest circuit that can be used to connect a computer with an RS232 serial port (or a Centronics parallel port) to a transmitter requires just one resistor and one general-purpose NPN transistor. It is suitable for keying CW and PTT. For use in keying the PTT, make sure that your transmitter has diodes across the changeover relays to suppress the back EMF that inevitably arises when they release, or the transistor may be destroyed the first time the PTT signal goes off! The circuit is shown in **Fig 15.1**. Typical connections are shown in **Table 15.1**. Such circuits are often

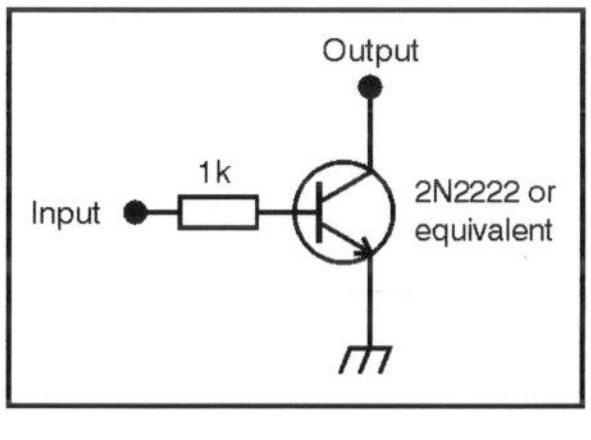

Fig 15.1: Simple CW keying and PTT interface.

Keying	9-pin RS232	25-pin RS232	Centronics
Input	4	20	17
Ground	5	7	1
PTT	9-pin RS232	25-pin RS232	
Input	7	4	
Ground	5	7	

Table 15.1: Simple CW keying and PTT interface connections.

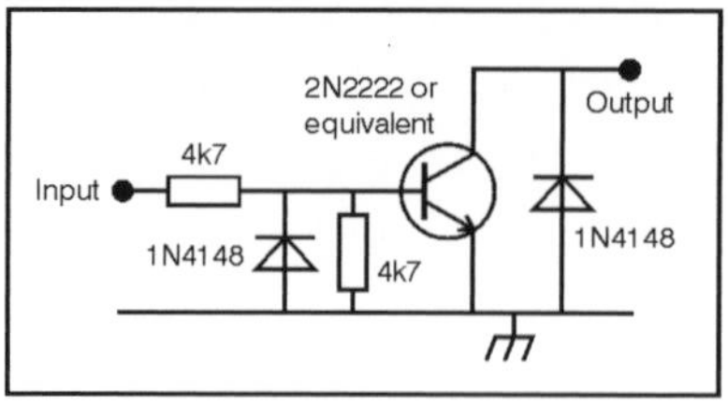

Fig 15.2: Superior non-isolated interface.

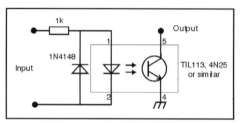

built into the body of a D-type connector.

A superior circuit is shown in **Fig 15.2**. This is more likely to be built into a small project box between the computer and transmitter.

Fig 15.3: Keying interface using an opto-isolator.

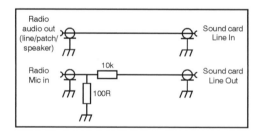

Isolated

A better method still of keying which removes the possibility of hum loops and reduces the possibility of RF pickup is to use an opto isolator. The circuit for this is shown in **Fig 15.3**. The type of opto isolator is not critical. Darlington and non-Darlington types should work equally well. The pinout of many opto isolators is as shown in **Fig 15.4**. If you use a different type to the ones mentioned in the circuit, check before you build the interface that the pinout is the same.

Once again, if you are going to use a curcuit such as this to key the PTT, make sure the relays in the transmitter have diodes across them.

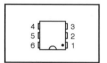

Fig 15.4: The pinout of typical opto-isolators.

Audio

For datamode operation via a sound card, screened cables are called for. The simplest connection will be two screened cables, one to carry audio from the sound card of the computer to the radio and a second to carry audio from the radio to the sound card. If your transmitter has a 'phone patch' (external, high level audio) input, it is recommended that you use it in favour of the microphone input. This is because most transmitter microphone inputs are very sensitive and it is all too easy to overload the input stage, which will result in distorted audio when you transmit. If you connect to a high level audio socket, remember to unplug your microphone during datamode operation or it is possible that it will pick up and transmit the sound of whatever is going on in your shack while you are transmitting.

Fig 15.5: Cabling and audio attenuator, suitable for connecting a computer to a radio that does not have a high level audio input.

If your radio does not have a phone patch input you should build the circuit shown in **Fig 15.5**, which includes a 100:1 attenuator. If your radio does have a phone patch input, it is likely that you will be able to omit the two resistors and connect the sound card output direct to the radio input. Either way, adjust the microphone gain to a level that does not cause the audio stages of the transmitter to be over driven.

If you experince problems with RF pickup when transmitting, the first remedy to try is clip-on ferrites on the cables. It is good practice to wind an audio cable through a ferrite several times, but make

Fig 15.6: A clip-on ferrite correctly installed on an audio cable.

sure the two halves close firmly together when you clip it shut or it will have no effect. **Fig 15.6** shows a clip-on ferrite correctly installed. Alternatively, use ferrite rings of an appropriate material for the frequency that is causing problems. Unless you are starting with a cable on which connectors are not already fitted, select a core size through which the smallest of the connectors can easy pass, and wind several turns onto the core. The cable should not be wound randomly, rather it should be wound from a start point and and around no more than 3/4 of the ring. Secure each end with a cable tie. Alternatively, the cable should be wound around about 3/8 of the ring, then crossed over and wound around another 3/8 of the ring. This is more effective, as it reduces capacitive coupling between the points where the cable enters and exits the ring.

There are *big* differences between the materials used in differing varieties of ferrite ring, so not all types of material are suitable for all

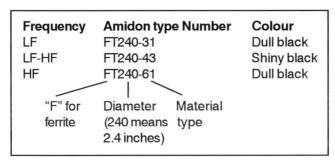

Frequency	Amidon type Number	Colour
LF	FT240-31	Dull black
LF-HF	FT240-43	Shiny black
HF	FT240-61	Dull black

"F" for ferrite — Diameter (240 means 2.4 inches) — Material type

Table 15.2: Ferrite rings/ cores suitable for winding on audio cables.

frequencies. Suitable types to use are shown in **Table 15.2**. Do not use iron dust cores (eg T200-6), which can often be identified by the fact that they are colour coded.

If you experince hum on your data transmission, caused by a hum loop, you may need to use audio transformers to electrically isolate the computer from the transmitter. The circuit for a suitable system is shown in **Fig 15.7**.

Audio transformers can be recovered from ancient transis-

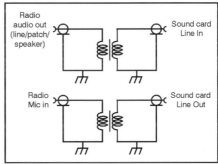

Fig 15.7: How audio transformers can be used to electrically isolate a radio from a computer.

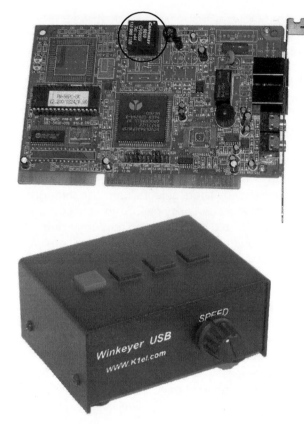

Fig 15.8: An old modem card from a computer, with the audio transformer circled.

tor radios, PC modem cards, or purchased from various retailers. **Fig 15.8** shows an old modem card from a PC, with the audio transformer circled.

Kits

There are numerous CW keyers available as kits, but perhaps the most popular computer-linked model is the WinKeyer2 from K1EL (see **Fig 15.9**). It conforms to the WinKey standard and integrates well with many popular logging programs. The kit is available in RS232 and USB versions and can take an experienced constructor less than two hours to build.

Fig 15.9: The WinKeyer USB from K1EL.

Commercial

A range of products for various purposes are available from a number of manufacturers.

MicroHAM produce several products. All their models that support datamodes include transformer isolation of audio signals between computer and transceiver. Some models contain sound card hardware, eliminating the need to use the sound card in a computer. Their 'Station Master' is a controller for antenna switching, bandpass filter switching and SteppIR control, while the 'MK2R' is an advanced controller for SO2R operation that features a host of facilities.

The EZMaster from Ham Radio Solutions is a USB device that interfaces your PC with several devices in your shack; radios, antennas and filter switching, microphone and headphones. It supports phone and data modes, and incorporates CW and digital voice keyers. SO2R is also supported.

K1EL produces a variety of CW-related products. Apart from the WinKeyer, already mentioned, a standalone CW keyer which operates from a computer keyboard is offered. Versions of the WinKeyer are also available with high voltage outputs, suitable for keying virtually any transmitter, not just modern ones which run on low voltage and/or require little current to flow through the keying contacts.

Some antenna rotators are capable of being connected directly to a computer, giving software that supports rotator control the ability to point an antenna automatically, according to the direction of the stations being worked. For rotators that do not include direct support for interfacing to a computer, Idiom Press offer a number of products that will add this function.

Instrumentation

If you own high-end test equipment it is quite likely to contain a General Purpose Interface Bus (GPIB) socket. The GPIB permits the user to connect the equipment to a computer to automate measurements, but historically this was an expensive process.

These days, with interfaces such as those produced by Prologix (see **Fig 15.10**), it is rather less expensive. Versions for connection to a USB or network socket on a computer are available.

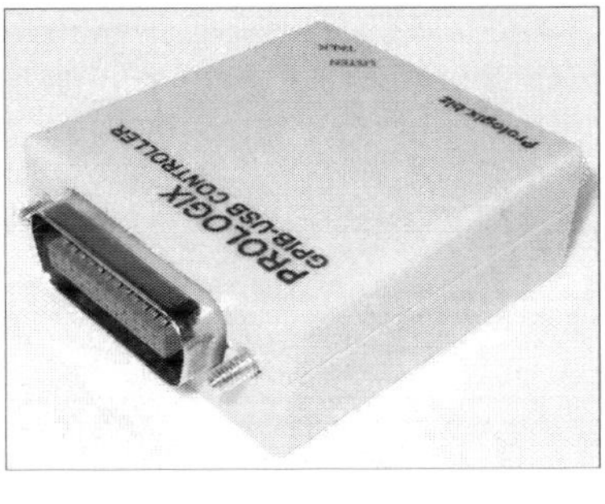

To use in conjunction with such a controller, the KE5FX GPIB Toolkit is a collection of free Windows utilities that will help you make and record research-quality measurements with GPIB-based electronic test equipment.

Fig 15.10: The Prologix General Purpose Interface Bus to USB converter.

The latest release is always available for downloading from www.thegleam.com/ke5fx/gpib/ readme.htm For troubleshooting help and additional application notes, check the FAQ.

The Toolkit is provided with full C++ source code for public- and private-sector, educational and amateur radio / hobbyist use. Comments and feedback are always welcome.

16.
Live Internet
Applications

by Steve White, G3ZVW

Chat Rooms

The most popular amateur radio chat rooms for arranging QSOs are run by ON4KST (see **Fig 16.1**). They are available at www.on4kst.com/chat/ These text only chat rooms are used mainly by VHF/UHF DX enthusiasts (there are separate rooms for 50/70MHz, 144/432MHz, JT6M/EME/ CW and microwave), but there is also a chat room for 160m/80m. The chat rooms are used primarily to arrange QSOs and as an instant messaging type talkback facility. A login is required, but this is free and it takes only moments to fill in the application, receive an e-mail response and activate an account.

Fig 16.1: One of the ON4KST chat pages.

Left panel - chat.

Centre panel - DX Cluster.

Right panel - current users.

The ON4KST chat rooms also include cut-down DX Cluster information (receive only). Additional windows can be opened, containing such things as ionospheric data and beacon lists.

Online Receivers

For a number of years there have been receivers available for use online. The problem with conventional receivers is that only one person can use them at a time, so usage by any given individual tends to be very time limited. These days a whole new world has been opened up because there are Software Defined Receivers (SDRs) available online.

As **Fig 16.2** shows, at this time the SDR at the University of Twente in the Netherlands (see http://websdr.ewi.utwente.nl:8901/) is perhaps

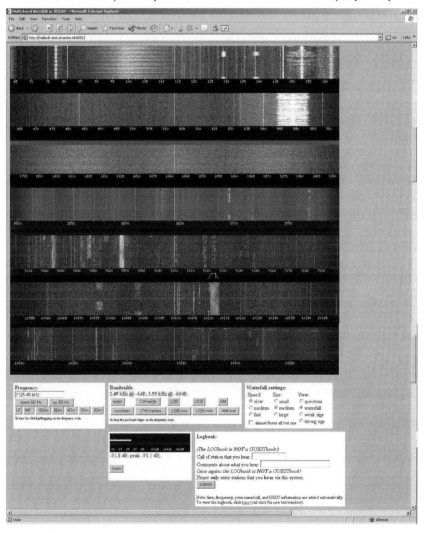

Fig 16.2: Composite of the seven bands on which the University of Twente DSP receiver listens on.

Fig 16.3: A map of the 7MHz band, showing who is listening to which frequency.

the most useful for HF enthusiasts. It can be tuned across any amateur band up to 14MHz, with the audio being heard via your computer's sound card. The receive mode, frequency, sideband and bandwidth are highly adjustable, and the receiver has an S-meter and simultaneous waterfall displays for all bands.

Fig 16.3 shows details of the usage of one band (7MHz). At the time of capturing the image, 26 people were using the receiver simultaneously on this band alone. If you give your callsign, it shows up against the frequency you are listening on, otherwise it shows your IP address.

See www.websdr.org for a list of online SDRs.

Reverse Beacons

The Reverse Beacon Network (RBN) is a revolutionary idea, which has only become possible because of the Software Defined Receiver (SDR) and Skimmer software. Instead of relying on beacon stations actively transmitting signals, the RBN is a worldwide network of SDRs that listen continuously to the amateur bands and report what stations they hear, when and at what signal strength.

Fig 16.4: The Reverse Beacon Network web page, showing recently heard stations.

Logging in to www.reversebeacon.net (see **Fig 16.4**) gives access to the site. There are numerous possible ways to use it:

- After transmitting and being received by one or more of the SDRs, you can compare how well you are being received at the various locations.
- You can compare the performance of different antennas, by switching to a new one and waiting to be spotted a second time.
- You can compare how strongly you are being received, compared to other people in, say, a contest or your own country.
- You can search spots tailored to individual (or groups of) amateur bands, by individual callsign, etc.
- You can see which amateur bands are open and carrying traffic.

The number of online SDRs is not constant. At the time of writing it was typically 20.

PSK Reporter

PSK Reporter (http://pskreporter.info) is a similar system for datamodes, particularly PSK31. Users of the site (see map of where monitor stations are located in **Fig 16.5**) can search by band, callsign, country, Locator square, mode and time, to receive reports on whether a station is being received (and if so how strong). Typically there are over 100 monitors active, mainly in Europe and North America.

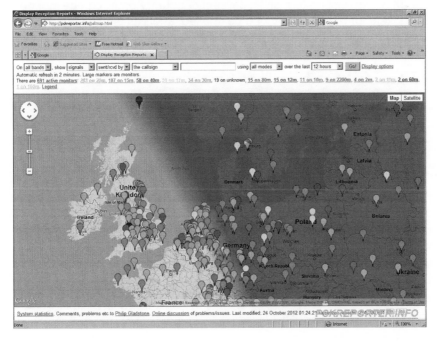

Fig 16.5: The PSK Reporter page, showing where SDRs are located and darkness moving across Europe.

DX Clustering

The DX Cluster came into being as a near real-time alert system in the mid 1980s, soon after the widespread adoption of Packet Radio around the start of that decade. A large network of stations (mostly on VHF/UHF, but some on HF) would pass 'DX Spots' around; information on DX stations that had been spotted on the air. When you view DX Spots it enables you to identify new or rare countries that you may wish to contact, and when you input DX Spots it helps others to do the same. The DX Cluster also has live online keyboard-to-keyboard chat, mail and conference facilities.

In the early days it could take several minutes for a DX Spot to propagate around the world. Even before the Internet became popular, the radio network was linked to it. These days a high percentage of DX Spots are input and viewed via the Internet, so much so that in many countries the number of radio-based nodes has diminished. Even so, the command structure of online cluster nodes that you can Telnet into is still the same as it was in the 1980s.

There are a number of web sites and applications devoted to DX clustering.

There are numerous web-based DX Clusters in existence, the 'DX Summit' by Radio Arcala, OH8X (www.dxsummit.fi) being one of them. It gives users the opportunity to view DX Spots and Announcements. Spots can be filtered by band, if required. DX Spots can also be input (no login or user validation required), for onward passing around the network. DX Summit also has a search facility, whereby - for example - all DX Spots relating to a given callsign or country prefix can be looked up. Filters for mode or year can be applied, and lists of differing length can be selected. To provide an easy link for additional information, when DX Spots are displayed, the callsign of the spotter and the spotted

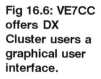

Fig 16.6: VE7CC offers DX Cluster users a graphical user interface.

station can be clicked on. Doing so will open www.qrz.com in a new window, with the callsign that was clicked on already entered. Some other web-based clusters are less sophisticated, while some of the newer ones are optimised for use with the iPhone.

DX Spider is one of many software packages that DX Cluster nodes use to run, others being CC Cluster, CLX, Clusse, and DxNet. DX Spider is a clone of the earlier packet cluster software, developed by Dick Newell, AK1A. The user commands are the same as those used by stations accessing the DX Cluster via Packet Radio. Most commands can be abbreviated. A comprehensive list is available online at: www.drhnet.com/cluster.htm

VE7CC is a software package for cluster users. As **Fig 15.6** shows, it offers a Graphical User Interface (GUI), so it is not necessary to key commands in.

Registration is usually required to use a DX Cluster fully. This is normally free of charge and was introduced to prevent false information being sent. Without registration it is generally possible to log in and see DX Spots and Announcements, but only registered users can send Spots and Announcements.

Live VHF DX Maps

Taking information from the DX Cluster network and placing it onto maps, the DX maps on www.dxmaps.com/spots/map.php give VHF/UHF users the facility to see the points between which QSOs have recently taken place. A snapshot of the European map for 50MHz is shown in **Fig 16.7**. Maps are available for different parts of the world

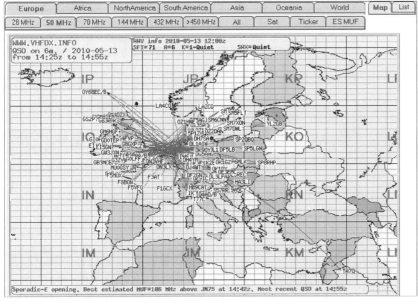

Fig 16.7: DX maps. When a DX QSO is spotted, the callsigns at each end of the QSO are added to the map in the appropriate place and a line is drawn between them.

and for individual bands from 28MHz to 432MHz. The maps are constantly updated, providing a near real-time picture of what is going on DX-wise on the VHF bands. They should not be relied upon 100% though, because the informstion used to create them is what has been input by users of the DX Cluster, and mistakes are sometimes made. There is a perfect example of this in Fig 16.7, because it shows TA7Q in KM91 when he is actually in KN91.

Path lines are shown in different colours, according to the propagation mode via which a QSO took place and users soon get accustomed to looking at where red path lines cross, because that is where the Sporadic-E clouds are. There is also a page that gives estimates of Sporadic-E MUFs.

An alternative to the DX Sherlock facility is the Live MUF program by Dave Edwards, G7RAU. It is available as a free download from http://g7rau.demon.co.uk/default.aspx?menu=5000

Live MUF is a DX Cluster Telnet client that attempts to resolve propagation modes from spots and also attempts to calculate Sporadic-E possibilities, based purely on incoming data from the DX Cluster. It has great circle mapping built in to the application for the live mapping of spots. Live MUF can also be used as a worldwide converse Telnet client, ON4KST Telnet client and DX Cluster at the same time.

Near Real-time Magnetometer

For propagation enthusiasts, the web site of Roger Blackwell, GM4PMK, at www.marsport.org.uk/observatory/index.php contains the feed from a Simple Auroral Magnetometer located at his home on the Isle of Mull, Scotland (locator, IO66XJ). It

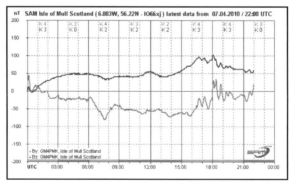

Fig 16.8: GM4PMK's live magnetometer.

is designed to give advance warning of possible auroral activity. **Fig 16.8** shows a graph captured from the site. Disturbances of K5 or more on the graph indicate there may be such activity.

Near Real-Time MUF Map

The image displayed at www.spacew.com/www/realtime.php (shown in **Fig 16.9**) is a recent high-resolution map of Maximum Usable Frequencies (MUFs) for 3,000km radio signal paths. It also shows the current

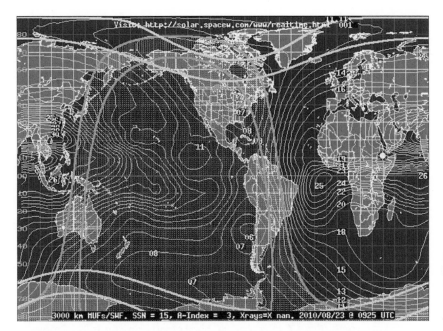

Fig 16.9: The near real-time MUF map.

location of the auroral ovals, the sunrise/sunset terminator and the regions of the world where the sun is 12° below the horizon (which estimates the greyline corridor where HF propagation is usually enhanced) and the sun. The map is updated every five minutes.

17.
The Raspberry Pi

by Peter Goodhall, 2E0SQL

The Raspberry Pi (**Fig 17.1**) is a credit card sized computer (85.6mm x 56mm x 21mm) developed by the Raspberry Pi Foundation (www.raspberrypi.org). This small, bare-bones, low cost computer, which is supplied without a keyboard, monitor and power supply, is designed to change the way children interact with and understand computers. The current curriculum at schools is heavily biased towards using Word, Excel and writing basic html web pages, but the Foundation wanted to change this.

After the demise of the Amiga, BBC Micro, Sinclair ZX Spectrum and Commodore 64, which previous generations used to learn to program on, a suitable replacement was needed. This is because they were replaced by the home PC and games consoles, which aren't really designed for children to learn to program or tinker with, especially if it is the family's computer. In 2008 the Foundation decided to use processors which were designed for mobile devices to make a low cost computer. Three years later these units were licensed to Element 14, Farnell and RS Electronics and entered production.

Even though the Raspberry Pi is designed to teach children how to code, this doesn't limit its usage. This chapter will explore how it can be used in the amateur radio shack.

Technical Specification

The Raspberry Pi is available in two 'flavours'. The Model A (not yet released) and Model B (£30) vary slightly in specification which might sway your purchasing decision. The Model A has 256Mb of RAM, one

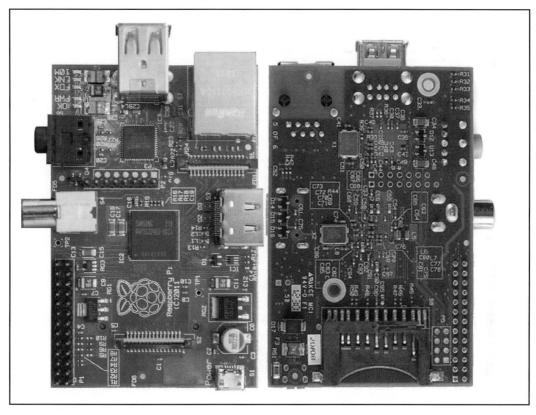

USB port and no Ethernet (network connection), whereas the Model B has 512Mb RAM, 2 USB ports and a 100Mbps Ethernet port.

Both models use a Broadcom BCM2835 that contains an ARM1176JZFS with floating point, running at 700MHz, plus a Video core 4 GPU (Graphics Processing Unit) which has more than enough power to play Blu-ray quality video using H.264 at 40Mbits/s.

Overall the real-world performance of the Raspberry Pi is similar to a 300MHz Pentium 2 and the CPU is on par with the Microsoft Xbox 1.

Fig 17.1: Life size top and bottom views of the Raspberry Pi.

Fig 17.2: Raspberry Pi Model B layout.

Connections

The Raspberry Pi's PCB edges are filled with connectors that you can use to interact in different ways with the hardware. **Fig 17.2** shows the Model B layout.

The power requirements are via a 5V micro USB connector, which you'd use normally on mobile phones, tablets or even the Amazon Kindle. The Model B,

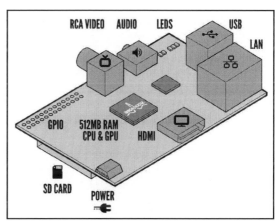

using networking and high current USB peripherals (keyboard, mouse), will require around 700mA. The Model A will likely require around 300mA. If you want a more 'green' option or to use it portable, it's possible to run it using 4 x AA cells. It is however recommended you use a voltage regulator.

You have two options for connecting the Raspberry Pi to a visual display; you can use the composite connector and an old style analogue television or the HDMI connector which provides a 1080p high-quality output. If you don't have an HDMI input on your monitor or television, you can get adapters to convert HDMI into DVI or VGA.

Audio output via a 3.5mm plug. It is also possible to get audio out via the HDMI connector. What isn't available is an audio input, so if you're looking at feeding audio in from your radio you will need a USB soundcard.

Next are the USB connectors. Depending on which model you choose you will either have one or two USB2.0 ports. Both ports use the same bus, so if you want to connect lots of USB devices it is highly recommended you purchase a powered hub to go along with your Raspberry Pi.

Networking is provided on the Model B via a 100Mbps Ethernet port. If you buy a Model A and require networking capabilities, you will need to purchase USB Wireless (http://elinux.org/RPi_VerifiedPeripherals#USB_WiFi_Adapters) or Ethernet devices (http://elinux.org/RPi_VerifiedPeripherals#USB_Ethernet_adapters) that are suitable for Linux.

Storage for the Linux-based operating system is provided by the SD card slot on the underside of the board. You can use any class of SD card, but most users seem to use between Class 4 and Class 10 with reasonable successes. However, it is worth noting that not all SD cards will work well with the Raspberry Pi. The eLinux Wiki (http://elinux.org/RPi_VerifiedPeripherals#SD_cards) has a comprehensive list of what others have tried and tested, to find what works or doesn't.

Operating System and Basic Setup

Unlike most desktop computers that you can buy on the high street running Microsoft Windows or Apple OSX, the Raspberry Pi uses the Linux operating system. This is nothing to worry about. You'll quickly get used to using it.

The Raspberry Pi Foundation recommends that you use the Raspbian Linux distribution (http://www.raspberrypi.org/downloads), which is based on the Debian (http://www.debian.org). This is one of the most popular Linux distributions in the world. Of course, if you're a more technical user, there are a couple of other flavours of Linux available including Arch and RiscOS, and many more being ported to the ARM architecture.

Once you've downloaded the Raspbian image and un-zipped it you'll be left with a file ending .img. This will need to be flashed onto the SD card using Win32DiskImager (https://launchpad.net). **Fig 17.3** shows a screen shot of Win32 Disk Imager. This can be download free of charge, but remember to get the binary version. In this utility you select the image file that you downloaded and the drive letter which represents your SD card, then press Write. Once complete you're ready to plug it into the Raspberry Pi.

On its first boot up the Raspberry Pi will normally load straight away into the Raspi-Config tool (see **Fig 17.4**), but if it doesn't the default login information is as follows:

Username: pi
Password: raspberry

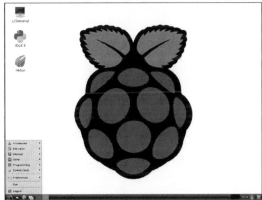

If the tool didn't load after this you can do a 'sudo raspi-config' within this area. You can resize the SD card, set a new password (highly recommended) and also enable over-clocking. I'd recommend doing this. It doesn't void the warranty (http://www.raspberrypi.org/archives/2008). In the Overclock section enable the Turbo mode. This allows the CPU to boost up to 1GHz, rather than the default 700MHz.

In the config tool you may also want to enable SSH if you plan on connecting to the Raspberry Pi remotely. If you selected the Expand_rootfs the Pi will need to reboot. Once it has and you've logged in with your newly created password you can start the graphical inter-face by typing:

start x

You will then be presented with a desktop screen (**Fig 17.5**) that you might find similar to Windows. You'll notice the familiar taskbar with the clock and CPU usage graphs on the right and the icon on the far left is the start button. Once clicked you'll notice it pops up with application types which break down

Fig 17.5: Desktop.

to further programs which have been installed. You'll notice as you install more applications they won't all show and you'll have to run them from the terminal screen.

To install other applications you can normally find them via the Advanced Packaging Tool. From the Terminal screen, type:

sudo apt-get install <application>

Shack Usage

The Raspberry Pi could and can have many uses within the amateur radio shack. Due to it being a new product the possibilities are only just starting to be explored.

In this section we are going to explore using the Raspberry Pi to do some basic tasks. This should give you a sufficient understanding, so that you can then start exploring what's possible and push the boundaries of the device yourself.

APRS

There are numerous software packages available for Linux that will decode APRS packets. Some of these are pre-compiled binaries that you can install via APT. Alternatively they will need to be compiled manually from source. Don't let this stop you though, because most have comprehensive guides on how to set them up.

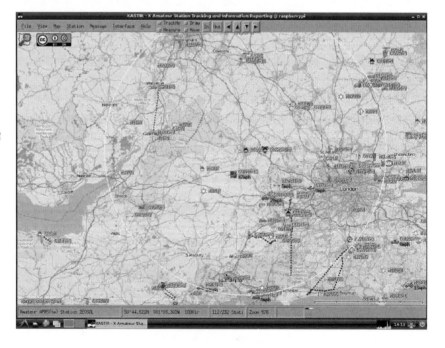

Fig 17.6: XASTIR APRS package.

Due to the fact the Raspberry Pi doesn't have any soundcard inputs you will either have to connect a TNC or try one of the sound modem packages such as Multimon – Packet Soundcard (http://www.baycom.org/~tom/ham/linux/multimon.html)

A great package to get started with is XASTIR (http://www.xastir.org). This is sown in **Fig 17.6**. Installation is straightforward. Open-up the terminal screen then issue the command to install:

sudo apt-get install xastir

This process might take some time, depending on the speed of your Internet connection and what else your Pi is currently doing, but it will tell you when it is complete. Once installed if you click on the start menu icon then go to 'other' you should find xastir. If not, type the following on the command line and it should load up:

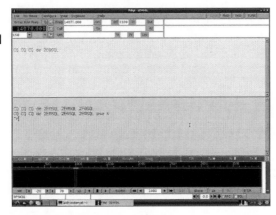

Figure 16.7:
FL-Digi in PSK-31 mode.

./xasitr

You'll now need to configure the interface that you want to use and also the maps. You can either use the basic world outlines or the highly comprehensive Open Street Map tiles.

Digital Modes
Even though the Raspberry Pi doesn't have audio inputs, don't let this put you off. With the help of a cheap external soundcard or a data interface which has a built in soundcard you can achieve good results.

A great application to start with is FL-Digi (**Fig 17.7** shows a screenshot of FL-Digi in PSK-31 mode). It's simple enough to install, just by installing though the APT package manager:

sudo apt-get install fldigi

Once it has successfully completed, load the application via the start menu. You will need to configure the soundcard and also any other add-ons like CAT control and PTT keying. It is also possible to interface with online callbooks for grabbing station information.

If you're more interested in SSTV, you'll find QSSTV (http://users.telenet.be/on4qz/) by ON4QZ works very well. A great guide on how to build it can be found at: http://blog.dale.id.au/archives/1246.

Figure 17.8: GPredict.

Satellite Tracking

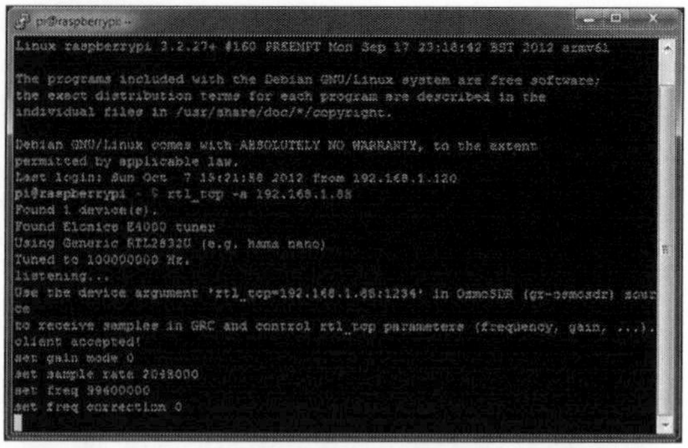

Satellite tracking is really easy using the Raspberry Pi, using the excellent GPredict program shown in **Fig 17.8** (http://gpredict.oz9aec.net/) by OZ9AEC, which allows interfacing to radios and rotators using the Hamlib library (http://sourceforge.net/projects/hamlib/). It's a perfect companion for anyone who wants to operate through amateur satellites; track cubesats or - as **Fig 17.9** shows - just monitor the pass times for the International Space Station.

Setup couldn't be simpler. Within the terminal window type:

sudo apt-get install gpredict

Then follow the on-screen instructions. Configuring the radio and rotators can be more complex, depending on the equipment concerned, so it's worth consulting the help documentation.

Remote SDR IQ Server

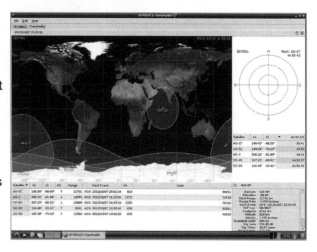

Figure 17.9: RTL_TCP running inside a Putty Window SSH.

A very useful application for the Raspberry Pi might be as a remote SDR IQ streaming server for RTL chipset SDRs (Funcube dongles coming soon). This will allow you to remotely control the dongle via a range of software packages like SDRSharp (http://sdrsharp.com) on Windows (see **Fig 17.10**). This is made possible using the RTL-SDR toolset which is available from http://sdr.osmocom.org/trac/wiki/rtl-sdr.

Getting it to work on the Raspberry Pi requires a little work, but it's worth the effort. To do this type the commands below in the terminal.

sudo apt-get install git
git clone git://git.osmocom.org/rtl-sdr.git
sudo apt-get install cmake, pkg-config, libusb1.0

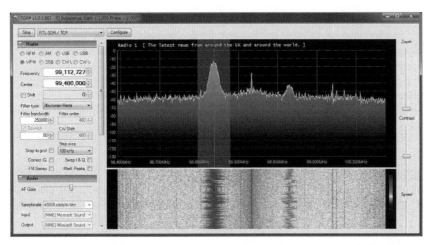

You then need to compile what you have done with the following:

**cd rtl-sdr/
mkdir build
cd build
cmake ../ -DINSTALL_UDEV_RULES=ON
make
sudo make install
sudo ldconfig**

Once it's completed and you've restarted the Raspberry Pi, type:

rtl_tcp -a 192.168.1.883

Please note that the IP address should be the one assigned to your Raspberry Pi, so you'll probably need to change it. As long as you get no errors you're now ready to connect to the RTL_TCP server from another application. I'm going to use SDRSharp, but there are other applications available for Linux.

SDR# is easy to use. I'd recommend you download the nightly build as it has all the latest features, then it's just a matter of selecting RTL-SDR / TCP and filling out the IP information to match the Raspberry Pi and clicking Play! You can now use SDRSharp normally.

External Interfaces

The Raspberry Pi comes with a 26 GPIO (General Purpose Input/Output) pins on an expansion header. These can be programmed through software. These pins break down to provide 8 GPIO lines plus access to I2C, SPI, UART, +3.3V, +5V and GND supply lines. It is worth noting that no over-voltage production is included, so if you plan on using these pins it will need to be added.

A number of expansion boards have been developed to make using the GPIOs easier and also to provide some more functions. These vary from simple, with the Slice of PI/O (https://www.modmypi.com/shop/raspberry-pi-expansion-boards/slice-of-pio-raspberry-pi-breakout-boad), to the Gertboard which is great board for learning more about electronics. This is also available from Farnell.

Other options are the popular Ardunio board (http://www.arduino.cc), which is an open-source electronics prototyping platform. This supports many add-on boards (shields), including a TNC shield (http://goo.gl/mHQiP).

Regardless of the platform you choose you should be able to program the Raspberry Pi to complete most tasks.

18.
Useful Programs and Web Links

by Steve White, G3ZVW

Besides the useful software that can be found on the CD that accompanies this book (and listed in Appendix 2), here are some suggestions.

Drawing
A basic drawing package will enable you to create circuit symbols and draw lines between them to create a circuit diagram. Such a package will also enable you to draw block diagrams, flow charts, antennas and simple plans.

Circuit Drawing and PCB Layout Packages
There are a number of programs dedicated to the drawing of circuit diagrams. Many can be downloaded free from the Internet, although versions that are downloaded sometimes have restrictions placed on them. Some packages also enable you to design a printed circuit board. Free versions often have limitations in terms of board size and the number of layers of tracks.

Circuit simulators
Designing RF filters used to involve a lot of mathematics. It still does, but now your computer can do that for you and show you graphically the response of a filter that you have designed. Such a package will contain virtual test equipment, so it will also be capable of taking a circuit diagram andsimulating its operation, to give you confidence in it working. Most packages work to the SPICE (Simulation Program with Integrated Circuit Emphasis) standard.

Circuit simulator packages will not design circuits for you and are not easy to learn, but they are capable of similating quite accurately any design and finding a fault in it.

Antenna design

There are numerous tools available to designing antennas. Some exist as web based applications, while others exist as downloadable programs or spreadsheets.

Test and measurement

Given the appropriate software, a computer with a sound card can be used to make numerous kinds of measurement. Audio analysis software can be used to measure distortion, noise, modulation and oscillator drift. A sound card can also be used as a frequency counter, sometimes up to hundreds of kilohertz.

Internet Resources

With something as dynamic as the Internet it would be impossible to list all the useful online calculators and downloadable programs, but the pages that follow include information on some of them.

QRZ.COM
(www.qrz.com)

Well-known for its worldwide callsign database, this site also has discussion forums, an online swapmeet, practice amateur radio exams (US syllabus) and an amateur radio trivia quiz.

VHF-Microwave Path Profiler
(www.mike-willis.com/software.html)

'Path Profile' by Mike Willis, G0MJW, is a utility that generates the profile of a given radio path and computes path loss for frequencies between 30MHz and 3GHz. It uses Shuttle Radar Topography Mission (SRTM) .HGT data, which you need to download separately. You will need the one degree tiles. This means downloading a lot of data, but you need large files to get high resolution. The entire database is 30+ gigabytes, but it is entirely possible to download if you have a broadband Internet connection.

There is a terrain map display facility and you can also plot the climatic zone data, which is used for estimating the probability of ducting. There is also a display for climatic zone, that is Inland, Sea and Coastal as per ITU definitions. A prototype area coverage model is also included.

GEOG.ZIP
(www.g4jnt.com/hdbase.htm)

This suite of programs from Andy Talbot, G4JNT including programs for calculating distances and bearings, the spot height for any given site, Locator system conversions and distance / bearing measurement, troposcatter loss for two sites, the path profile between two sites, maps of paths worked between many sites, a local height colour map, 3D representation of local heights, a Great Circle world map based on any locator, a wide area height colour map, the horizon view from any site and more.

The programs were written for a DOS environment, but you should have no problems running them under Windows. You will need PKUNZIP or WINZIP to open the download file.

OFCOM
(www.ofcom.org.uk)
The regulator for the UK communications industries, with responsibilities across television, radio, telecommunications and wireless communications services. The site contains a number of information sheets of interest to radio amateurs.

Special Interest Groups
Just about every special interest group, from AMSAT to WACRAL, has its own site. Topics covered include, caravanning, television, DXing, Morse, low power operation, listening, the Armed Forces, the disabled, old timers, emergency comms, VHF, microwaves and more.

Yahoo! Groups
Discussion boards on just about every amateur radio topic, from individual models of equipment, through DXing to local clubs.

Locator calculators
Calculate Locator from latitude and longitude (and *vice-versa*):
www.amsat.org/cgi-bin/gridconv
Find Locator direct from Google maps:
http://f6fvy.free.fr/qthLocator/fullScreen.php
Calculate Locator from UK National Grid Reference:
www.ntay.com/contest/NGR2Loc.html

IARU Societies
Most national societies have web sites. They are all accessible via a page at the IARU web site, www.iaru.org/iaru-soc.html

Software collections
There are so many web sites that contain collections of utilities and programs it would be impossible to list them all. Here are three worthy of mention:

AC6V
(www.ac6v.com/software.htm)
A site that contains links to numerous utilities.

AmSat
(www.amsat.org/amsat/ftpsoft.html#win)
Contains numerous links to programs and utilities. The emphasis is on satellites, but there utilities of all kinds.

g3vfp
(www.g3vfp.org/download.html)
Utilities and software mainly for MS Windows.

RSGB
(www.rsgb.org)

This is the starting point for the site. Navigation buttons are provided to take you to the rest of the site. The latest news headlines are displayed prominently, as are links to special offers and new features. There are links to pages for news, local information, membership, committees and operating.

Members' area
The Members' Area of the RSGB website offers a selection of valuable amateur radio resources to members of the society. The weekly news is published here two days before is appears on the piblic pages, plus there are news archives, the minutes of Broad and Council mettings, downloadable logos, the RSGB bylaws, planning advive, a searchable version of the small ads that is found every month in RadCom, information on operating abroad, the RSGB QSL Bureau, details of the insurance offered to affiliated groups, hundreds of links to the web sites of national and local clubs and societies, links to technical leaflets etc.

Fig 18.1: Join this Yahoo! Group if you need technical advice or can help others.

RSGBTech
(http://groups.yahoo.com/group/ rsgbtech/)
RSGBTech is technical help for the 21st Century. It is an RSGB Internet site located on Yahoo!(see **Fig 18.1**). Its purpose is to be the first port of call for technical queries on amateur radio matters. It is open to all radio amateurs and within a short period of time from its inception had hundreds of registered users. Not only are there people from the Society on the site, but people from other special interest groups and radio amateurs from overseas.

Emergent Technology Coordination Committee
(www.etcc.rsgb.org/)

The ETCC was formed when the Datacommunications Committee (DCC) and Repeater Management Committee (RMC) were merged.

In terms of repeaters, there ar eare pages that list the operational status of existing units and the vetting process of as yet unlicensed repeaters, plus lists of repeaters sorted by callsign, frequency and type. However, the largest and most graphic part of the site is devoted to operational units. There are national coverage maps for every channel and individual coverage colour maps for every repeater (see **Fig 18.2** for an example).

On the datacomms side, the site contains pages associated with Internet linking and other data modes, lists of packet mailboxes, Internet gateways, etc.

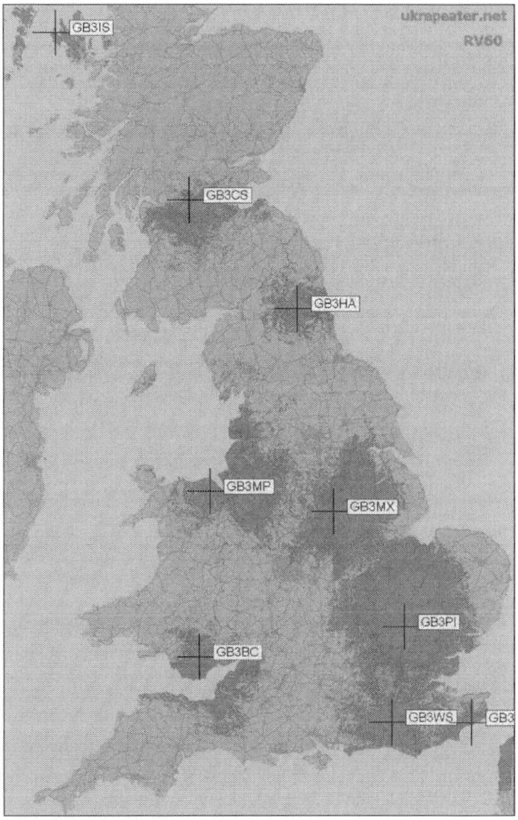

Contest Committee
(www.rsgbcc.org/)

Since the merger of the HF and VHF Contest Committees, there has been a major reorganisation of their web pages. There is still a frequency distinction between HF and VHF events, but all RSGB contesting pages now come under one site.

The major part of the site is devoted to results. There are results for RSGB HF contests going back to the year 2000. The results of the IOTA Contest can be searched and sorted in more ways than other events.

For those who do not use a computer for logging in a contest, there is a web-based log generator. Via the Claimed Scores page you can subscribe to an e-mail reflector that will mail you an alert of claimed scores, either for all events or just the ones you enter. On the Results page you can similarly subscribe to an e-mail reflector that will mail you an alert of declared results, either for all events or just the ones you wish.

Recent innovations include e-mail alerts prior to contests and the ability to see on a Google map where you made all the contacts in a contest.

Fig 18.2: One of many repeater coverage maps.

Electromagnetic Compatibility Committee
(www.rsgb.org/emc/)

The EMC web site contains a wealth of information on the subject, including news updates on PLT.

Clicking on 'EMC Help' will take you to a page with links to numerous EMC leaflets, to help you identify and resolve problems. There are also links to lists of EMC/technical advisors. Another page lists all the different models and uses of the ferrite rings and EMC filters that RSGB stock.

Propagation Studies Committee
(www.rsgb.org.uk/psc/)
The front page contains links to numerous other pages associated with propagation ascross the frequency spectrum, plus specific types of propagation.

Planning Advisory Committee
(www.rsgb.org/committees/pac/)
Source material for planning applications.

Amateur Radio Direction Finding Committee
(www.rsgb.org/radiosport/ardf/?id=ardf)
The home page of this site has links to news of IARU style ARDF in the UK, rules for events, results from 2006 to date, a newcomer's view of IARU DF, hints and tips on IARU DF events, an events calendar, links to IARU ARDF sites and technical information.

Spectrum Forum
(www.rsgb.org.uk/spectrumforum/)
The Forum was launched in 2004. It is a grouping of all RSGB spectrum-related voluntary bodies and close affiliates. The Forum replaced the earlier RSGB structure, whereby separate committees focused upon different areas of the spectrum. The Forum looks across the whole spectrum, forming short-term Working Groups or ad hoc teams to focus on specific issues. Thus, the Forum is agile, better linked both internally and externally with other groups and is able to be seen as a single point of representation for the UK amateur radio enthusiast.

A major part of the site is devoted to band plans, with HTML and Excel spreadsheet versions available. Other parts of the site deal with news, awards, consulation documents, developments,

Radio Communications Foundation
(www.commsfoundation.org)
The RCF is a charity set up by - but independent from - the RSGB, to create a fund which can support efforts to bring radio communications into classrooms, universities, indeed any place where a hands-on public demonstration can deliver our message.

The RCF supports projects which demonstrate radio communication to the public through the expertise of the UK radio amateur.

On 16 January 2007 an agreement was signed between Ofcom and the RCF, setting out the terms under which the RCF agrees to conduct amateur radio examinations and under which Ofcom agrees to recognise a candidate's result in those examinations for the purpose of granting an amateur radio licence. A Standards Committee is responsible for oversight of the management structure and policies.

Islands On The Air
(www.rsgbiota.org)

A site devoted to RSGB's highly-rated award program. Additionally, there are lists of operations approved for island credit, imminent island activities and the latest DX spots from island stations, the Honour Roll and Annual Listing, Research Resources, IOTA Meeting Frequencies, IOTA Contest information and Google Earth Files.

National Radio Centre
(www.nationalradiocentre.com/)

The world-class Radio Communications Centre, located at the former WWII code-breaking centre at Bletchley Park in Buckinghamshire, is a showcase for radio communications technology. From the first inventors in the late 19th century through to future radio developments, the Centre provides visitors with the opportunity to get 'up close and personal' with the history of radio communications.

Visitors will find films, interactive displays, hands on experiments and even the opportunity to go on the air at the state-of-the-art amateur radio station.

Appendix 1
The Modern Personal Computer

by Steve White, G3ZVW

There's a basic precaution that should always be observed when working inside a personal computer. Don't do it while its switched on! Power it down and unplug the power lead first.

The next thing you need to be aware of is that many of the components in a computer are sensitive to static electricity. If you have a static discharge wriststrap,use it when working inside your computer. Failing that, touch the chassis of the machine every time you approach it, because static electricity accumulated by walking across a carpet can destroy sensitive components. Keep components in anti-static bags or in anti-static foam until you are just about to instal them.

Power Supply
The power supply converts the AC supply from the mains to various DC voltages used by the PC. More powerful machines need supplies capable of delivering more current. In desktop systems such as the one shown in **Fig 19.1**, the power supply is almost always at the top back of the machine. It will require a mains cable with a female IEC connector. Some power supplies have power and/or voltage selector switches, while some don't. Some power supplies also have an IEC female (outlet) connector on the back, for powering additional equipment, for example the display screen.

Memory
The Random Access Memory (RAM) used in PCs comes in standard sizes (256MB, 512MB, 1GB etc). Depending on the operating system and software you run, you may require more or less of it. Systems with less momory tend to run slower, so a relatively inexpensive way of increasing your computing power is to increase the amount of memory.

This type of memory is 'volatile', which means that data is not retained when the machine is switched off.

There are a variety of memory module types and technologies. They have different connectors and run at different speeds, so make sure you use the correct type for your machine.

Power cabling

A wiring loom with a variety of connectors will emerge from the power supply. Each device installed in the machine will need power connecting to it. Even in machines that are loaded-up with a lot of devices, some of the connectors are likely to remain unused.

CD/DVD Drive

For installing programs, listening to music, backing-up data, etc. Older drives were CD-only read-only types. More modern drives can also read DVDs, as well as write to a variety of media. The most modern machines may have a BluRay drive.

Fig 19.1: Inside a modern desktop computer.

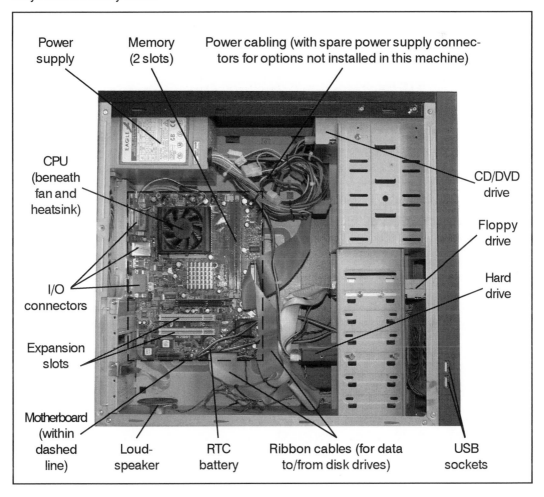

Power supply — Memory (2 slots) — Power cabling (with spare power supply connectors for options not installed in this machine)

CPU (beneath fan and heatsink)

CD/DVD drive

Floppy drive

Hard drive

I/O connectors

Expansion slots

Motherboard (within dashed line) — Loud-speaker — RTC battery — Ribbon cables (for data to/from disk drives) — USB sockets

Floppy Drive
Almost obsolete now, but used for installing small programs, backing up small amounts of data etc. New machines are not equipped with floppy disk drives, because it has become more convenient to move or store small amounts of data on memory sticks or across networks.

Hard Drive
Sealed disk that stores most of the information (programs and data) on the machine. Data is retained when the machine is switched off. Some machines may be equipped with more than one hard drive.

USB Sockets
The Universal Serial Bus is used for the connection of a wide variety of hardware, such as printers, scanners, external disk drives, memory sticks etc. USB sockets are often found on the back of computers and some-times on the front as well.

Ribbon Cables
Used for devices that require parallel connection to carry data, typically disk, CD and DVD drives. Different drives (e.g. floppy disk and hard disk) use different cables, which are not interchangeable.

RTC battery
Used to keep the Real Time Clock running when the machine is switched off, this battery also enables the machine to retain basic settings (disk drive types and capacities etc) when it is switched off. Most systems use a flat, button-shaped lithium battery. Expect such a battery to last about five years. The battery can be unclipped from its holder and replaced.

Loudspeaker
Used by the machine for basic sounds, e.g. error warnings on startup.

Motherbaord
Populated with components that carry out many of the functions of the machine. There will be a Basic Input Output System (BIOS) chip that enables the computer to boot from disk, the Real Time Clock (RTC) and controllers for the keyboard, mouse, video graphics, network, sound, joystick, USB etc. The CPU chip invariably plugs into a socket. On different motherboards expect the components shown in Fig 17.1 to be in different places.

Expansion Slots
Printed circuit boards that can be used for numerous purposes plug into these sockets. In early PCs is was common for several boards to be required, indeed older motherboards were larger and has more sockets.

As more and more functions became incorporated onto motherboards and peripheral devices standardised onto USB, there has become less of a need to plug in anything at all.

I/O Connectors

Accessed from the rear of the machine, there will be sockets for the kayboard, mouse, network, USB devices, sound, joystick, video display etc. Some motherboards are equipped with sockets for a parallel printer and/or RS232 serial comms. See the following paragraphs.

Central Processing Unit (CPU)

The CPU is the computer's engine. The faster the chip, the more instructions it can execute per second. CPUs with multiple cores overcome the 'speed limit' of technology as it currently stands.

Connectors and Connections

Fig 19.2 shows the back panel of a typical personal computer.

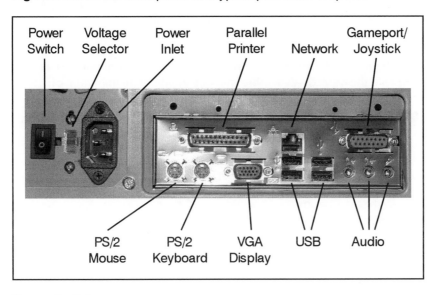

Fig 19.2: The back panel connectors of a typical personal computer.

Power Switch

Typically a small rocker switch, this can be used to power the computer completely off. Of left 'on', the power supply will in fact be in standby mode when the computer appears to be 'off'.

Voltage Selector

Used for switching between 115/230V operation. Some power supplies are 'universal' types that can accommodate any input voltage, in which case this switch will not be present.

Power Inlet

Male IEC connector. Power supplies that have an outlet will be equipped with an additional IEC female connector.

Pin	Name	Colour
1	Neutral	Blue
2	Earth	Green/yellow
3	Live	Brown

1 2 3

Network

The most popular wiring scheme for IEE 802.3 networking uses Unshielded Twisted Pair (UTP) cable. The standard plug and socket is the RJ45 'jack'. Cables need to be made with care to work efficiently at higher speeds. When used for 10/100/1000BASE-T networking, the maximum cable length for Cat5e is 100m (90m horizontal). When used for 10GBASE-T, Cat6 is limited to 37m or 55m, depending on its environment. Cat6 cables must not be kinked or bent too tightly.

For connecting a computer to a router, switch or hub, a straight cable is required. For connecting two computers together without a router, switch or hub, a crossover cable is required.

If you are going to make a cable, you must use the correct cable type, because the guage of the conductors and the twists in the pairs are critical to performance. You will require a special crimping tool to terminate the cables. Also, there must be an absolute minimum of untwisting of the pairs as they enter the plugs. Either wiring scheme shown below is OK.

Pin	TIA/EIA 568A Wiring Colour	TIA/EIA 568B Wiring Colour	Signal name
1	White + Green	White + Orange	TX+_D1
2	Green	Orange	TX-_D1
3	White + Orange	White + Green	RX+_D2
4	Blue	Blue	BI+_D3
5	White + Blue	White + Blue	BI-_D3
6	Orange	Green	RX-_D2
7	White + Brown	White + Brown	BI+_D4
8	Brown	Brown	BI-_D4

Crossover Wiring

Pin 1 - Pin 3
Pin 2 - Pin 6
Pin 3 - Pin 1
Pin 4 - Pin 7
Pin 5 - Pin 8
Pin 6 - Pin 2
Pin 7 - Pin 4
Pin 8 - Pin 5

1   8

1   8

VGA

The Video Graphics Adapter connector is a 15-pin high density D-type.

Pin	Name	Description
1	Red	Red Video (75-ohm, 0.7V p-p)
2	Green	Green Video (75-ohm, 0.7V p-p)
3	Blue	Blue Video (75-ohm, 0.7V p-p)
4	ID2	Monitor ID Bit 2 (to PC)
5	Gnd	Ground
6	R Gnd	Red Ground
7	G Gnd	Green Ground
8	B Gnd	Blue Ground
9	Key	Key (no pin)
10	S Gnd	Sync Ground
11	ID0	Monitor ID Bit 0 (to PC)
12	ID1 or SDA	Monitor ID Bit 1 (to PC)
13	HSYNC or CSYNC	Horizontal Sync (or Composite Sync)
14	VSYNC	Vertical Sync
15	ID3 or SCL	Monitor ID Bit 3 (to PC)

HDMI

High Definition Multimedia Interface. The Type A is commonplace. Type C is the newer mini HDMI plug. The pinouts shown below apply to the Type A and Type C. The 29-pin Type B is able to carry an expanded video channel, but is rarely used.

Pin	Name
1	TMDS data 2+
2	TMDS data 2 shield
3	TMDS data 2-
4	TMDS data 1+
5	TMDS data 1 shield
6	TMDS data 1-
7	TMDS data 0+
8	TMDS data 0 shield
9	TMDS data 0-
10	TMDS clock+
11	TMDS clock shield
12	TMDS clock-
13	CEC (control)
14	No connection
15	SCL (DDC clock)
16	SDA (DDC data)
17	DDC/CEC ground
18	+5V
19	Hot plug detect

Gameport

Analog joystick interface. On Gameport connectors fitted to sound cards, pins 12 and 15 are usually devoted to MIDI (Musical Instrument Digital Interface) usage.

Pin	Name	Description
1	+5V	+5V DC
2	/B1	Button 1
3	X1	Joystick 1 X-axis
4	GND	Ground (switch 1)
5	GND	Ground (switch 2)
6	Y1	Joystick 1 Y-axis
7	/B2	Button 2
8	+5V	+5V DC
9	+5V	+5V DC
10	/B4	Button 4
11	X2	Joystick 2 X-axis
12	GND	Ground (switches 3 and 4) or MIDI out
13	Y2	Joystick 2 Y-axis
14	/B3	Button 3
15	+5V	+5V DC or MIDI in

PS/2 Connectors

The keyboard and mouse on an IBM-compatible PC are connected with a 6-pin miniature DIN plug of the same type. A mouse plug and socket are usually green, while a keyboard plug and socket are usually purple.

Mouse

Pin	Name	Description
1	DATA	Data
2	N/C	Not connected
3	GND	Gnd
4	VCC	+5 VDC
5	CLOCK	Clock
6	N/C	Not connected

Keyboard

Pin	Name	Description
1	DATA	Data
2	N/C	or DATA2 for dual PS/2
3	GND	Gnd
4	VCC	+5 VDC
5	CLOCK	Clock
6	N/C	or CLOCK2 for dual PS/2

RS232

There are two connectors in common use, both D-types. In older equipment it tends to be 25-pins (which supports the full specification), while on modern PCs it is 9-pin. This smaller connector means that only a subset of the modem control signals are supported, but it is sufficient for normal communication.

RS232 was introduced to enable electronic equipment to communicate serially via modems. This led to two terms being introduced - Data Terminal Equipment (DTE) for the main equipment (originally Teletype terminals, but now also computers and USB-RS232 adapters, etc) and Data Set Equipment (DSE) for modems. DTE equipment will have a 9-pin male connector, the female connector being on the cable.

Pin	Name	Direction	Description
1	CD	To PC	Carrier Detect
2	RXD	To PC	Receive Data
3	TXD	From PC	Transmit Data
4	DTR	From PC	Data Terminal Ready
5	GND		Ground
6	DSR	To PC	Data Set Ready
7	RTS	From PC	Request to Send
8	CTS	To PC	Clear to Send
9	RI	To PC	Ring Indicator

USB

Designed to connect peripherals such as mice, keyboards, scanners, digital cameras, memory sticks, printers and hard disks. Up to 127 devices may be connected in a tree-like fashion on a USB bus. Hubs may be cascaded.

Pin	Name	Colour	Description
1	VCC	Red	+5 VDC
2	D-	White	Data -
3	D+	Green	Data +
4	GND	Black	Ground
x			May be disconnected, GND, or used as attachment I/D

Firewire (IEE1394)

A high speed serial interface that uses differential signals. Used typically for high-end equipment and applications such as scanners, digital video, digital audio mixing, etc.

4-pin	6-pin	9-pin	Name	Description	Colour
-	1	8	Power	Unregulated DC (30V no load)	White
-	2	6	Ground	Ground return for power and inner cable shield	Black
1	3	1	TPB-	Twisted-pair B	Orange
2	4	2	TPB+	Twisted-pair B	Blue
3	5	3	TPA-	Twisted-pair A	Red
4	6	4	TPA+	Twisted-pair A	Green
-	-	5	A shield		
-	-	7	-		
-	-	9	B shield		
Shell	Shell	Shell	Outer	Cable shield	

Audio

On desktop systems there are usually three 3.5mm stereo jack sockets, for the inputting and outputting of audio. In terms of left and right audio, all the sockets are wired the same. The microphone input is usually red, the line input is usually blue and the output is usually green. Many laptop computers only have one input socket.

Connection	Usage
Sleeve	Ground
Ring	Right
Tip	Left

Parallel (Centronics) Printer

The Centronics printer was the one-time standard for high speed printers. Largely replaced by USB these days, it is still sometimes used by
radio amateurs to drive keyers. The full Centronics standard is not
supported by the 25-pin D-type on a personal computer. The wiring and
signals are shown below.

Pin (PC)	Pin (Prtr)	Name	Description
1	1	/Strobe	Strobe
2	2	D0	Data Bit 0
3	3	D1	Data Bit 1
4	4	D2	Data Bit 2
5	5	D3	Data Bit 3
6	6	D4	Data Bit 4
7	7	D5	Data Bit 5
8	8	D6	Data Bit 6
9	9	D7	Data Bit 7
10	10	/Ack	Acknowledge
11	11	Busy	Busy
12	12	POut	Paper Out
13	13	Sel	Select
14	14	/Autofeed	Autofeed
	15	n/c	Not used
	16	0 V	Logic Ground
19	17	Chassis Gnd	Shield Ground
	18	+5 V Pullup	+5 V DC (50 mA max)
20	19	Gnd	Signal Ground (Strobe)
	20	Gnd	Signal Ground (Data 0)
	21	Gnd	Signal Ground (Data 1)
	22	Gnd	Signal Ground (Data 2)
	23	Gnd	Signal Ground (Data 3)
	24	Gnd	Signal Ground (Data 4)
	25	Gnd	Signal Ground (Data 5)
	26	Gnd	Signal Ground (Data 6)
	27	Gnd	Signal Ground (Data 7)
	28	Gnd	Signal Ground (Ack)
	29	Gnd	Signal Ground (Busy Ground)
25	30	/GndReset	Reset Ground
16	31	/Reset	Reset
15	32	/Fault	Fault (Low when offline)
	33	0 V	Signal Ground
	34	n/c	Not used
	35	+5 V	+5 VDC
17	36	/Slct In	Select In (Taking low or high sets printer on-ine or off-line respectively)

Appendix 2
Software on the CD that accompanies this book

The following are brief descriptions and information from the maker's websites of the included shareware/freeware on the CD that accompanies this book. Please note this software is supplied with no warranty or implied approval by the Radio Society of Great Britain. The producers of this CD have made no charge for the software listed below and provide no technical support for it. Most of these programs are designed for PC use only and not all will work with Vista, Windows 7 or 8. If you choose to use the software it is entirely at your own risk and you are bound by any conditions applied by the makers or their agents. Should any feature of the software's use be illegal or have restrictions placed on its use in your jurisdiction, you must only make legal use of this software or its features. The Radio Society of Great Britain will not accept any responsibility for losses or damage arising from the use of this software. We provide no installation instructions, but all items are either zip or self installing files.

Amateur radio programs

AALog
A comprehensive logger program designed for amateur radio station operators. It has a convenient interface, a good set of tools, is fast and very easy to use. It looks like your paper logbook and uses all power of your computer. It can be integrated with the CW terminal program CwType, Morse decoder, CwGet and RTTY/PSK31 software TrueTTY. Also you can use AAVoice for voice operations. AALog is LoTW and eQSL.cc compatible.

AGW Software
This package includes:

AGW Packet	This application will allow your sound-card-equipped PC to function as a packet TNC, without an external modem.
AGW Tracker	This is an APRS(c) compatible program. It works using AGW Packet Engine or Packet Engine Pro.
AGW Monitor	This application allows you to monitor packet radio activity.
AGW GMT Clock	GMT time display for DXers.
AGW DX Robot	Displays the DX Robot Aurora and Sporadic-E Propagation for Europe.
AGW DX Net Manager	Rag Chewing Net Manager.
AGW DX QSL Print	Design and Print your QSL.

Airlink Express
A user-friendly digital mode software package for the amateur radio operator. The software is compatible with Microsoft Windows XP, Microsoft Windows Vista and Microsoft Windows 7. It offers PSK, MFSK and RTTY digital modes, with logging and macro capabilities. If you have ever used Digipan software you will be immediately familiar with Airlink Express.

Amateur Contact Log
An easy-to-use general logging program that has many great features, including tracking of Worked All States, Counties and Countries.

Contest Trainer
A great contest trainer, produced by G4FON. Please note that this is shareware and limited to 20 QSOs.

CW Decoder
Translate Morse code to printed text with your PC sound card. Version 2.81.2, Vista Compatible.

CwGet
A program to decode Morse code (CW) via sound card to text. It can also work as a narrowband DSP filter. No additional hardware is required - you need only a receiver and a computer with a sound card. Can integrate with AALog logger.

CW_PLAYER

A program to learn and train the Morse code, which needs a sound card and Win95/98/ME/2000/NT/XP. The Morse message of page amateur radio has been generated with CW_PLAYER. CW_PLAYER includes automatic CW keying of the transmitter, through serial and parallel ports, or manual keying through the Joystick port. A special menu will add some fun for children.

CW Skimmer

Version 1.6. Multi-channel CW decoder and analyzer used with the software defined radios.

Features
- A very sensitive CW decoding algorithm based on the methods of Bayesian statistics;
- Simulatneous decoding of *all* CW signals in a receiver's passband (up to 700 signals can be decoded in parallel on a 3GHz P4 if a wideband receiver is used);
- A fast waterfall display, with a resolution sufficient for reading Morse code dots and dashes visually;
- Callsigns are extracted from the decoded messages, and the traces on the waterfall are labeled with stations' callsigns;
- Extracted callsigns are exported as DX cluster spots via the built-in Telnet cluster server;
- A DSP processor with a noise blanker, AGC, and a sharp, variable-bandwidth CW filter;
- An I/Q recorder and player.

CwType

The terminal program for CW operators. You can transmit both from the keyboard and from a paddle connected to game or LPT port. You can also operate in iambic mode. Control of the transceiver (PTT and CW keying) is made through the LPT or one of the COM ports. Can integrate with AALog software.

DX Lab

A suite of interoperating applications designed to automate amateur radio DXing activities. Each application can be independently installed and utilized. When multiple applications are running, they sense each other's presence and interoperate appropriately. All DXLab applications are free and contain no advertising. They run on Windows 95, 98, 98SE, NT, 2000, and XP. Commercial use is expressly forbidden. You will also find the latest development releases of the same software.

Features
- Commander allows you to control your Alinco, Elecraft, Flexradio, Icom, JRC, Kachina, Kenwood, TenTec, or Yaesu radio from a PC (Vista compatible).
- DXKeeper is comprehensive amateur logging software.
- DXLab Launcher makes it easy to control individual DXLab applications, or a specified group of DXLab applications.
- DXView presents a world map, upon which beam headings, stations you spot, the sun's position, and the solar terminator are continuously displayed.
- Pathfinder makes it easy to find QSL information from web-accessible sources like address and manager databases and country-specific callbooks.
- PropView uses VOACAP, ICEPAC, and IONCAP propagation prediction engines, to forecast the minimum and maximum useable frequencies between two locations over 24 hours.
- SpotCollector is a free application that captures spots from up to four additional telnet-accessible DX Clusters, the DX Summit spotting network (via the #CQDX IRC channel) and local PacketCluster (via a TNC or the AGW soundcard packet engine).
- WinWarbler allows you to conduct QSOs in PSK31, PSK63, PSK125 and RTTY modes using your soundcard's analog-to-digital and digital-to-analog conversion functions.

Great Circle Map
Produce your own Great Circle map with this program from SM3GSJ. Other programs by SM3GSJ mapping islands, lakes, rivers etc are also enclosed.

Ham Radio Deluxe
Version 6 is an integrated suite of software products for amateur radio. The five modules in the suite provide rig control, logging, digital communications, satellite tracking and rotator control.

Rig Control
Provides rig control through a richly-featured full-screen interface and other products in the Ham Radio Deluxe Suite via a direct connection or TCP/IP remote access.

Logbook
Provides QSO logging, DX cluster connectivity, callsign lookup, awards tracking (with integration to LOTW, eQSL, and Ham Radio Deluxelog.net), and contesting. Microsoft Access and MySQL are supported, with strong features for backup and recovery.

Digital Master (DM-780)
Provides the most popular sound card digital modes, with direct integration to the Ham Radio Deluxe Logbook.

Satellite Tracking
Provides satellite operations, with rig control and Google Earth integration.

Rotator
Provides control for 15 popular models of antenna rotators.

Jason Mode
Jason is a weak signal communication program, especially tailored for LF work.

MMSSTV
This program is for transmitting and receiving SSTV using a PC's soundcard.

MMTTY
Superb RTTY software program.

MMVARI
A multi-mode sound card amateur radio program for receiving and transmitting in RTTY, PSK, FSK and MFSK modes.

MMANA-GAL
Antenna analyzing tool based on the moment method, which was introduced in MININEC.

Morse Runner (Version 1.68)
Contest simulator for Windows 95/98/ME/NT4/2000/XP.

Morse Trainer
Version 9 of the great Morse trainer produced by G4FON.

Multi PSK
Multimode program by F6CTE that supports phase shift keying modes, on-off keying modes, frequency shift keying modes, multi frequency shift keying modes, baseband modes, Hellschreiber modes, graphic modes, DSP filters / analysis / bnaural CW reception, RTTY, CW, BPSK31, BPSK63 and PSKFEC31 panoramics, and Video ID / RS ID / Call ID identifiers, a TCP/IP digital modem and an integered SDR demodulator/modulator

N1MM Logger
The world's most popular contest logging program. For CW, phone and digital modes, its combination of contest-optimized features is unmatched. All major and many minor HF Contests are supported. Includes general DX logging, DXpedition, DXSatellite and VHF DX. SSB, CW and digital support. Multi-user support, rover support for QSO parties and other contests which support this. VHF and up contesting. Transverter support (SHF bands supported up to 10, 24, 47, 76, 142 and 241GHz). Dxpedition mode (stay in run, or S&P).

QSL Maker
This nice software, developed by WB8RCR, lets you design and print your own QSL cards, allowing you to personalise the background by importing pictures or just filling with a plain colour, and lets you person-alise headings and address, as well as your own callsign. It can import ADIF log file for auto-filling fields during the print process, or allows you to insert QSO data directly into a table.

Satscape
Satellite tracking program for Windows, Mac OS and Linux. You can use it to find out the position of any of the 8000+ satellites and orbital debris in orbit around the earth right now. Anything from the Interna-tional space station to a misplaced spanner can be tracked right on your screen, with no special equipment. Your very own NORAD com-mand and control on your computer desktop. If you are a star-gazer and want to see (with the naked eye) the International Space Station fly over your house, or you're a radio amateur who wants to know when you can have a QSO with your buddy thousands of miles away, this is the program you need. It is easy to use, looks pretty and there's no need to be a rocket-scientist because it will do all the maths for you.

SAT_EXPLORER
Freeware for satellite tracking and antenna positioning. Handles the following antenna tracking interfaces: PourSat, FODTrack, EA4TX, GS232, EASYCOM, TRAKBOX, KCT, PROSISTEL and other compatible interfaces such as LVBTracker and SatDrive. SAT_EXPLORER is com-patible with TRX-Manager for piloting transceivers and other antenna systems.

SD

Sets the standard for fast, simple logging and editing in the major international contests and in dozens of others worldwide. It is intended for single-op unassisted entries, on both SSB and CW. SD runs on all versions of Windows, from Win95 to Win7, with a character-based display.

SD is free and unrestricted in the following contests. There's no need to register - just download and away you go! All RSGB SSB and CW events, for both sides where applicable, including: IOTA, RSGB DX, Commonwealth, Field Day, 1.8MHz, 21/28MHz, 80m Club Sprints, 80m CC, AFS, RoPoCo, Low Power, 160m Club Calls,   ARSI Himalayan, CQMM DX (PY), CW Open, CWops Mini Tests, FOC Marathon, FOC QSO Party, INORC, IRTS 80m Counties, WAPC (China - both sides). In all other contests logging is delayed after 10 QSOs if you're not registered.

SDV for VHF Contests is free, and is unrestricted.

SIMPLEX

This repeater software quickly creates a free radio repeater. Handles simplex, duplex, transponder and mixed repeaters. Requires a sound card and Win95/98/ME/2000/NT/XP.

The program includes a lot of recording functions and a watching function program. WATCHDOG is also included in the zip. Time beacons through the french COUCOU or the multilingual Speaking Clock Deluxe.

WinDRM

Amateur radio digital voice with high-speed data transfer mode.

WinGrid

This program calculates grid squares from latitudes and longitudes, the reverse, and calculates distances and headings from two sets of lat/long or grid squares. The program saves your home QTH information.

Also Includes:

RF Safety Calculator (Version 1.0)
This program calculates RF field strengths and compares them to ~1998 FCC safety standards.

Power Loss / dB Calculator (Version 2.0)
Calculates transmission line power loss and input/output power.

Solar/Lunar Tracking Program (Version 5.3)
This program locates the Sun and Moon in real-time using a full set of ephemeris factors.

P3T AO-40 Telemetry Program
This is a comprehensive program for logging, interpreting, and replaying the telemetry from AO-40.

IPS Emulator for Windows
A fully functional emulator for IPS (Interpreter for Processor Systems) used on Phase3 amateur satellites.

WSJT - by K1JT
Open-source programs designed for weak-signal digital communication by amateur radio. Normal usage requires a standard SSB transceiver and a personal computer with soundcard. Some SDR-style hardware including the SDR-IQ, Perseus, SoftRock, and FUNcube Dongle are also supported. SimJT is a utility that generates simulated signals for test purposes.

WSJT
Weak Signal Communication by K1JT offers specific digital protocols optimized for meteor scatter, ionospheric scatter, and EME (moonbounce) at VHF/UHF, as well as HF skywave propagation. The program can decode fraction-of-a-second signals reflected from ionized meteor trails and steady signals 10dB below the audible threshold. Check the WSJT page for details about new modes in WSJT 9.3 and the experimental program release WSJT-X.

MAP65
Version 2 implements a wideband receiver for JT65 signals. It can be used together with Linrad (by SM5BSZ) or SDR-Radio (by HB9DRV), or with direct input from a soundcard. The program decodes all detectable JT65 signals in a passband up to 90kHz wide, producing a band map of decoded callsigns sorted by frequency. The principal application of MAP65 is EME on the VHF and UHF bands. In a dual-polarization system, MAP65 optimally matches the linear polarization angle of each decodable signal, thereby eliminating problems with Faraday rotation and spatial polarization shifts. Check the MAP65 page for details on modes JT65B2 and JT65C2 in MAP65 v2.4.

WSPR
Pronounced 'whisper', Weak Signal Propagation Reporter is designed for sending and receiving low-power transmissions to test propagation paths on the MF and HF bands. Users with Internet access can watch results in real time at WSPRnet. Version 2.11 of WSPR includes FMT, a package of command-line utilities that can help you make highly accurate frequency measurements without expensive laboratory equipment.

SimJT
Generates JT65 and CW test signals with a user-specified signal-to-noise ratio. It is useful for testing the JT65 decoder and the relative capabilities of these two modes.

Winlog32
Logging software designed and working on all Microsoft Windows platforms, e.g. 95/98/ME/NT4/2000/XP/Vista/W7/W8. This software has been in development for many years and is ongoing, In the true 'Ham Spirit', the author (G0CUZ) provides this software free to use by all radio amateurs and SWL's. As such no warranty is implied or given as to it's suitability or reliability.

Although Winlog32 is general purpose logging software, it has a definite slant on DXing on both HF and VHF, with comprehensive tracking of various awards programs like DXCC, IOTA, WAZ etc. It also includes all the features you would expect from good quality logging and DXing software, and more.

youLOG
The easiest logging software available for free to the amateur radio community. Made in Italy, youLOG is a simple and efficient logging system suitable for DXpeditions, special events, or just simple fun. youLOG full includes the WCall by IK1MTT, with 1.7 Million callsigns included. It runs even on a small display netbook and is portable, as it doesn't need to be installed (you can run it from a USB memory stick). No mouse is required, as it has been designed for those operators who require time on the air without being distracted by their software.

Non amateur radio program that may be useful

Adobe Reader XI
This indispensable product lets you read and print from any system any document created as an Adobe Portable Document Format (PDF) file, with its original appearance preserved. PDF files are compact and can be shared, viewed, navigated, and printed exactly as the author intended by anyone with Adobe Reader.

Doro PDF Writer
If you need to create PDFs that you can view and use inside of the many free standalone PDF viewers, then Doro PDF Writer is a versatile, compact alternative in the form of printer-based PDF tool. Doro adds an additional printer to your system, but instead of connecting to an external device, it formats your documents and saves them as PDFs. You create PDFs simply by selecting Print and choosing Doro from your print menu. Doro PDF Writer is freeware.

PDF-XChange

An alternative to Adobe's Acrobat Reader (above) and much more. Viewing PDFs is incredibly simple and it excels with its added features. The program's interface looks and feels remarkably like Acrobat Reader, but with more command icons along the top. Users who are familiar with viewing PDFs will find this fairly intuitive and the control panel along the top displays a long list of options for editing your PDFs. The most useful we found was the option for making bright red shapes and lines, which can be utilized to mark errors and make comments (an element that has always been one of Acrobat's best tools).

Open Office

A free and credible rival to MS Office, OpenOffice.org includes powerful applications for making text documents, spreadsheets, presentations, diagrams, and databases, as well as HTML and XML documents. Not only does it let you edit basic documents, it also handles equations and complex and multipart documents with bibliographies, reference tables, and indexes. The interface is similar to that of MS Office, and even advanced Office users will find almost everything they're used to: templates, macros, and even a programming language. You can open and save documents in formats as diverse as MS Office formats, PDF, HTML, and XML and import files in a huge range of formats. It normally saves files in the open-standard Oasis Open Document XML format, for maximum compatibility with other applications.

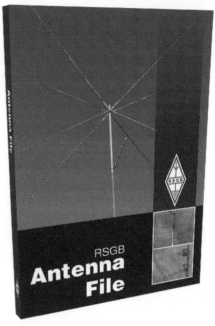

RSGB Antenna File

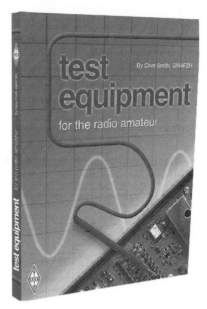

Test Equipment for the Radio Amateur
4th Edition

By Clive Smith, GM4FZH

Many of us would like to analyse the performance of our stations but find that professional test equipment such as spectrum analysers prohibitively expensive. Yet it can be easy to make many pieces of very useful test equipment yourself at home. *Test Equipment for the Radio Amateur* is a book that provides the definitive guide to the equipment that can be made or used to measure the various parameters of an amateur radio station.

This fourth edition of *Test Equipment for the Radio Amateur* has been fully updated to show what can be achieved today with the simple, inexpensive and easily obtainable. Test equipment for measuring current, voltage, the value of components, frequencies, receiver performance, RF power, modulation, antennas and transmission lines, noise, transmitter linearity and much more is all covered. For the home builder there are numerous projects, from a simple fuse tester to a high quality 1.3GHz signal source and much more. One chapter even covers software based test equipment that runs on a PC and includes specialist calculators, oscilloscope and spectrum analyser programs, signal generators, SINAD analysis and even design tools for RF filters. Surplus equipment often appears on the amateur market and the use of this equipment such as frequency counters and oscilloscopes, is well documented in this book. There is an appendix of useful reference data with everything from resistor colour coding to discrete semiconductor coding and surface mount device identification to common coaxial cable equivalents. There is even a second appendix of PCB and component layout diagrams for many of these projects.

Size 174x240mm, 256 pages, ISBN: 9781 9050 8672 6

RRP £14.99

Radio Society of Great Britain www.rsgbshop.org
3 Abbey Court, Priory Business Park, Bedford, MK44 3WH. Tel: 01234 832 700 Fax: 01234 831 496

The Low Power
Sprat Book

QRP – the art and science of low-power operation – is one of the most popular aspects of amateur radio. In the UK, the G QRP Club has been a leading light in this area of operation since its formation in 1974. Its journal, *SPRAT* is recognised as one of the world's leading QRP publications and it has now reached its 150th edition. This milestone is marked by this publication of this book, which is a selection the best of nearly four decades of low-power amateur radio circuits and ideas that have been published in *SPRAT*.

The Low Power Spratbook is divided into seven parts, covering transmitters, receivers, transceivers, antennas, ATUs, Morse keys and keyers, and a section for those circuits which might best be categorised as 'miscellaneous'. Circuits vary in complexity from an "ultra-simple" 80m CW transceiver using just 14 parts to the more sophisticated 'Sparkford', designed by Walford Electronics and also for use on 80m CW. You will find early 'classics' within these pages, including the 'OXO' transmitter and the 'ONER' both GM3OXX designs. *The Low Power Spratbook* also includes QRP classics such as versions of the 'FOXX' transceiver, the 'Pixie', the 'Epiphyte' and the 'Naxos'. All are presented as they were originally printed.

The Low Power Spratbook will appeal to the dedicated QRP enthusiast through to all those who have never tried QRP construction work before. This book is a veritable gold mine of ingenious designs and circuits and provides a superb introduction and reference book dedicated to the art and science of low-power or QRP amateur radio.

Size 174x240mm 320 pages ISBN: 9781 9050 8686 3

RRP £14.99

E&OE All prices shown plus p&p

Radio Society of Great Britain www.rsgbshop.org
3 Abbey Court, Priory Business Park, Bedford, MK44 3WH. Tel: 01234 832 700 Fax: 01234 831 496

Index